IN CONTEXT

ANTHOLOGY ONE

Clayton Graves
Christine McClymont

Nelson Canada

PROJECT DEVELOPMENT: Joe Banel

COORDINATING EDITOR: Jean Lancee

DEVELOPMENTAL EDITORS: Maggie Goh,
Mary Beth Leatherdale, Debora Pearson

CONSULTING EDITOR: Margaret Cameron

EDITOR: Trina Preece

RESEARCH: Sheila Fairley, Marjorie Hale,
Colleen Nielsen-Hyde, Elinor Phillips

DESIGN, ART DIRECTION AND TYPOGRAPHY:
Pronk&Associates

COVER PHOTOGRAPHS

Freeman Patterson/Masterfile: (top); Barrett & Mackay/
Masterfile: (bottom); Rukuo Kawakami/The Image Bank
Canada: (centre); Larry Dale Gordon/The Image Bank
Canada: (left).

PHOTOGRAPHS

Nancy Randall: 17; Gerard Sweeny: 25; Tony Freeman–
PhotoEdit: 30; Tony Thomas, reprinted with permission
of the publisher, *The Young Naturalist Foundation*: 30;
McClelland and Stewart: The Canadian Publishers;35 Elsie
Morris: 47; Canada's Fitweek Project Centre: 50–51; Image
Bank: 62–63; Anansi Press: 67; Masterfile: 71, 72, 73, 74;
Athletes' Information Bureau: 69, 70, 72 (above); Joy
Kogawa: 106–107 (above); Vancouver Public Library:
106–107 (below); Fiona McCall: 124–128; McGraw Hill
Ryerson: 138; ©Mori/Image Bank: 168–169; Miller-Comstock:
170; Niagara Parks Commission: 172; Niagara Falls Museum:
171 & 173; Joe Lepiano: 175; Madison Press and Penguin
Books Canada: 178–187 & 190–197; Eva Hart: 189; Greg
Holman: 203; Doubleday Canada: 205; Durantes-Liason:
211; CanaPress Photo Service: 212 & 215 & 221–226;
Penguin Books Canada: 235, 236, & 237; Image Bank: 243;
©Curto/Image Bank: 247; Joe Lepiano: 249; ©Rossi/Image
Bank: 252; Zoot Capri Magazine and the AADAC: 260–264;
Kulwant Saluja: 267; McClelland and Stewart: The Canadian
Publishers: 293; Alain Choisnet/The Image Bank Canada: 294;
B. C. Productions/The Image Bank Canada: 295; E. Stuart
McDonald Estate and the L. M. Montgomery Collection,
University of Guelph: 300.

ILLUSTRATIONS

Don Gauthier: 8–9; Paul Zwolak: 10–18; Rodney Dunn:
19–21 & 139–141; Vicki Elsom: 22–25; June Lawrason:
26–27; Sandra Dionisi: 28–29; Harvey Chan: 31–37; Graham
Bardell: 38–46; Mike Schiell: 52–58; Odile Ouellet: 59–61; Kim
Lafave: 64–67; Paul McCusker: 75–79 & 132; Craig Terlson:
80–81; Thach Bui: 82–85; Steve Redman: 90–94; Val Fraser:
95 & 267; David Bathurst: 96–105 & 206–209; Tomio Nitto:
108–112; Courtesy of the Royal Ontario Museum, Toronto,
Canada: 113; Nick Vitacco: 114–121; Alan Barnard: 122–123;
Joanne Fitzgerald: 133–135; Ted Harrison: 137; Peter Grau:
142–148; Greg Douglas: 149–151; Steve Van Gelder: 152–165;
Ken Marschall: 176–177, 179, 186; Jan Fatum: 198–199; Laurie
Lafrance: 216–220; Renee Mansfield: 227–231; Doug Thoms:
242–259; Paul McCusker: 272–273; Greg Ruhl: 280–293; Barb
Massey: 296–301; Sean Leaning: 302–303; Frances Clancy:
304–308; Gerry Lagendyk: 309–313; Joe Morse: 314–320; Rick
Sealock: 321–331.

I(**T**)**P**® International Thomson Publishing

The ITP logo is a trademark under licence

Published by **I**(**T**)**P** Nelson
A Division of Thomson Canada Limited
1120 Birchmount Road
Scarborough. Ontario M1K 5G4

Visit our Website at http://www.nelson.com/nelson.html

Copyright © 1998, 1990

ISBN 0-17-603048-4

Canadian Cataloguing in Publication Data

Main entry under title:
In context: anthology one

2nd ed.
First ed. (1981) published under title: Contexts.
Anthology one
for use in schools.
Includes bibliographies and index.
ISBN 0-17-603048-4

1. Readers (Elementary). I. Graves, Clayton.
II. McClymont, Christine. III. Title: Contexts.
Anthology one.

PE1121.C655   1990   428.6   C89-094614-0

Printed and Bound in Canada

11 12 13   TP   00 99 98

IN CONTEXT

ANTHOLOGY ONE

TABLE OF CONTENTS

Dark Water, Deep Water

Words and Music

Getting the Message

Challenges

Indexes

FRIENDS AND RELATIONS

I tried to remember the last time I'd walked to school without Kim.

The Trouble with Friends/10

If there was anybody who didn't notice Klutter's Kobras, it was Priscilla.

Priscillia and the Wimps/19

"That was some shot, mister."
The Wild Goose/31

There was little comfort for her just then. If Grandma succeeded it would mean the end of Katia's plan.

The Education of Grandma/38

With My Foot in My Mouth

By Dennis Lee

The reason I clobbered
Your door like that,
Is 'cause it's time
We had a chat.

But don't start getting
Talkative—
I've got a speech
I want to give:

"A person needs
A pal a lot,
And a pal is what
I'm glad I've got,

So thank you. Thank you."
There, it's said!
I feel my earlobes
Getting red,

And I wish you wouldn't
Grin that way!
It isn't healthy,
Night or day.

But even though
You're such a jerk,
With your corny jokes
And your goofy smirk,

I'm sort of glad
You're my old pard.
You're cheaper than
A bodyguard,

And smaller than a
Saint Bernard,
And cleaner than a
Wrecker's yard.

I like the way
You save on socks:
You wear them till they're
Hard as rocks.

And I think those missing
Teeth are keen:
Your mouth looks like
A slot machine

And every time
I see you grin,
I stick another
Quarter in.

You make me laugh
Till we trip on chairs;
One day we nearly
Fell downstairs.

But I think you're kind of
Brave, I guess:
Your no means no,
Your yes means yes.

And even if
It makes you shrink,
You say the things
You really think.

In fact your mouth
Is never closed—
Your tonsils blush,
They're so exposed.

And your tweety voice
Is never quiet;
They must put birdseed
In your diet.

Still, you seem to know,
When we kid a lot,
A time for kidding
A time for not—

Cause often things
I say to you,
I'd ache if any
Body knew.

You choke me up,
You make me sneeze,
I've caught you like
A rare disease:

I'd like to come and
Rub your back;
I'd like to feed you
Crackerjack

And send you messages
In code
And walk along you
Like a road.

And bath you till your
Fleas are gone
And stuff you like
A mastodon.

And let's go play
In Kendal Park;
There's still an hour
Before it's dark.

Cause some things last and
Some things end—
I want you always
For my friend.

The Trouble with Friends

BY FRANCES DUNCAN

*im Ferris was my best friend until she started talking about leaving Vancouver and going back to Korea to find her real parents. I mean, I understand why she's interested in her homeland, but when it came to hurting her Canadian parents, the ones who'd adopted her and cared for her all her life — well, I thought she'd really gone too far.*

The sky hung down like wet fuzz, making the air and trees and grass damp and dark. The closer I came to school, the more damp and dark became my mood. I tried to remember the last time I'd walked to school without Kim and, except for colds or flu, couldn't. It had been that long. I wasn't so angry any more — my temper never lasts long — but I felt miserable. I wasn't sure the world was all it was cracked up to be. The older I got, the more difficult everything became.

A group of kindergarten or Grade One kids passed me, all laughing and shouting. What a blissful age. No worries except learning to tie your shoelaces and to make your buttons match the holes. Someone to look after you, shield you from the world. I sighed again. I could just hear my mother, Kate, saying in a very irritating fashion, "Contrary to the song, life is not a bowl of cherries!"

By the time I reached school the only thing I wanted was my very own hole which I could crawl into and close behind me and be left entirely alone. I had my head down and nearly tripped over Kim before I saw her.

"Where were you?" she asked. "You didn't call for me!"

"Sorry," I lied.

"I've been waiting to tell you I won the free skating! And I came third over all, so I can go to the next competition for all of Western Canada!"

"That's nice."

"What do you mean—nice? I thought you'd be pleased!"

"I said it was nice. Congratulations. What more do you want? Do you want me to admire you all the time so you can step on me too?" My anger of yesterday was growing again. "I'd think you'd want your real Korean friend that you left in the orphanage as a baby to be proud of you—not your second-hand Canadian friend! I'm just like your parents—I don't count! So don't expect me to be pleased!"

There were great tears in the corners of Kim's eyes and I was so mad I didn't care. She opened her mouth as if to say something, then closed it again, and quietly walked up the stairs into school, her shoulder blades making punctuations of sadness through her jacket.

And still I didn't care. Well, not much. She was being so stupid. She had everything and all she wanted to do was hurt people. So, I'd hurt her first. Let her go back to Korea. Who cared? Not I. Well, not much. I looked at my foot. It was prying a piece of moss loose from its crack in the sidewalk.

I wanted to ask the teacher if I could change desks but he was busy with a new girl. I sat on the very edge of my seat away from Kim and stared out the window. Once I turned my head by mistake. Kim was leaning over, talking very loudly to Jennifer about the competition. After that, I got a crick in my neck from looking the other way.

"Class," Mr. Taggart said, "this is Bindu Khan. She's from Uganda, which is in Africa."

He couldn't resist getting the social studies in there, I thought.

"Bindu hasn't been in Canada long," Mr. Taggart continued. "I'm going to assign some girls to show her around, help her get used to us."

The girl stared at the floor. She must have been horribly embarrassed.

"Let's see." Mr. Taggart looked around the class. "Michelle — and Kim," he smiled as though he'd done something very clever, "will you look after Bindu?"

"No!" I wanted to shout. "Not with Kim!"

But of course I nodded.

Mr. Taggart showed the new girl to an empty seat in the front row. He kept interrupting his lesson to smile at her. I suppose he wanted to put her at ease, and make her feel welcome, but I could tell by the look on her face he just made her more uncomfortable.

She was nearly as tall as me, but skinny, with long black braids that made her face look even thinner. She was wearing a tartan pleated skirt and white blouse that emphasized her darkness. She was even darker than Kim. On her feet, which she tucked under the seat, were brown lace-up oxfords, the kind old ladies or English boarding school girls wear. She really stuck out in a class where everyone was wearing blue jeans or cords and joggers. She didn't look easy to look after. And to have to team up with Kim!

I didn't hear a thing Taggart said. I watched the clock hands march closer to the end of the period wishing they'd get stuck somewhere. But of course they didn't and of course the bell rang.

Without waiting for Kim I marched up the aisle and said, "I'm Michelle Macdonald. Call me Mish. We get science now."

"I'm Kim Ferris," she said behind me. I didn't turn around. "After that we get Home Ec. *Michelle* here is the brain of the class." The scorn in her voice would have frizzled bacon.

I tried to ignore Kim, but my back felt twitchy. "Do you have any books or anything?" It was obvious she didn't.

"No," Bindu said. "I did not know what to bring."

"I'll lend you some paper and a pen," I said.

"I have an extra pen," Kim added. I could tell she was glaring at me.

"Thank you." Bindu looked at us curiously.

"You speak English well," I said as we walked down the hall to the science room.

"In my country everyone but the poor people speaks English. All the schools are — were — English." She had, in fact, an English accent.

"I guess you're finding everything different," Kim said from Bindu's other side.

"Yes. What is your country?"

"I was born in Korea. I'm going back as soon as I can. I hate Canada."

"I'm going back to Uganda too," Bindu said. "As soon as I can."

I wanted to say, "You can both go right now as far as I'm concerned," but instead I asked, "Have you been here long?"

"One month. I couldn't start school until we found a house. In my country houses are much cheaper. There are more of them too. And the gardens are much nicer. We had pawpaw trees in ours."

I curled my lips and wondered if I could leave the two Canada-haters to look after themselves, but then I thought, if I left, it would look as though Kim had won.

"In my country," Bindu continued, "we don't wear pants to school, and certainly not jeans."

"Yeah?" Kim and I said at the same time. Kim finished, "We do here."

Kim opened the science room door. I stood back to let Bindu through but Kim pushed in front and the door banged my shoulder. I managed to step on Kim's toe and get to Mr. Zilbe first so I could introduce Bindu.

I just love Mr. Zilbe. He's short and fat, but he knows a lot of chemistry.

"Uganda, eh?" He smiled sympathetically. "That's quite a trip. Look through Michelle's lab book to see what we're doing. Things will be different for a while. Take your time getting used to us."

I led Bindu to a table and placed her between Kim and me. It was a squish and Kim had to move over to the corner. She had hardly enough room for her books. I opened the lab book to the section on light.

"Don't you have a text? I did this last year."

"We use lots of different books." I dug out an old report on copper sulphate. "Have you done this?"

"Yes. At my old school we had a very advanced program."

"My," I said. "Did you do much microscope work?"

"We had a microscope. All those with good marks were allowed to look through it. We saw human hair and pond water."

"When we do anything with microscopes we all get our own to use. Last year we learned to prepare slides. We saw pond water too. Did you see any rotifers? I think they're cute. They look like bugs on bicycles."

"I don't think there are any in Uganda," she said slowly.

"Have you done anything with computers?"

Bindu shook her head and I wondered if her advanced program was so advanced after all. "We had lots of computer time last year. We went to the universities to see their computers."

"Oh," Bindu said.

"I guess you studied different things in Uganda."

"Yes, probably." Bindu smiled. "Kim said you were good in science."

"I'm going to be a biochemist when I grow up. That's what Kim's mother is…" It hit me then. I'd not only lost my best friend, I'd also lost her mother and our trips to her lab. My eyes started to sting. " Excuse me," I mumbled and dashed to the washroom.

I locked the door of the cubicle and leaned my head on the wall. I still felt I was right. Kim had been hurting people. But should I have been so mean to her? Maybe I could have said the same things in a nicer way. Maybe we could have stayed friends. But then maybe Kim had wanted to be rid of me, and she was glad I'd got mad so she'd have an excuse. That was how she was acting.

But never to have dinner at her house again! No more chess with her brother Brent, or visits to the lab, or sleeping in Kim's room and telling secrets. No one to tell secrets to. No more best friend. I'd have to get my clothes and things back. My new blue T-shirt I'd left there and my second-best jeans. I cried some more and wished I hadn't got up that morning.

Finally I took a paper towel and washed my face with cold water. I looked in the mirror — red and blotchy. It took another ten minutes before my face was presentable enough to take back to class.

Mr. Zilbe looked at me curiously when I opened the door but he didn't say anything. Kim had her lab book sprawled in front so Bindu could look at it too. They'd both edged into the centre of the table. Now I had to balance at the corner.

So, what? I thought. *You can have each other! Neither of you likes it here!*

By lunchtime I had a crashing headache. I hadn't even cared that Bindu had gone to Home Ec. with Kim, leaving me tagging behind. By English, Kim had taken complete possession of the new girl. It was Taggart's fault for putting two people in charge, not one.

But, still doing my duty, I sat with them in the lunchroom. It was not the best companionship for a meal, because Jennifer, who could not stand being left out of anything, wangled her way in. I sat as far away from Kim as possible while still being at the same table.

Bindu said, "I can see you girls are not friends."

"I guess we're not," Kim replied, "since one of us can't stand the sight of the other."

"Oh, which one?" Jennifer asked with delight. There's nothing she likes better than someone else's business.

"None of your business," Kim said, before I could.

Bindu looked totally confused. "I'm sorry you have to bother with me. I can manage."

"You're no bother," I lied, feeling horribly guilty.

"Do you skate?" Jennifer asked and for once I was glad she'd butted in.

"Oh yes, in Uganda everyone skates. The sun shines so much, not like here, all the children skate."

Jennifer laughed. "I meant *ice* skating. Did you think I meant *roller skating*?"

Kim glared at her. "How's she to know, for goodness' sake?"

Bindu said stiffly, "In my country we do not have ice. It is too hot. In my country it doesn't rain like this drizzle, drizzle, drizzle." She waved her hand up and down. "I find it very cold in Canada. My mother has had a stuffed head and arthritis since we came here. I do not think I would like the skating on ice. It would be too cold."

"This isn't *that* bad a place," Kim said. I stopped chewing, I was so amazed. "You just have to get used to it. Why'd you come here, if you don't like it?"

"We had to." Bindu folded her wax paper neatly and put it in her bag. "The government made my father give them his business and said, 'Get out of the country.' All the people who weren't true Ugandans had to leave. They said we weren't true Ugandans because we look different. My great-grandparents moved to Uganda from India seventy-five years ago. How long does it take to become a true Ugandan?"

She paused, sounding as though she'd asked that question before and was still waiting for an answer.

"We lost our house and our two stores *and* our country. They want Uganda to be black and African. 'Get out, all you East Indians!' That's what they said. But my family isn't East Indian any more."

"But a government can't kick people out of a country, not if they're born there!" Kim said.

"Uganda did."

I was stunned. Fancy being told your country doesn't want you any more. Sort of the opposite of Kim's problem. She has two countries — in a way.

Bindu said, "I have to go to the office to collect some books. Could one of you please show me the way? This is a more confusing school than the one in my country — in my old country, I mean."

"Sure," we all said, but Jen was on her feet first. "I'll do it."

Kim and I were left alone with an uncomfortable silence. She looked at me, then gathered the rest of her lunch and moved to another table where some kids from our class were sitting.

I have never known a longer or more desolate day. My head continued to throb like mad and I didn't hear one thing the teachers said. P.E., last period, was a real drag. Kim and I ended up on the same team for floor hockey and she went out of her way not to pass me the puck, although once I had a clear shot at goal. She just passed it to someone else and the other team took it away and scored. Each step I took up and down the gym jarred my head fiercely.

It was still raining after school. I dragged myself home and flopped on the bed. For once I was glad Kate worked. I just wanted to be alone. Why was the world such a mixed-up place? Why had I been so hard on Kim? Maybe she had been moody lately, but she had her problems, and now I'd lost her forever. And her mother. And Brent.

Settling In

Moving can be exciting, but it can also be confusing. Even if you just move from one street to another, it takes a while to settle in.
Farhaneh Khalani, 13, Omar Nurse, 12, and Al-Karim Datoo, 12, all moved great distances from other countries to Canada. Margo Beggs talked to them about what it feels like to move to another country, and how they got used to their new home.

INTERVIEWER: *Where did you live before moving to Canada, and how long have you been here?*

FARHANEH: My two sisters and I came here about eight months ago. We joined my parents, who came first to find a house. Before that we lived in Kenya, and before that, Pakistan, where I was born.

OMAR: Six months ago I moved to Canada from Barbados to be with my mother.

AL-KARIM: My family moved here from England five years ago.

INTERVIEWER: *Can you remember what you felt like when you first stepped off the plane?*

OMAR: I felt good because it was summer. I didn't know about the cold weather yet.

AL-KARIM: I was excited, but kind of scared. I was afraid that people I would meet might think I was really weird with my English accent, and that I might not fit in. And I did feel like that sometimes at first.

INTERVIEWER: *Do you find the schools different here?*

FARHANEH: In Pakistan and Kenya we didn't play sports like we do here. We just did exercises, like jumping up and down, so I enjoy playing the

Why wasn't Kate like some other mothers? Why didn't she stay home sometimes? Why did she have to work so much? Even Mrs. Ferris baked cookies and she worked. Why did I call her Kate anyway?

I started calling her Kate one day a year ago, just for fun. It made me feel grown-up. She'd seemed to like it, so I kept on.

I sighed and rolled over, but the movement made my head throb. Why did things never come out equally? Why was there always too much or not enough? I wished the world were like a chemistry experiment. If you did things exactly right, you could count on the results. Things didn't get mixed up for no reason.

"Mommy," I said aloud.

Then the tears came, great stinging welts of them, hot and hurting. I wished I were dead. Nothing happened if you were dead. You could just lie there. I wished I hadn't been born.

I must have fallen asleep, for I suddenly became aware of the doorbell ringing. It was dusk already, close to seven. Where was Kate? Had she forgotten her key and had to ring the bell?

It was Kim, holding a brown paper shopping bag.

"Here are your things," she said stiffly. "I think I found them all."

"Thanks." I took the shopping bag.

games here. But some of the work we're doing now, like in math, I did before I came here, so I find it very easy.

OMAR: My school in Barbados didn't have four closed-in walls. Two of the walls were open, because the weather is always warm.

INTERVIEWER: *Can you remember anything funny that happened to you when you first came here because you weren't used to things?*

AL-KARIM: I remember when snow first came piling down, I thought it was like fluff and jumped on it. I didn't know it would be so cold.

OMAR: When I first arrived I got lost in the elevator in my apartment building. I forgot my floor number, and when the doors opened the floors all looked the same.

Omar Nurse, Farhaneh Khalani, and Al-Karim Datoo after settling in to a new life in Canada.

She shifted from one foot to the other. "I guess that's all. I won't bother you again."

I wanted to say, you don't bother me, but all I did was start to cry again. I turned away so she wouldn't see and half shut the door.

"Aw gee, Mish, I'm sorry." Her voice sounded funny and I looked at her. She was crying too. "You were right this morning. I've been horrible. Will you forgive me?"

"I was horrible too. I shouldn't have said all those things. I was mad at everyone."

"No, you were right."

"No, I wasn't."

"You were right and I'm sorry."

"Don't say sorry."

"Sorry." She half laughed. "Sorry I said sorry." Her laugh changed to a sob. "I'm only sorry I'm me."

"I'm sorry I'm me, too." I shivered and realized we were still standing in the door. "Come on in." I put down the bag.

"You can't feel the same as me," Kim said. "You're so smart and always know what to say. You're sophisticated. And good-looking."

"Yeah, sure," I replied sarcastically. "Tell us another one."

"Yes. Really. I'm the one that's different."

"Come off it. You've got everything going for you. You're good-looking, you've got talent, and you're smart too. You don't have a mother who's always looking after other people. See, she's not even home yet! You don't have divorced parents. You have a family, and you're not a great big moose!" I started to cry again.

The door opened and Kate came in. "That meeting took longer than I thought. Hello, Kim. Good heavens, what's wrong?"

"Nothing," we both said.

"Looks like a pretty big nothing," Kate replied.

"Where have you been?" I asked.

"At a meeting. Didn't you see my note? I asked you to warm up some TV dinners."

"I'd better go," Kim said. "Will you call for me tomorrow, Mish?"

I nodded. "Hey," I shouted, "you'd better take these back!" I held out the shopping bag and Kim grinned.

From Kap-Sung Ferris by Frances Duncan

Priscilla and the Wimps

BY RICHARD PECK

Listen, there was a time when you couldn't even go to the *rest room* around this school without a pass. And I'm not talking about those little pink tickets made out by some teacher. I'm talking about a pass that could cost anywhere up to a buck, sold by Monk Klutter.

Not that Mighty Monk ever touched money, not in public. The gang he ran, which ran the school for him, was his collection agency. They were Klutter's Kobras, a name spelled out in nailheads on six well-known black plastic windbreakers.

Monk's threads were more…subtle. A pile-lined suede battle jacket with lizard-skin flaps over tailored Levis and a pair of ostrich-skin boots, brass-toed and suitable for kicking people around. One of his Kobras did nothing all day but walk a half step behind Monk, carrying a fitted bag with Monk's gym shoes, a roll of restroom passes, a cashbox, and a switchblade that Monk gave himself manicures with at lunch over at the Kobras' table.

Speaking of lunch, there were a few cases of advanced malnutrition among the newer kids. The ones who were a little slow in handing over a cut of their lunch money and were therefore barred from the cafeteria. Monk ran a tight ship.

I admit it. I'm 165 cm, and when the Kobras slithered by, with or without Monk, I shrank. And I admit this, too: I paid up on a regular basis. And I might add: so would you.

This school was old Monk's Garden of Eden. Unfortunately for him, there was a serpent in it. The reason Monk didn't recognize trouble when it was staring him in the face is that the serpent in the Kobras' Eden was a girl.

Practically every guy in school could show you his scars. Fang marks from Kobras, you might say. And they were all highly visible in the shower room: lumps, lacerations, blue bruises, you name it. But girls usually got off with a warning.

Except there was this one girl named Priscilla Roseberry. Picture a girl named Priscilla Roseberry, and you'll be light years off. Priscilla was, hands

down, the largest student in our particular institution of learning. I'm not talking fat. I'm talking big. Even beautiful, in a bionic way. Priscilla wasn't inclined toward organized crime. Otherwise, she could have put together a gang that would turn Klutter's Kobras into garter snakes.

Priscilla was basically a loner except she had one friend. A little guy named Melvin Detweiler. You talk about The Odd Couple. Melvin's one of the smallest boys above midget status ever seen. A really nice guy, but, you know — little. They even had lockers next to each other, in the same bank as mine. I don't know what they had going. I'm not saying this was a romance. After all, people deserve their privacy.

Priscilla was sort of above everything, if you'll pardon a pun. And very calm, as only the very big can be. If there was anybody who didn't notice Klutter's Kobras, it was Priscilla.

Until one winter day after school when we were all grabbing our coats out of our lockers. And hurrying, since Klutter's Kobras made sweeps of the halls for after-school shakedowns.

Anyway, up to Melvin's locker swaggers one of the Kobras. Never mind his name. Gang members don't need names. They've got group identity. He reaches down and grabs little Melvin by the neck and slams his head against his locker door. The sound of skull against steel rippled all the way down the locker row, speeding the crowds on their way.

"Okay, let's see your pass," snarls the Kobra.

"A pass for what this time?" Melvin asks, probably still dazed.

"Let's call it a pass for very short people," says the Kobra, "a dwarf tax." He wheezes a little Kobra chuckle at his own wittiness. And already he's reaching for Melvin's wallet with the hand that isn't circling Melvin's windpipe. All this time, of course, Melvin and the Kobra are standing in Priscilla's big shadow.

She's taking her time shoving her books into her locker and pulling on a very large-size coat. Then, quicker than the eye, she brings the side of her enormous hand down in a chop that breaks the Kobra's hold on Melvin's throat. You could hear a pin drop in that hallway. Nobody'd ever laid a finger on a Kobra, let alone a hand the size of Priscilla's.

Then Priscilla, who hardly ever says anything to anybody except to Melvin, says to the Kobra, "Who's your leader, wimp?"

This practically blows the Kobra away. First he's chopped by a girl, and now she's acting like she doesn't know Monk Klutter, the Head Honcho of the World. He's so amazed, he tells her. "Monk Klutter."

"Never heard of him," Priscilla mentions. "Send him to see me." The Kobra just backs away from her like the whole situation is too big for him, which it is.

Pretty soon Monk himself slides up. He jerks his head once, and his Kobras slither off down the hall. He's going to handle this interesting case personally. "Who is it around here doesn't know Monk Klutter?"

He's standing real close to Priscilla, but since he'd have to look up at her, he doesn't. "Never heard of him," says Priscilla.

Monk's not happy with this answer, but by now he's spotted Melvin, who's grown smaller in spite of himself. Monk breaks his own rule by reaching for Melvin with his own hands. "Kid," he says, "you're going to have to educate your girl friend."

His hands never quite make it to Melvin. In a move of pure poetry Priscilla has Monk in a hammerlock. His neck's popping like gunfire, and his head's bowed under the immense weight of her forearm. His suede jacket's peeling back, showing pile.

Priscilla's behind him in another easy motion. And with a single mighty thrust forward, frog-marches Monk into her own locker. It's incredible. His ostrich-skin boots click once in the air. And suddenly he's gone, neatly wedged into the locker, a perfect fit. Priscilla bangs the door shut, twirls the lock and strolls out of school. Melvin goes with her, of course, trotting along below her shoulder. The last stragglers leave quietly.

Well, this is where fate, an even bigger force than Priscilla, steps in. It snows all that night, a blizzard. The whole town ices up. And school closes for a week.

Papa's Parrot

BY CYNTHIA RYLANT

Though his father was fat and merely owned a candy and nut shop, Harry Tillian liked his papa. Harry stopped liking candy and nuts when he was around seven, but, in spite of this, he and Mr. Tillian had remained friends and were still friends the year Harry turned twelve.

For years, after school, Harry had always stopped in to see his father at work. Many of Harry's friends stopped there too, to spend a few cents choosing penny candy from the giant bins or to sample Mr. Tillian's latest batch of roasted peanuts. Mr. Tillian looked forward to seeing his son and his son's friends every day. He liked the company.

When Harry entered junior high school, though, he didn't come by the candy and nut shop as often. Nor did his friends. They were older and they had more spending money. They went to a burger place. They played video games. They shopped for records. None of them were much interested in candy and nuts anymore.

A new group of children came to Mr. Tillian's shop now. But not Harry Tillian and his friends.

The year Harry turned twelve was also the year Mr. Tillian got a parrot. He went to a pet store one day and bought one for more money than he could really afford. He brought the parrot to his shop, set its cage near the sign for maple clusters and named it Rocky.

Harry thought this was the strangest thing his father had ever done, and he told him so, but Mr. Tillian just ignored him.

Rocky was good company for Mr. Tillian. When business was slow, Mr. Tillian would turn on a small colour television he had sitting in a corner and he and Rocky would watch the soap operas. Rocky liked to scream when the romantic music came on and Mr. Tillian would yell at him to shut up, but they seemed to enjoy themselves.

The more Mr. Tillian grew to like his parrot and the more he talked to it instead of to people, the more embarrassed Harry became. Harry would stroll past the shop, on his way somewhere else, and he'd take a quick look

inside to see what his dad was doing. Mr. Tillian was always talking to the bird. So Harry kept walking.

At home things were different. Harry and his father joked with each other at the dinner table as they always had — Mr. Tillian teasing Harry about his smelly socks; Harry teasing Mr. Tillian about his blubbery stomach. At home things seemed all right.

But one day, Mr. Tillian became ill. He had been at work, unpacking boxes of caramels, when he had grabbed his chest and fallen over on top of the candy. A customer had found him and he was taken to the hospital in an ambulance.

Mr. Tillian couldn't leave the hospital. He lay in bed, tubes in his arms, and he worried about his shop. New shipments of candy and nuts would be arriving. Rocky would be hungry. Who would take care of things?

Harry said he would. Harry told his father that he would go to the store every day after school and unpack boxes. He would sort out all the candy and nuts. He would even feed Rocky.

So the next morning, while Mr. Tillian lay in his hospital bed, Harry took the shop key to school with him. After school he left his friends and walked to the empty shop alone. In all the days of his life, Harry had never seen the shop closed after school. Harry didn't even remember what the CLOSED sign looked like. The key stuck in the lock three times, and inside he had to search all the walls for the light switch.

The shop was as his father had left it. Even the caramels were still spilled on the floor. Harry bent down and picked them up one by one, dropping them back in the boxes. The bird in its cage watched him silently.

Harry opened the new boxes his father hadn't gotten to. Peppermints. Jawbreakers. Toffee creams. Strawberry kisses. Harry travelled from bin to bin, putting the candies where they belonged.

"Hello!"

Harry jumped, spilling a box of jawbreakers.

"Hello, Rocky!"

Harry stared at the parrot. He had forgotten it was there. The bird had been so quiet, and Harry had been thinking only of the candy.

"Hello," Harry said.

"Hello, Rocky!" answered the parrot.

Harry walked slowly over to the cage. The parrot's food cup was empty. Its water was dirty. The bottom of the cage was a mess.

Harry carried the cage into the back room.

"Hello, Rocky!"

"Is that all you can say, you dumb bird?" Harry mumbled. The bird said nothing else.

Harry cleaned the bottom of the cage, refilled the food and water cups, then put the cage back in its place and resumed sorting the candy.

"Where's Harry?"

Harry looked up.

"Where's Harry?"

Harry stared at the parrot.

"Where's Harry?"

Chills ran down Harry's back. What could the bird mean? It was like something from "The Twilight Zone."

WHERE'S HARRY.

"Where's Harry?"

Harry swallowed and said, "I'm here. I'm here, you stupid bird."

"You stupid bird!" said the parrot.

Well at least he's got one thing straight, thought Harry.

"Miss him! Miss him! Where's Harry? You stupid bird!"

Harry stood with a handful of peppermints.

"*What*?" he asked.

"Where's Harry?" said the parrot.

"I'm *here*, you stupid bird! I'm here!" Harry yelled. He threw the peppermints at the cage, and the bird screamed and clung to its perch.

Harry sobbed, "I'm here." The tears were coming.

Harry leaned over the glass counter.

"Papa." Harry buried his face in his arms.

"Where's Harry?" repeated the bird.

Harry sighed and wiped his face on his sleeve. He watched the parrot. He understood now: someone had been saying for a long time, "Where's Harry? Miss him."

Harry finished his unpacking, then swept the floor of the shop. He checked the furnace so the bird wouldn't get cold. Then he left to go visit his papa.

IN CONTEXT
AUTHOR PROFILE

Cynthia Rylant: "Thank You Miss Evans"

I had a teacher named Miss Evans back in Beaver, West Virginia. Miss Evans was the first, and last, person who ever told me stories. I don't mean the reading aloud of books. I mean the spinning of tales. Let me tell you what this woman in Beaver, West Virginia created.

It was an ongoing saga entitled *The Journey*. The main characters in *The Journey* were the twenty-five of us sitting in her classroom. Once a week, Miss Evans led us on an adventure into the jungles of Africa or the glaciers of the Antarctic or some equally harrowing place, and she narrated, in a tense, mysterious, breathless

voice, the epic battles we won, together and individually.

One time in the Sahara Desert, I was bitten by a rattlesnake. And Randy Meadows carried me to a safe place, slit my flesh into an X, and sucked the poison from my foot. Sitting at my desk, I was nearly overcome with nervous exhaustion before Miss Evans finished this particular installment.

That is the power of what a story can do to you.

When Someone I Love Is Hurt

When someone I love is hurt,
I never know what to say.
I scowl and growl.
I slam doors.
I shut myself up in my room and put KEEP OUT on the door.
I glare at people who say things like,
"You certainly got out of bed on the wrong side
    this morning!"
I can't even run away into my favourite books.
The hurting follows me there and won't let me stay.
I just lie on my bed and concentrate on not crying.
I am not one tiny bit helpful.
I act dumb with everybody,
Even people who are completely outside it all,
Like the paper boy or Emily's aunt.
Even when I know I'm being stupid
    and only making things worse,
I can't help it.

But, all the time, I'm hurting too.
I yearn, with every atom of me, to make things right
    for the person I love.

It would be better to be comforting,
To be cheery, to make little jokes,
Or even just to say how sorry I am.

I can't. Hardly ever.
I just ache and ache and ache.

By Jean Little

Together

Because we do
All things together
All things improve,
Even weather.

Our daily meat
And bread taste better,
Trees are greener,
Rain is wetter.

By Paul Engle

Two Girls of Twelve...

Two girls of twelve or so at a table
in the Automat, smiling at each other
and the world; eating sedately.
And a tramp, wearing two or three tattered coats,
dark with dirt, mumbling, sat down beside them—
Miss Muffet's spider.
But, unlike her, they were not frightened away,
and did not shudder as they might if older and look
    askance.
They did steal a glance
at their dark companion and were slightly amused:
in their shining innocence seeing
in him only another human being.

By Charles Reznikoff

TWIN *TELEPATHY*

BY JAY INGRAM

There are hundreds of reports of twins reading each other's minds, but unfortunately twins don't seem to do it when scientists are there, recording what goes on. On the other hand, so many twins have reported that one can sense what the other is doing that it's hard to ignore them. Here's one account, first told by Charles Crail in his book *My Twin Joe*.

A teacher suspected that Charles and his twin brother Joe were cheating on exams, because they always wrote the same answers, right or wrong, even when they were sitting on opposite sides of the room. So the teacher decided to put Joe in the principal's office for the next exam. On exam day, Charles sat in the classroom with the exam in front of him, but he didn't start when everyone else did. "I'm not ready," he said, and continued to wait.

Then the principal came in and asked for an exam paper to give to Joe. He'd been busy with something else. Joe was still waiting for his exam paper in the principal's office. You guessed it: as soon as Joe got his exam, both twins started writing. Their exam papers turned out to be exactly the same: the same right answers and the same mistakes. It was as if they were sharing the same brain.

That story is one of those that can't be proven to be true. But there are others like it. In the French army during World War I there were

TWIN TELEPATHY

twin generals, Félix and Théodore Brett. They were so similar in their thinking when they were military students that the head of the French War College ordered an inquiry, because their exam papers were so much alike. The twins were cleared of cheating. Sounds a lot like Charles and Joe, doesn't it? Again, the problem with proving the story is that we don't know just how much alike those exam papers were.

Fifteen-year-old Brian Blackett was walking by himself near London, England, on Thursday, October 13, 1960. He suddenly became scared. At that very moment, on the other side of the city, his twin brother Lennie was being sentenced to prison for breaking into a house. Brian had no idea that Lennie was being sentenced that day.

Then there was Barbara Morgan, who got labor pains when her twin Gillian was having a baby. Kenneth Main felt sharp pains in his chest at 12:15 p.m., November 13, 1958, the exact time when his brother Keith was having a heart operation.

BRAIN WAVES AND DREAMS

There are many more stories like this, but they all share the same weakness—it's hard to know, years later, just how accurate they are. But if even some of them are true, it means some twins can actually communicate with each other—mind to mind—without talking, and

sometimes over great distances. Can twins read each other's minds? If anyone could prove they can, it would be a sensational discovery.

Maybe part of the answer is that twins' brains can be very much alike. There are some startling bits of evidence that twins' brains are so similar that they think almost identically. Their results on IQ tests can be almost identical and their brain-wave patterns are just about the same.

Brain waves are pulses or bursts of electricity that go through your brain when you're thinking. Measuring them can't tell you what thoughts someone is having, but they do give you an idea of how the brain is processing those thoughts.

Reading brain-wave patterns is a little like looking at city lights from an airplane. It would be pretty hard to see the exact moment when the corner store turns its lights off. But you could see that the light patterns in the city change from time to time and you could tell that each city's pattern is different. Twins' brain waves would

"Twin Telepathy" describes how the relationship between some twins is so close that they can read each other's minds. Other twins just enjoy having a good time together.

look like two cities with exactly the same pattern of lights.

French researchers have now discovered that IQ tests and brain waves are only part of the story. They have found by looking at those same electrical brain-wave patterns that twins share the same dream habits. They don't necessarily dream the same dreams (although some twins say they do), but they do dream at the same times of night, for about the same length of time. If you're not a twin, you don't share your dream patterns with anybody else.

None of this scientific evidence is good enough to prove that twins can read each other's minds. But these brain-wave measurements do show that even though brains are very complicated, twins' brains are amazingly alike.

A SPECIAL BOND

There are twins who think too much like each other. Greta and Freda Chaplin are English twins who have been described as having "one mind in two bodies." They talk in unison, dress alike and sleep in the same bed. When they make breakfast, they both hold onto the handle of the frying pan at the same time. Some scientists have said that the Chaplin twins are the closest thing they've ever seen to telepathy: reading each other's minds. They do so many things together that they seem to be communicating in secret ways.

Many twins feel that they have a special kind of bond with each other—a relationship that other people don't have. Sometimes it makes them act as if they were one person instead of two. There's a story about little twin girls who were very upset. One was crying, one was not. When the dry-eyed twin was asked why she wasn't crying, she said, "Sister's crying, so I don't need to."

The Wild Goose

BY ERNEST BUCKLER

I've never stopped missing my brother Jeff.

I'm all right; and then I pick up the rake he mended so perfectly for me where the handle went into the bow; or I come across where he'd scratched the threshing count on the barn door, with one of those clumsy fives of his in it; or it's time for someone to make the first move for bed; or some winter dusk when the sun's drawing water down beyond the frozen marshes — do you know that time of day? It's as if your heart slips into low gear.

(I'm glad Jeff can't hear me. But I don't know, maybe he wouldn't think it sounded soft. Just because he never *said* anything like that himself — you can't go by that.)

I always feel like telling something about him then. I don't know, if I can tell something to show people what he was really like it seems to help.

The wild goose flew over this evening. The sky was full of grey clouds. It looked as if it was worried about something. I could tell about Jeff and the wild goose. I never have.

It really started the afternoon before. We went hunting about four o'clock. I was fourteen and he was sixteen.

You'd never know we were brothers. You could tell exactly how he was going to look as a man, and I looked like a child that couldn't make up his mind *what* shape his face would take on later. He could lift me and my load (though he'd never once glance my way if I tackled anything beyond my strength — trying to lead a steer that was tough in the neck, or putting a cordwood butt on top of the pile, or anything). But I always seemed the older, somehow. He always seemed to — well, look up to me or something, it didn't matter how often I was mean to him.

I could draw the sprawling back field on a piece of paper and figure out the quickest way to mow it, by algebra; but when I took the machine out on the field itself I wouldn't know where to begin. Jeff could take one look at the field and know exactly where to make the first swath. That was the difference between us.

And I had a quick temper, and Jeff never lost his temper except when someone was mad at *me*.

I never saw him mad at me himself but that one day. The day was so still and the sun was so bright the leaves seemed to be breathing out kind of a yellow light before they fell to the ground. I always think there's something sort of lonesome about that, don't you?

I'm no kind of a hunter. You wouldn't think I was a country boy at all.

But Jeff was. He was a wonderful shot; and the minute he stepped into the woods there was a sort of brightness and a hush in his face together, I can't describe it. It wasn't that he liked the killing part. He seemed to have a funny kind of love and respect for whatever he hunted that I didn't have at all. If I don't see any game the first half a kilometre I get to feel like I'm just walking around on a fool's errand, dragging a heavy gun along. But Jeff's spell never slacked off for a second.

You'd have to live in the country to know what hunting meant to anyone like Jeff. And to know how he rated with the grown-up men; here's just this kid, see, and he knows right where to find the game, no matter how scarce it is, and to bring it home.

Anyway, we'd hardly gone any distance at all — we were just rounding that bend in the log road where there's the bit of open swamp and then what's left of the old back orchard, before the woods start — when Jeff halted suddenly and grabbed my arm.

"What's the matter?" I said.

I guess I spoke louder than ordinary, because I was startled. I hadn't thought of having to be cautious so soon.

Jeff's gun went up, but he didn't have time for even a chance to shoot. There was a flash of the big buck's flag. He'd been standing under the farthest apple tree. Then in a single motion, like the ripple in a rope when you hold one end in your hand and whap the other against the ground, he disappeared into the thicket.

Deer will sometimes stand and watch you for minutes, still as stone. Stiller than thunder weather. Stiller than holding your breath. So still you can't believe it. They're cocked for running, but you get the feeling they weren't there before you saw them. Your eyes seem to have plucked them right out of the air. Their feet don't seem to quite rest on the ground.

But the second you speak, they're off. The human voice is like a trigger.

It would have been a sure shot for Jeff. There wasn't a twig between them. It would have been the biggest buck anyone had brought home that year. Even I felt that funny sag in the day that you get when game's been

within your reach except for carelessness and now there's nothing. You just keep staring at the empty spot, as if you should have known that was the one place a deer would be.

Jeff turned to me. His eyes were so hot in his head I almost crouched.

"For God's sake," he said, "don't you know enough to keep your tongue still when you're huntin'?"

It was like a slap in the face.

The minute Jeff heard what he'd said the anger went out of him. But you'd have to live in the country to know what a funny feeling it left between us. For one hunter to tell another he'd spoiled a shot. It was as if you'd reminded someone to take off his cap inside the house.

I didn't say a word. Only in my mind. I seemed to hear my mind shouting, "You just wait. You'll see. I'll never…never…" Never what, I didn't know — but just that never, never again…

Jeff rumbled with a laugh, trying to put the whole thing behind us, as a joke.

"Well," he said, offhand like, "that one certainly moved fast didn't he? But we'll circle around. Maybe we'll ketch him in the choppin', what?"

I didn't say a word. I just broke down my gun and took out the cartridge, then and there. I put the cartridge into my windbreaker pocket and turned toward home.

"Ain't you comin'?" Jeff said.

"What d'ya *think*?" I said.

I glanced behind me when he'd gone on. I don't know, it always strikes me there's something sort of lonesome about seeing anyone walk away back-to. I almost changed my mind and ran and caught up with him.

But I didn't. I don't know why I could never smooth things over with Jeff right away when I knew he was sorry. I wanted to then, but I couldn't. I had to hang on to the hurt and keep it fresh. I hated what I was doing, but there it was.

It was pitch dark when Jeff got home that night, but he didn't have any deer.

I sort of kept him away from me all the next day. I hated myself for cutting off all his clumsy feelers to make up. ("What was the algebra question you showed the teacher how to do when you was only ten?") It always kind of gets me, seeing through what anyone is trying to do like that, when they don't know you can. But I couldn't help it.

(Once Jeff picked up about fifty bags of cider apples nights after school. The day he took them into town and sold them he bought every single one of us a present. I followed him to the barn that evening when he went to tend the horse. He didn't hear me coming. He was searching under the wagon seat and shaking out all the straw around the horse. He didn't want to tell me what he was looking for, but I made him. He'd lost a five-dollar bill out of the money the man at the cider mill had given him. But he'd kept the loss to himself, not to spoil our presents. That's what he was like.)

It was just about dusk when Jeff rushed into the shop the day after I'd spoiled his shot at the deer. He almost never got so excited he forgot himself, like I did. But he was that way then.

"Git your gun, Kenny, quick," he said. "There's a flock o' *geese* lit on the marsh."

It would be hard to explain why that gave even me such a peculiar thrill. Wild geese had something — well, sort of mystic — about them.

When the geese flew south in the fall, high in the sky, people would run outdoors and watch them out of sight. And when they turned back to the house again they'd have kind of a funny feeling. The geese seemed to be about the most — distant, sort of — thing in the world. In every way. You couldn't picture them on the ground, like a normal bird. Years and years ago Steve Hammond had brought one down, and it was still the first thing anyone told about him to a stranger. People said, "He shot a wild goose once," in the same tone they'd say of some famous person they'd seen, "I was close enough to touch him."

I was almost as excited as Jeff. But I kept rounding up my armful, pretending the geese didn't matter much to me one way or the other.

"Never mind the *wood*," Jeff said. He raced into the house for his gun.

I piled up a full load before I went into the house and dropped it into the box. It must have almost killed him to wait for me. But he did.

"Come on. Come on," he urged, as we started down across the field. "And put in a ball cartridge. We'll never git near enough fer shot to carry."

I could see myself hitting that small a target with a ball cartridge! But I did as he said.

When we got to the railroad cut, we crawled on our bellies, so we could use the embankment the rails ran along as a blind. We peeked over it, and there they were.

They were almost the length of the marsh away, way down in that mucky spot where the men cut sods for the dike, but their great white breasts looked big as pennants. They had their long black necks stretched up absolutely straight and still, like charmed cobras. They must have seen us coming down across the field.

Jeff rested the barrel of his gun on a rail. I did the same with mine. But mine was shaking so it made a clatter and I raised it higher.

"I'll count five," Jeff whispered. "Then both fire at once." I nodded and he began to count.

"One. Two. Three…"

I fired.

Jeff's shot came a split second afterward. He gave me a quick inquisitive glance, but he didn't say a word about me firing before the count was up.

He threw out his empty shell and loaded again. But the geese had already lifted, as if all at once some spring in the ground had shot them into the air. They veered out over the river.

All but one, that is. Its white breast was against the ground and we didn't see it in the blur of wings until its own wings gave one last flutter.

"We got one!" Jeff shouted. "Well, I'll be…. We got one!"

He bounded down across the marsh. I came behind, walking.

When I got there he was stroking the goose's soft down almost tenderly. It was only a dead bird to me now, but to him it seemed like some sort of mystery made flesh and shape. There was hardly a mark on it. The bullet had gone through his neck, fair as a die.

Then Jeff made a funny face. He handed the goose to me. He was sort of grinning.

"Here," he said. "Carry her. She's yours. That was some shot, mister."

"Mine?" I said.

"Sure." He looked half sheepish. "I'm a hell of a hunter, I am. I had two ball cartridges in this here pocket, see, and two shot in this one." He put his hand into the first pocket and held out two ball cartridges in his palm. "I guess I got rattled and put the shot in my gun instidd o' the ball. You know how far shot'd carry. It was you that got him, no doubt about *that*."

I carried the goose home.

It didn't mean much to me, but he didn't know that. He could only go by what it would have meant to him, if he'd been the one to carry it home. I knew what he was thinking. This would wipe out what I'd done yesterday. And the men wouldn't look at me now the way they looked at a bookworm but the way they looked at a hunter.

I'm glad that for once I had the decency to pretend I was as excited and proud as he'd thought I'd be. I'm glad I didn't say a word — not then — to let him know I saw through the trick.

For I knew it was a trick. I knew I hadn't shot the goose. While he was counting I'd felt that awful passion to wreck things which always got into me when I was still smarting over something. I had fired before he did, on purpose. Way over their heads, to scare them.

The day Jeff went away we sort of stuck around close to each other, but we couldn't seem to find anything to say.

I went out to the road to wait for the bus with him. Jeff had on his good clothes. They never looked right on him. When I dressed up I looked different, but Jeff never did. I don't know why, but every time I saw Jeff in his good clothes I felt sort of — well, like *defending* him or something.

The bus seemed to take a long time coming. He was going away in the army. He'd be with guys who were twice as much like him as I was, but just the same I knew he'd rather be with me than with them. I don't know, buses are such darned lonesome things, somehow.

When the bus was due, and I knew we only had left what few minutes it might be late, I tried to think of something light to say, the way you're supposed to.

The only thing that came into my mind was that day with the goose. It was a funny thing to bring up all of a sudden. But now we were a couple of years older I thought I could make something out of it to amuse him. Besides, when someone's going away you have the feeling that you ought to get everything straight between you. You hardly ever can, but you get that feeling.

"You shot the goose that day," I said, "didn't you?"

He nodded.

I'd never have opened my fool mouth if I'd known what was going to happen then. I'd felt sort of still and bad, but I hadn't felt like crying. How was I to know that the minute I mentioned that day the whole thing would come back so darn plain? I'd have died rather than have Jeff see my face break up like that.

But on the other hand, I don't care how soft it sounds, I'm sort of glad I did, now. He didn't look embarrassed, to see me cry. He looked so darned surprised — and then all at once he looked happier than I believe I ever saw him.

That was Jeff. He'll never come back. I don't even know which Korean hill it was — the telegram didn't say. But when I tell anything about him like this I seem to feel that *somewhere* he's sort of, I don't know, half-smiling — like he used to when we had some secret between us we'd never even discussed. I feel that if I could just make him absolutely clear to everyone he wouldn't really be dead at all. Tonight when the geese flew over I wished I knew how to write a book about him.

The geese didn't light this time. They never have since that day. I don't know, I always think there's something lonesome about wild geese.

But I feel better now. Do you know how it is?

The Education of Grandma

BY ELSIE MORRIS

The victim was Katia Zubkoff, whose rigid body lay across her bed, straining to catch her mother's muffled voice. She knew what Grandma was saying for she had been hearing it for the past two weeks, since the very first day of the old lady's visit, but she wanted to know her mother's reply. Rising noiselessly from the bed, Katia crossed the cold wooden floor to open the door a crack.

"I've told you before, Dasha," stormed Grandmother in Russian, "the girl is fifteen years old and she's still in school. What do you plan to do about it?"

"There's not much for her to do at home," Katia's mother replied with the usual timidity reserved for Grandmother.

"Not much!" Grandmother was sounding shrill. "Will you be knitting stockings for her all your life? And what does she know about spinning, I ask you? She won't even *look* at a spinning wheel. People all around you are going on relief and all she does is stick her nose in those books. Are you trying to make a useless lady out of her?"

"She helps around the house," Mother replied. "She churns the butter."

"With a book on her knee!" came Grandma's scornful reply.

"And will that change the taste of the butter?" Katia wanted to yell, but didn't because Grandmother was not the kind of person you yelled at. Instead, she closed the door and crept into the comfort of her feather bed. But with anxiety bordering on desperation, there was little comfort for her just then. If Grandma succeeded, it would mean the end of Katia's plan to become a teacher.

"Mother is weakening," she thought helplessly. "Will she give in completely?" Reaching up, she jerked down the shade, oblivious to the charm of moonbeams playing silent rhythms with the leafless poplars outside her window. Her hand brushing against the mud-plastered wall increased her irritation, as memories flooded with anger came rushing back.

Each spring Mother had whitewashed those walls with clay and water. Katia, who disliked the grey, was promised a pink room next spring.

"Why wait till spring?" Grandma had decreed. "Might as well do it now and get rid of those cobwebs."

"But we have no pink calcimine," Mother had protested. "We'll have to go to town and get some."

"Waste thirty kilometres of gas for calcimine! We'll do it with clay and water like it's always been done."

Upon returning from school, Katia stared in disbelief at the fresh grey walls, while Grandma stood by looking tired but pleased, like a surgeon who had just performed a successful operation.

"The spiders won't bite you any more *Katushachka*," she explained warmly, reverting to the diminutive endearing form which Katia loved but seldom heard.

But the thankless *Katushachka* remained unmoved. "Our spiders don't bite," she muttered, turning away to hide her smarting eyes.

"What's that?" demanded Grandma. "Spiders don't bite you say? Is that what they teach you in school? I should think it's time you stayed home and learned something useful instead of filling your head with nonsense."

Katia had walked away annoyed with Grandma, with Mother, with all of them. Why did they suddenly turn to jellyfish in the presence of this woman? Father, who usually had definite opinions, seemed to lose his backbone, and Mother turned to putty.

Why did they have to fall into her ways? Why did they always have to speak Russian? Though it was natural with adults, it seemed ludicrous with her two younger brothers. "Grandmother says it's so we won't forget Russian, but I know it's so she won't miss anything she can stick her nose into," thought Katie resentfully.

Her resentment burned into the night till she fell asleep. She was awakened early by the turning of the grate in the kitchen stove. Above the droning of the cream separator came Grandma's reprimanding voice, "You know Dasha, if that boy keeps turning the separator like that, you'll end up feeding all your cream to the pigs."

Almost at once the hum changed tempo.

When Katia reached the kitchen door, Father was standing by the table with a pen in hand waiting for Grandma to sign her "X" on a cheque.

It was a two-dollar payment for some spun wool, and it took both parents to convince the old lady of its worth before she would sign.

Holding the pen awkwardly in her hand as though it were an instrument of torture, she seemed uncertain what to do with it.

"Why don't you sign it in Russian if you don't know English?" suggested Katia.

Grandma, looking confused, pulled her kerchief forward to hide her embarrassment, and Katia remembered that Grandma could neither read nor write even in her native language.

"So there's something she can't do!" thought Katia gleefully. Armed with this knowledge she left for school feeling strangely exhilarated. Yet a lingering thought persisted that this should not be so. Suppose she tried to teach her to read and write? "She spends all her time spinning and knitting those horrid itchy stockings, and inventing ways to make me quit school. If she did something else, it might keep her out of my hair for a while."

With the last thought in mind Katia made her decision. One question remained. How?

Later in her room, as she searched the titles in her apple crate book shelf, she pondered. "Surely Grandma at sixty should be able to read what I could at five, if I helped her."

It seemed plausible, except for one detail which she dared not overlook. If Grandma had the least suspicion that she was being "educated," she would most likely burn the book.

"So," concluded Katia, "Grandma must not know. There's more than one way to skin a cat."

Next morning the sound of Grandma's voice indicated it was time to act. Removing her squeaky shoes, Katia picked up two books and crept stealthily toward her grandmother's room, hoping to slip unseen past the kitchen door where Grandma stood in full view.

Katia stood riveted to the floor wondering how long it would be before she turned away. Luckily six-year old Nick dropped his bread into the open stove, sending up a shower of sparks.

"Dasha," Grandmother turned to Mother, "the way you let this boy make his own toast he'll burn down the house."

Mother sighed.

"Sit down Nick. I'll make the toast after this," Grandma ordered as Katia slipped quickly past.

The cold lean-to at the end of the hall where the boys used to play before Grandma's arrival was now warmed by a heater. Shadows of its dancing flames darted from the braided floor mats to the plush rug on the wall, from the red geranium on the sill to the chair between the heater and the spinning wheel. Carelessly placing her books on the chair where Grandma would see them when she came to check the fire, Katia eyed the spinning wheel, malevolently remembering the scratchy stockings. Not even for a visit would Grandma leave it behind.

"She'd be as lost without it as without her arm," Mother had said.

Until Nicki caught his finger in the spindle it had graced the kitchen.

"Those boys will ruin it before I'm done with the fleece," Grandma had snorted. Katia hoped they would.

Now it reposed majestically in the corner of Grandma's room, impervious to Katia's glare.

Pleased with her success, she sped incautiously past the kitchen door when she stopped dead in her tracks at the sound of Grandma's booming voice.

"Dasha, did you see that girl? The floor is like ice and she's running about in stocking feet. Do you want to catch pneumonia before your time?" she demanded.

"I was looking for my shoes," flushed Katia.

"Did you hear that, Dasha? Fifteen years old and she's lost her shoes. I tell you, that girl has no sense of responsibility."

Mother sighed again. "Katia, put on your slippers."

Grandma left for her room and Katia returned with her shoes on.

"Has anyone seen my Russian primer?" she asked casually after breakfast.

"So you've lost your book now. What did I tell you Dasha, irresponsible. The way that girl leaves things lying about you'll have everything stolen off the place."

Like most of Grandma's puzzles, Katia gave up trying to solve that one.

"There are two books in my room," she continued. "Which did you want?"

"The one that says cat on the first page."

"Cat, shmat! Come with me."

Katia followed, meekly matching her brisk step to Grandma's barely perceptible limp, the result of an injury received while helping to move the granary.

"Which one is it?" asked Grandma, holding up the books.

Katia quickly flipped the page. "This one," she pointed. "This says 'cat'."

Grandma looked at it long and hard, tracing the mysterious letters with her gnarled fingers.

"And I suppose that says 'dog'?" She pointed to the next word.

"No, that says 'house'," replied Katia, picking up her pencil and printing it for her. "The letters are different."

Knowing the right moment had arrived, she hurried towards the door, leaving Grandma studying the words.

"I have to go now," she called back. "The van is almost here. I'll get the books after school."

In school Katia found herself impatiently glancing at the clock, wondering if Grandma's curiosity would lead her beyond the second page.

When at last she stepped off the van she could see Grandma's shawled head in the field, arms waving about like a conductor's, instructing Father how to spread manure. With one final grand gesture she left him, making her way towards the chicken coop.

"I wonder what she's telling the hens?" murmured Katia, stepping into the well-scrubbed porch where shiny milk pails stood neatly on their shelf. Only a day after her arrival Grandma had persuaded Father to build the shelf.

"The way you strew things under foot you'll end up with broken noses," she told them unceremoniously.

Katia rather suspected that it was not so much the noses as Grandma's tongue which had moved Father.

In the same way the pails which had previously been given a hurried wash were now scrubbed to perfection.

"You can't put dirty pails on a clean shelf, Dasha," she told Mother, proceeding to wash them thoroughly.

Katia paused in the kitchen doorway, inhaling deeply the yeasty fragrance of new baked bread, when Grandma arrived with an apronful of eggs.

"Come into my room for a minute," she said aside to Katia.

With the door closed carefully behind them, Grandma picked up the book. "Now then, you told me that this was 'cat' and this was 'house.' I went to the next page and found the same words there but there were some others I didn't know. Can you tell me what they are?"

Katia, delighted at this unexpected luck and hiding her dancing eyes lest they betray her delight, told her.

Grandma, amazed at the similarities of the letters, went on to sound a few more.

"I wonder," she said thoughtfully after a pause, "if you would mind coming in after school each day to show me some more words?"

No, Katia wouldn't mind, but before she left, Grandma intercepted her. "You won't bother telling the others about this, will you?" she added as an afterthought. "They'll probably think I'm shirking my work."

Katia agreed to the conspiracy and later found herself looking forward to those twilight hours spent in the coziness of Grandma's room. Grandma, who had not known a single printed word before, was now reading simple stories.

One day she said to Katia, "Sit down, we won't do word finding today. I want you to write a letter to Grandpa."

Katia reached for the paper.

"My dear Fedya," dictated Grandma.

"My dear Fedya," tittered Katia.

"Now what?" snapped Grandma. "Why are you giggling like a ninny?"

"You really ought to be writing your own love letters," twinkled Katia.

"Would I be asking you if I knew how? Love letters indeed! What next?"

"It's really quite easy. You start with 'A' and make it like this." Slowly and carefully Katia drew a large letter. Grandma, watching closely, remarked, "I'm too old to start this writing nonsense."

Katia continued to print more letters and Grandma, peering over her shoulder, exclaimed, "Why that's my name! A-n-a-s-t-a-s-i-a!" After a long pause she added, "Here, give *me* the pencil."

"You'll have to go over my 'A' first," Katia told her, remembering how she herself had first struggled with the letters.

While Grandma laboured over the letters, Katia noticed a pile of wool nearby. Reaching down she picked up a strand and pulled it apart. The fibres felt soft and silky in her hands. She picked up some more and lifted the carders. Grandma looked up from her writing only long enough to tell her to wear an apron if she was going to card wool. Katia reached for the voluminous covering. By the time Grandma had finished her writing, Katia had a pile of snowy rolls beside her.

"Tomorrow you can do the 'n'," Katia told her, leaving her with the sample letter.

She hurried home next day knowing there was butter to churn before she could begin to think of lessons. Grandma met her in the doorway.

"I churned it up for you," she informed the delighted granddaughter out of earshot of others, "so you can show me some more letters. Better give me the rest for tomorrow. Besides, I want to know what happened to that silly boy and his goat in the book. I don't know some of the words."

The day arrived when Grandma proudly announced to Katia that she now knew how to write her full name. "Now I can get back to my knitting."

Katia's face fell. What if Grandma took the notion to stop now?

"You've learned so many letters already, why don't you learn the rest of the alphabet as well. Then you can write anything you like," she suggested hopefully.

"Write anything, even letters?"

"Anything," repeated Katia.

Grandma paused for a few moments looking at a sock she had started. "Nicki needs socks."

Katia looked at the needles uncertainly before she spoke. "Maybe I can knit the socks."

Grandma looked surprised. "But you don't know how."

"I know a simple stitch I learned long ago."

Hesitating at first, Grandma finally handed her the needles, watching Katia's feeble attempt. At first, Katia's stitches were as awkward as Grandma's writing, but with time she became more adept. With fascination she watched the growing inches while Grandma, with her shawled head bent studiously over her books, seemed to have forgotten all about the socks till Katia asked for help with the heel.

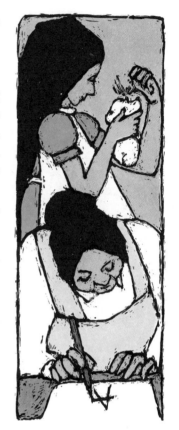

It was then Katia noticed for the first time Grandma's rough, gnarled hands and cracked fingers. She had been hanging wet clothes in the cold wind with bare hands ever since she had arrived and informed Mother, "The way you hang those clothes all bunched up together, they'll never dry." Although she had been quick to supply all the family with socks and mittens, she didn't seem to own a pair of mittens herself.

Katia suddenly noticed Grandma's stooped form and realized that it was a result of all the hard physical labour she had been doing all her life. Nor did a visit stop that work. If Dad was at the barn, Grandma brought water from the well; if the boys were at school, she brought in the coal. Although she had been short with the family at times, she never spared herself. And had she ever had a single holiday?

Then Katia realized with a pang that reading and writing were something that Grandma had done solely for herself for the first time in her life, and had been ashamed of doing it because she felt it wasn't work. Tears welled up in her eyes.

Grandma looked sharply at her. "What are you snivelling for now?" she demanded. "I suppose you've caught a cold?"

"I think I have," choked Katia.

"The way you go about bareheaded, you'll be in your grave before you're twenty."

Grandma's visit was fast drawing to a close and Katia shrank from the thought. On the day of her departure she found herself loitering about till the van left. A lump filled her throat as she watched Grandma straighten her shawl and tuck her voluminous skirt about her in the cab of the truck. Katia, huddling beside her mother, watched the truck move away. But the next moment the window rolled down and they could hear a familiar voice.

"Get back into the house. The way you two stand around with nothing on you'll be left without lungs before Peter gets back."

They looked at each other and laughed through their tears.

Indoors, the house seemed very empty. Katia, wandering aimlessly, found herself back in Grandma's room. Nothing was changed. The rugs were still on the floor, the spinning wheel in its corner.

The spinning wheel!

"Mother!" exclaimed Katia, rushing through the kitchen. "Grandma forgot her spinning wheel."

Mother looked up from the pot she was scouring. "I don't suppose she'll have much time for spinning now. Spring comes early to B.C. She never did finish that fleece though," she added thoughtfully.

In Grandma's room Katia gazed at the spinning wheel. The hateful thing now seemed warm and friendly, a reminder of Grandma. Pulling up a chair, she reached for the wool and turned the wheel. Lumpy strands began to take shape, rough at first but gradually smoothing out. Katia was beginning to enjoy the wheel's rhythmic hum.

"I'll just move it to my room and finish off the fleece," she thought.

"I didn't know that you could spin," exclaimed Mother, walking in and looking at Katia's uneven yarn. "Yes, of course you may finish it. There's hardly enough for a pair of socks. What did you want to do with it?"

"I thought I'd knit a pair of mittens," replied Katia, remembering Grandmother's chapped hands.

Katia's spinning helped relieve the loneliness that persisted all week till Dad arrived home with the letter. Written on the back of a calendar sheet, its crudely formed letters sloped awkwardly to one side.

Dear Katia,

Now that I am in the peace and quiet of my own home I can think straight again. Tell your mother to set the brown hen soon if she wants to have chickens before Christmas. She always puts off things till the last minute. Remind your father to raise the two-by-four in the granary if he doesn't want to crack his skull. I told him once but I'm sure he has forgotten. Keep the boys away from the spinning wheel. There's lots of work to do so I can't write much. As for you Katusachka, at the rate you go about showing people words and writing, you'll make a fine teacher some day. I send you all my love.

From your grandmother
Anastasia

Katia held the letter for a long time while two big tears rolled down her cheeks. Grandma was finally "educated," and so was Katia.

Elsie Morris

Elsie Morris, the author of "The Education of Grandma," grew up in Alberta in a community of Doukhobors. The Doukhobors are a religious group who emigrated from Russia to Western Canada in the late nineteenth century, and whose beliefs are marked by pacifism. Elsie moved away from the Doukhobor community that she had grown up with in 1941, but her thinking and writing continues to be shaped by the beliefs and values of her childhood. Like the protagonist in the story you have just read, Elsie Morris taught the Russian alphabet to her Doukhobor grandmother, who thought it was more important that a girl learn to spin than to read. Elsie's grandma, too, sent a letter back to show off her new skill. Like Anastasia's in the story, it was written on the back of an old calendar.

Elsie Morris and her grandmother.

GOOD BOOKS

Friends and Relations

Homecoming/CYNTHIA VOIGT
Abandoned by their mother with no money and no home the four Tillerman children must struggle to survive on their own. Thirteen year old Dicey has the spirit, love and good sense to guide her family along to triumph.

The Friends/ROSA GUY
Everything about Phyllisia feels different and wrong. Teased in the classroom and beaten up in the schoolyard, she is lonely and badly in need of a friend. Edith may be a poor, abandoned, thieving "ragamuffin" but she is just the person Phyllisia needs.

The Keeper/PHYLLIS REYNOLDS NAYLOR
Something very strange is happening to his father and Nick is afraid. Why is his father convinced his family is being watched? Why would he think there were microphones hidden in the toilet? Nick must find help quickly before something terrible happens.

Summer of the Swans/BETSY BYARS
Sara's younger brother Charlie has not spoken a word since he was sick years ago. One morning fourteen-year-old Sara discovers that Charlie is missing, and she is sure his disappearance is her fault. A desperate search for her brother leads Sara to an understanding of the true meaning of love.

SPORTS PAGES

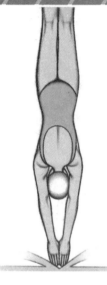

A strong feeling within her drew her to the edge for a short, quick look at the cool, blue water waiting to swallow her.

Fly Like an Eagle/59

I had one of the greatest disappointments of my life!

The Hockey Sweater/64

Athletes need to compete with their minds as well as their bodies.

Imaging For Success/68

Pam checked Black Sand abruptly as Becky's whip came hissing down.

The Finish Line/75

49

MOGA MADNESS

BY LAUREN E. WOLK

What do you get when you mix together a mountain of mashed potatoes, a heap of popcorn, and a few thousand feathers, throw in 150 000 Canadian teenagers, and let nature take its course? It's the national youth fitness contest, MOGA Madness...what else?

A popcorn party at Alberta's Trochu Valley School. All right, Trochu brought the popcorn — where's the movie?

Canada's Fitweek
May 20-29
Fitness Canada

The **M**ost **O**utrageous **G**roup **A**ctivity contest is organized by youth for youth, and is held annually during Canada's Fitweek. Every spring, high school students from across the country participate in hundreds of outrageous events that involve 20 minutes of continuous physical activity. Intended to promote physical activity to youth, MOGA madness gets the largest percentage of the student population possible to create original, creative, and outrageous events, and as much fun as possible, of course.

Last year, the judges awarded the coveted Pink Sneaker Award to Sir Frederick Banting Secondary School of London, Ontario for its Shower Power MOGA Hour. First, all 683 of Banting's MOGA maniacs, dressed in shower caps and garbage bag ponchos, spent half an hour slogging through some very creative messes. Then they shared a mass soaping and shampooing and, finally, a rinse, courtesy of the London Fire Department. All in the name of good, clean fun…and fitness.

So who gets *your* vote?

In the "Flamingo Stakes Extravaganza" at Westminster Secondary School in London, Ontario students ride pink flamingos through a 240 kg tub of jello.

Students from B.C.'s Pemberton Secondary School demonstrate the little-known mashed potato dance.

A Shattering Experience

BY DONALD HONIG

"Success does not come cheaply."

"Every triumph has its price."

You hear things like that spoken and you want to run in the other direction from the speaker before the wind becomes so great your ears get blown flat against the sides of your head. You have come to suspect that when certain words get bumped together they tend to blow up with air like birthday balloons.

That's what I believed until I was 12 years old. But now that I'm 13 and have seen a little more of the world, I'm beginning to believe that there might have been things I was wrong about. You see, experience can come into your life, and what it tells you goes something like this: *Listen again, and this time pay attention.*

This important information was brought home to me on a baseball diamond, where many important lessons are taught, and sometimes learned. We were one week away from our biggest game of the summer—Tuxdale (us) versus Palmerville (them). This game, between our neighbouring towns, had been topping off the summers for years and years.

The game was played on what was considered neutral turf—a field that lay between the two towns. A few days before the game some of us rode bikes down there to work out. I went with Alan Bennett on his two-seater bicycle—the kind that lets the guy on back look like he's peddling when he's really just along for the ride.

That was me. I was saving myself for the workout.

I really enjoyed the workout, because, for one thing, it gave me some time off from mowing the neighbourhood lawns, which I had been doing all summer to earn some pocket lining. Also, I wanted to get used to this field. I was Tuxdale's centre fielder, and I made a big deal of running around out there after fly balls, saying I wanted to see how the ball travelled and how it looked against the sky, as if the sky there were different from the sky anywhere else.

Then Alan, our star pitcher, asked me to go down the left-field line with him and warm him up.

"Why not Davey?" I asked. Davey was our catcher.

"No, Kenny," he said. "I want you."

I found out he wanted me to teach him how to throw a knuckle ball. You see, my big brother Dennis, who had been one of Tuxdale's best pitchers ever, had taught me how to throw the knuckler. Sometimes, before a game, when we were loosening up on the sidelines, I'd fool around and throw a couple of those dancers. I'd grip the ball with two fingertips and let it go, and once in awhile it would do something, like wobble in the air or suddenly drop. A knuckler is a crazy pitch.

"They're hard to control," I told him. "You shouldn't mess with it."

"Let's give it a shot," Alan said. "Throw me a couple and then show me how you hold it."

He walked on ahead, then turned around and crouched down in front of the fence like he was a catcher. The fence was about two metres high and right behind it were a couple of two-storey frame houses.

Alan punched the pocket of his glove and told me to throw.

The first knuckler I threw didn't do much, just shivered a bit on the air. The second one did less. I could see the disappointment beginning to form in his face.

"Okay," I said. "Here comes a good one."

I threw it too hard, which was a mistake, because you can't pressure a knuckler. It's a very independent pitch, almost with a mind of its own. Anyway, the ball slipped right off my fingertips and went way up in the air, too high for Alan to get, too high for anybody to get. It sailed right over the fence and a moment later there was the pure, sudden sound of glass shattering.

Well, if you've ever played ball, you know that sound. Sooner or later it comes to the ears of every ballplayer: that crisp, crashing noise which can freeze the air of even the hottest August afternoon.

Alan must have had more experience hearing that sound than I did, because the moment that window went splintering he was off, never fully straightened up from his crouch, running across the foul line and diving into the bushes that grew down there. But me, I didn't move. I guess I was too startled or scared or whatever.

Then all of a sudden this face appeared, the face of a very angry man, red as a ripe tomato. His shoulders must have come right to the height of the fence because all I saw was this red, glaring face that looked like it was balanced on top of the fence.

"You!" he yelled. "Hey, *you!*"

That got me moving in a way the crash never did.

I had to run. Alan was leaving, which meant my ride was leaving. And I didn't want to be left alone with the angry owner of a pile of newly shattered glass. I decided to come back later.

I wheeled around and began hightailing it down the left-field line. The rest of the guys — they'd heard the crash — were already hopping on their bicycles and taking off. I jumped over the players' bench, caught up to Alan, threw my glove into the basket behind the bike's back seat, and got aboard with a hop. We all went up the road at top speed, each guy bent over like competitors in a race. Without turning around, Alan said, "Boy, great knuckle ball, Kenny!"

When we got home we all went to the ice cream parlour and had some sodas. Everyone had a big laugh over the whole thing. Everyone but me — I'd broken the glass.

The Sunday of the big game was a real late August blazer, all yellow and hot like something fresh out of the oven.

I drove down to the field with my parents and brother, Dennis. When we got there the grandstands were already filling up with a couple of hundred people.

I sat down on our bench, and Alan came over to me. He had a foolish grin on his face.

"I was just thinking," he said, sitting down next to me. "Since that guy whose window you broke lives right over there, it's a good bet he'll be in the stands watching the game."

I hadn't thought of that. In fact, it would be just my luck that he'd come home midgame after I'd been knocking at his door for *days* trying to pay for the damage or work it off by mowing his lawn.

"Maybe he's not a baseball fan," I said.

"Well, he's probably forgotten you by now anyway."

"Probably," I said. But I didn't believe that for a second, not the way he'd looked at me. It was like his eyes were taking a photograph of my face and pasting it onto his memory.

We took batting practice and went through the pregame drills. Then, just before he went down to the bullpen to warm up — it was about 20 minutes to game time now — Alan came up to me in front of our bench and put his arm around my shoulder.

"Kenny," he said, "I didn't get much of a look at him last week, but I think he's here."

"Where?" I started giving suspicious little looks around the grandstand, keeping my head down and looking up from under the bill of my cap.

"Not there," Alan said. He jerked his thumb over his shoulder.

I looked, and then felt my knees turning to jelly. There he was, standing over by the Palmerville bench, big as a tractor, wearing a chest protector and holding an iron-barred mask in his hand.

He was the home plate umpire.

Alan gave me a silly grin and went off to warm up.

Talk about being in a boiling kettle! I was going to have to walk right up to him probably four times during the game and stand there. Jiggers, but I was a goner. He'd never believe I'd tried to make things right with him about the broken window. I could feel the panic starting all over me like the hives.

I would have to stall talking to him till after the game.

I looked over at Dennis and my parents. I'd never told them about the window. Then I got an idea. I went over to my brother. He was wearing sunglasses.

"Dennis," I said, "do me a favour. This sky is rough, not a cloud. Look at it. Lend me your shades."

He groaned, then reached up and lifted the glasses off his nose and handed them to me. The moment I put them on I felt better, safer. Then I went over to Mr. Pearson, our coach.

"Coach," I said, "this sun is burning my eyes something awful. I think I'd better wear these the whole game."

"You don't want to hit with them on, do you?"

"I'll be able to see the ball better."

"I'm not so sure about that, Kenny."

"No problem, Coach," I said. "Otherwise I'll be squinting up there and see only part of the ball. You see, I had—what do you call it, where your eyes get sticky?"

"Conjunctivitis?"

"That's it. I had it a few days ago and it made my eyes weak."

He just sighed. I guess he had so many other things on his mind at the moment, he just said okay and let it go.

So there I was, wearing sunglasses the whole game. Some of the guys laughed and called me Harry Hollywood and things like that, but I didn't care. Those shades could save me.

My first time at bat, in the bottom of the first inning, was the acid test. I walked up there wearing my shades, head down. But the umpire never glanced at me.

I had a hard time following the ball. I fouled one off, then took a couple of strikes and was gone. But he hadn't recognized me, I was sure of it.

I was a little more relaxed the next time up, but still couldn't manage more than a grounder back to the box, swinging at the first pitch just to get out of there in a hurry.

Soon I wasn't thinking about the umpire anymore because the game was ticking away as quiet and steady as a time bomb—inning after inning and no score. Once we got past the sixth inning you could just feel the tension growing. Baseball can be a funny game all right—the less that's happening, the more the tension.

Alan was pitching the game of his life for us—with no knuckle balls either—and a tall left-hander named Dawden was doing the same for them. Going into the top of the ninth it was still zip-zip.

"You hold 'em," the guys told Alan as he walked out to the mound to pitch the ninth, "and we'll win it for you."

Pitchers always hear that, but I don't think they always believe it. Anyway, I've never heard one say, "That's right," when somebody tells them that.

Alan put them down one-two-three in the ninth and we all hustled in. We had last up—the two teams alternated that every year—and all we had to do was nudge across just one thin run to win it.

I was leading off. Under the growing tension, I'd almost forgotten about the umpire and who he was.

Almost.

When I saw him looking at me as I walked to the plate it suddenly came back to me with a rush. I stopped right in my tracks, as still as a telephone pole. But then I realized he just happened to be looking in my direction and that the shades were still keeping me safe.

I stepped into the batter's box and dug in and pumped my bat back and forth in practice swings. I was a little frustrated; being a right-handed hitter, I figured I should have clipped this left-hander Dawden for a couple of hits. But I hadn't gotten anything out of the infield. I was tempted to take off those glasses, but didn't. For one thing, Mr. Pearson would want to know why I hadn't done that before, and for another thing, I didn't want the umpire to suddenly recognize me.

I tell you, I had a lot on my mind.

On the second pitch, Dawden came with a good fast ball that was a bit outside. I went for it, and the moment the bat cracked it, I knew I was in business. The ball shot out on a line over the first baseman's head and went travelling down the right-field line. With the right fielder swung over toward centre, this was at least a triple.

I took off and went sweeping around first base with all cylinders whirling, and as I went into second base I saw that the right fielder still hadn't picked up the ball. Coming into third I figured the coach would hold me up, but he was wheeling his arm around and around like a windmill and jumping up and down like a guy doing some crazy exercise.

I kept going.

I cut third base just right, hitting the inside corner of the bag with my foot, and went flying down the line. The catcher, his mask off, was in a half crouch, facing out toward right field waiting for the throw, his lips compressed in a tight line like he'd sworn never to speak again.

I was closing in on the plate when I saw the first baseman take the relay and whirl and fire. The ball and I arrived at about the same time. I went in head first, reaching out for the plate with my hand just as the catcher received the ball and spun around and whacked the tag onto the side of my head, but my hand was on the plate a split second before. As the catcher went tumbling over me I looked up at the umpire crouched enormously over us, legs spread so wide you could have pushed a wheelbarrow through them.

"Safe!" he roared, and then, glaring down at me eye for eye, he added in a highly dramatic whisper, *"You!"*

That's when I realized the sunglasses had been knocked loose by the tag. They were hooked over one ear and hanging sideways down my face.

Everybody came running off our bench to shake my hand and pound

me on the back and, finally, hoist me up on their shoulders. And over all the whooping and cheering, I could hear the umpire yelling, "What's his name? What's that kid's name?"

It was a strange ride home all right. My mother was excited because I was a hero. My brother kept smacking me on the back. And my father kept repeating: "One hundred twenty-five dollars. One hundred twenty-five dollars…"

I had broken a storm door, the umpire said. He also said he believed I had come and knocked on his door. They were the same days he had worked out-of-town games.

I, of course, had to pay my father back the one hundred and twenty-five dollars. Took every penny of the money I'd earned all summer cutting grass.

Which brings me back to what I said in the beginning: "Success does not come cheaply," and "Every triumph has its price." And there was something else I found out about too: mixed emotions.

Fly Like an Eagle

BY ELIZABETH VAN STEENWYK

"I've never been this high off the ground in all my life," Angie thought, as she climbed the ladder to the ten-metre diving platform. "I'm going to blow it. I can't possibly jump ten metres down to the water. Coach Hansen has to be crazy to think I'm going to dive from here. I won't…can't do it."

"The first dive is frightening from up there," Coach Hansen's voice came to her through the microphone and loudspeaker. His voice echoed through the dark, empty swim stadium. He was seated in his favourite spot near the pool.

"You can do it, Angie. I know you can dive from there."

"No, I can't do it," Angie thought, "and there's no way you're going to make me do this dive."

She stood well back from the edge of the platform, not even wanting to look down. Yet there was a strong feeling within her that drew her closer to the edge for a short, quick look at the cool, blue water waiting to swallow her.

"Come on, Angie. Time's wasting, and you know you're going to jump."

Angie shook her arms and legs again and again, as if she wanted to be free of them. Then she pulled and tugged at her suit so hard that it seemed to stretch down to her thighs.

"Think your dive through, Angie," Coach Hansen said. "Do it in your mind."

"Leave me alone," Angie thought. "I've done a front dive in the layout position a million times before on the three-metre platform. I know how to do it from down below, but this is different."

"Don't be ashamed to say you're afraid," Coach Hansen said. "Fear is something we all have."

"How would you know?" Angie thought. "When was the last time you stood up here?"

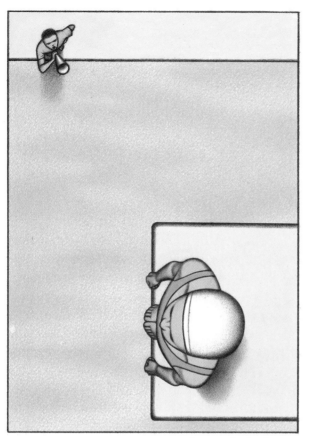

"Let's talk about what it is you're afraid of," Coach Hansen's voice went on. "Is it fear of landing wrong? I don't think so. You've done that before from the three-metre platform and from the edge of the pool when you first began to dive. What is it then? Fear of getting the wind knocked out of you?"

Angie looked towards him. She shook her head no.

"Of course not. You're not afraid of that either. Then what is it?" the coach asked. "I think I know. It's fear of the unknown. Is that what's bothering you?"

She nodded and walked back to the farthest edge of the platform. She wiped her hands on a towel.

"Of course that's it, Coach," she thought. "Is that so hard to understand? I've never done this before, never felt the dive in my body going down from here. I can't dive from here."

"Your fear is normal," the coach's voice went on. "It's not natural to want to dive from up there the first time. You need someone to know when you're ready to do something you've never done before. I wouldn't let you dive if you weren't ready. Confidence will come from the dive itself. You've learned that with each new one."

Angie stood at the edge of the platform. She put her toes in space and waited.

"You may not believe it, but your body will know what to do once you're in the air," Coach Hansen said.

Angie didn't believe it — not for one second. She walked to the back of the platform and dried her hands again. Then she turned and slowly took two steps towards the edge. Her mouth felt so dry she knew she'd have to swallow the whole pool to make it feel wet again. She pulled at her suit and shook her arms.

"Look, Angie, the thing you want most right now is to get this over with, right?"

Angie nodded. She couldn't have spoken, couldn't have made a sound.

"It will only take you two or three seconds to be down and out of the water. Don't think. Just do it."

Angie stood there, shaking inside until she was sure her blood was frothy.

"What about all your plans for the championship and the Olympics?" Coach Hansen asked.

"So he's going to use that old trick on me, is he," Angie thought. "Throwing the Olympics at me like a trainer throws fish to seals, as if I didn't know what he was doing."

She walked back on the platform and looked down the steps, longing to use them.

"Okay, I've had it," the coach said. His voice sounded cold and hard. "Just walk down the steps, and go home if you can't do this dive."

"No," she thought. "No, I won't. You aren't going to make a quitter out of me." She edged closer.

"That's better," the coach said softly. "Just remember to keep your body tightly controlled. If you're limp, that water will tear you apart. Now think it through, Angie. You're just about ready, I know you are."

She turned to get the towel again. Then she thought, "That's crazy. I keep drying my hands when I'm just going to get them wet in a second or two."

That's when she knew she was going to jump. She'd known it all along, but Coach Hansen had to remind her. There is that moment when you know it's going to happen. There is that moment when training takes over. That moment is now.

Angie took a deep breath and pushed off, her body rising into space. She spread her arms in the swan position and felt the air touch her body gently. For a lazy second Angie hung like a bird she had seen turning cartwheels in the sky. "Fly like an eagle," she told herself. "Fly." Then she felt her body begin to come down, and her mind took total control. She brought her arms over her head and kept her body and legs straight as she entered the water, causing hardly a ripple. Angie stretched her dive downward before she curved back to the surface.

"That wasn't bad, Angie," Coach Hansen said as she came out of the water and towelled herself dry. "But you can do better. Go back up there and try it again."

"Right," she said, and smiled. Her fear of diving from the platform had gone.

Pole Vault

He is running like a wasp,
Hanging on a long pole.
As a matter of course he floats in the sky,
Chasing the ascending horizon.
Now he has crossed the limit,
      And pushed away his support.
For him there is nothing but a descent.
Oh, he falls helplessly.
Now on that runner, awkwardly fallen on the ground,
Once more
      The horizon comes down,
Beating hard on his shoulders.

By Shiro Murano

Point Scored

By C. Cardenenas Dwyer

up against the backboard ...lolling... looping...leaning...almost in

Wild Pitch

In that Blue Jays/
Red Sox game
one beautiful
one hysterical moment
to stop all cameras—

batter set in the box,
big bat swinging,
sweat of concentration
beading his face;

the catcher crouched,
signal just given
and the big glove ready,
body taut spring
ready to uncoil anywhere;

umpire bent low,
set squarely behind him,
chest mask moved up
underneath his chin,
his attention focussed
on that white projectile
soon to hurtle in;

then all three frozen
in one glorious second
when the ball's released
from the pitcher's fingers;

comes bulleting in
to sail high high
higher
over batter
catcher
umpire
six feet above their heads;

with no motion made
so great their disbelief,

all eyes
refusing to look up
to catch,
winging high and wide and far

the screwball
that came unscrewed.

By Raymond Souster

The Women's 400 Metres

Skittish,
they flex knees, drum heels and
shiver at the starting line

waiting the gun
to pour them over the stretch
like a breaking wave.

Bang! they're off
careening down the lanes,
each chased by her own bright tiger.

By Lillian Morrison

The Hockey Sweater

BY ROCH CARRIER

TRANSLATED BY SHEILA FISCHMAN

The winters of my childhood were long, long seasons. We lived in three places—the school, the church, and the skating rink— but our real life was on the skating rink. Real battles were won on the skating rink. Real strength appeared on the skating rink. The real leaders showed themselves on the skating rink. School was a sort of punishment. Parents always want to punish children and school is their most natural way of punishing us. However, school was also a quiet place where we could prepare for the next hockey game, lay out our next strategies. As for church, we found there the tranquillity of God: there we forgot school and dreamed about the next hockey game. Through our daydreams it might happen that we would recite a prayer: we would ask God to help us play as well as Maurice Richard.

We all wore the same uniform as he, the red, white, and blue uniform of the Montreal Canadiens, the best hockey team in the world; we all combed our hair in the same style as Maurice Richard, and to keep it in place we used a sort of glue—a great deal of glue. We laced our skates like Maurice Richard, we taped our sticks like Maurice Richard. We cut all his pictures out of the papers. Truly, we knew everything about him.

On the ice, when the referee blew his whistle the two teams would rush at the puck; we were five Maurice Richards taking it away from five other Maurice Richards; we were ten players, all of us wearing with the same blazing enthusiasm the uniform of the Montreal Canadiens. On our backs, we all wore the famous number 9.

One day, my Montreal Canadiens sweater had become too small; then it got torn and had holes in it. My mother said: "If you wear that old sweater people are going to think we're poor!" Then she did what she did whenever we needed new clothes. She started to leaf through the catalogue the Eaton company sent us in the mail every year. My mother was proud. She didn't want to buy our clothes at the general store; the only things that were good enough for us were the latest styles from Eaton's catalogue. My mother

didn't like the order forms included with the catalogue; they were written in English and she didn't understand a word of it. To order my hockey sweater, she did as she usually did; she took out her writing paper and wrote in her gentle schoolteacher's hand: "Cher Monsieur Eaton, Would you be kind enough to send me a Canadiens sweater for my son who is ten years old and a little too tall for his age and Docteur Robitaille thinks he's a little too thin? I'm sending you three dollars and please send me what's left if there's anything left. I hope your wrapping will be better than last time."

Monsieur Eaton was quick to answer my mother's letter. Two weeks later we received the sweater. That day I had one of the greatest disappointments of my life! I would even say that on that day I experienced a very great sorrow. Instead of the red, white, and blue Montreal Canadiens sweater, Monsieur Eaton had sent us a blue and white sweater with a maple leaf on the front—the sweater of the Toronto Maple Leafs. I'd always worn the red, white, and blue Montreal Canadiens sweater; all my friends wore the red, white, and blue sweater; never had anyone in my village ever worn the Toronto sweater, never had we even seen a Toronto Maple Leafs sweater. Besides, the Toronto team was regularly trounced by the triumphant Canadiens. With tears in my eyes, I found the strength to say:

"I'll never wear that uniform."

"My boy, first you're going to try it on! If you make up your mind about things before you try, my boy, you won't go very far in this life."

My mother had pulled the blue and white Toronto Maple Leafs sweater over my shoulders and already my arms were inside the sleeves. She pulled the sweater down and carefully smoothed all the creases in the abominable maple leaf on which, right in the middle of my chest, were written the words "Toronto Maple Leafs." I wept.

"I'll never wear it."

"Why not? This sweater fits you...like a glove."

"Maurice Richard would never put it on his back."

"You aren't Maurice Richard. Anyway, it isn't what's on your back that counts, it's what you've got inside your head."

"You'll never put it in my head to wear a Toronto Maple Leafs sweater."

My mother sighed in despair and explained to me:

"If you don't keep this sweater which fits you perfectly I'll have to write Monsieur Eaton and explain that you don't want to wear the Toronto

sweater. Monsieur Eaton's an *Anglais*; he'll be insulted because he likes the Maple Leafs. And if he's insulted do you think he'll be in a hurry to answer us? Spring will be here and you won't have played a single game, just because you didn't want to wear that perfectly nice blue sweater."

So I was obliged to wear the Maple Leafs sweater. When I arrived on the rink, all the Maurice Richards in red, white, and blue came up, one by one, to take a look. When the referee blew his whistle I went to take my usual position. The coach came and warned me I'd be better to stay on the forward line. A few minutes later the second line was called; I jumped onto the ice. The Maple Leafs sweater weighed on my shoulders like a mountain. The coach came and told me to wait; he'd need me later, on defence. By the third period I still hadn't played; one of the defencemen was hit in the nose with a stick and it was bleeding. I jumped on the ice: my moment had come! The referee blew his whistle; he gave me a penalty. He claimed I'd jumped on the ice when there were already five players. That was too much! It was unfair! It was persecution! It was because of my blue sweater! I struck my stick against the ice so hard it broke. Relieved, I bent down to pick up the debris. As I straightened up I saw the young vicar, on skates, before me.

"My child," he said, "just because you're wearing a new Toronto Maple Leafs sweater unlike the others, it doesn't mean you're going to make the laws around here. A proper young man doesn't lose his temper. Now take off your skates and go to the church and ask God to forgive you."

Wearing my Maple Leafs sweater I went to the church, where I prayed to God; I asked him to send, as quickly as possible, moths that would eat up my Toronto Maple Leafs sweater.

IN CONTEXT
AUTHOR PROFILE

Roch Carrier:
Les Maples Leafs, Yes Sir!

"Toronto? Toronto? Through all the years of my childhood, Toronto was never a city. It didn't occur to me that Toronto was anything but a hockey team. In my little village in Québec, during those long winters when the snow piled up outside our warm wooden houses that sheltered us from the wind howling like a famished wolf, we would all sit around the old radio in its cabinet of dark varnished wood. Maurice Richard would dash across the red line with the puck, into the Maple Leafs' Zone, he'd shoot—and score! Toronto had lost and we danced with joy. The Montréal Canadiens had beat Toronto.

But a city called Toronto? There was no such thing.

Then there were those boxes of merchandise that came to my father's store; I remember them so well that just thinking of the way they smelled

still makes me sneeze. And I see on the sides of the boxes: W.T.X. Ltd., MONTREAL TORONTO MELBOURNE AUSTRALIA. For a long time, because of those boxes in my father's store, I thought Toronto was in Australia.

Years passed, I became a novelist and one day I learned that one of my novels had been translated into English and would be published in Toronto. I was invited to Toronto for the publication and that was when I learned that even though Toronto was still a hockey team, it was also a city."

— *Translated by Sheila Fischman*

FOR SUCCESS

An interview with Dr. John Durkin

BY AVERY GIETZ

"Imaging" is a term you hear a lot these days in the sports world. When athletes are striving to outrun, outskate, or outdance their extremely talented, extremely well-trained rivals, they need to compete with their minds as well as their bodies. Avery Gietz, a Grade Twelve student from Belmont Senior Secondary School in Victoria, B.C., decided to find out more about the mental training technique of "imaging." She spoke with Dr. John Durkin, a mental training expert at the University of Victoria.

INTERVIEWER: *What is imaging?*

DR. DURKIN: Imaging, in general, is forming some representation of events in the future or the past. People usually think of imaging as being only visual, but for some it is more natural to hear things or feel them. Imaging includes all kinds of sensory techniques.

INTERVIEWER: *How does imaging work?*

DR. DURKIN: Imaging can determine how well one performs any given activity. People who feel that they are klutzy at a particular activity invariably *are* klutzy. They are probably embarrassed to begin with and unconsciously resist the physical involvement needed to perform well. While I'm not a big fan of hypnosis, some staged hypnosis has shown that people perform elaborate activities well when they are rid of negative images. In sports and everyday life, imaging is used to set up positive expectations.

INTERVIEWER: *Can you give an example of athletes, swimmers, or runners going through an imaging process?*

DURKIN: First of all, they would fill their minds with an image or feeling of the activity in considerable detail. To give you an example, some swimmers I was working with could image their event to within a hundredth of a second; the same times they'd actually been achieving in the pool. They would feel the water, hear the sounds as if they were really there. They would image the activity from being "inside," as if they were performing the activity, or from the "outside," as spectators. From the inside, they could use the imaging to work out any difficulties in a turn, for example. As spectators they could see their arms and legs moving as they swam or positioned

"Ever since I've been young I have always done imagery. That is how I learned how to do a lot of my own jumps. I would be working on a triple toe loop for instance; I would be thinking about it so much and I would be at home in bed thinking about it and all of a sudden I would get the feeling of it in my head. The feeling is what you are after, rather than just picturing it. It was through actually feeling it in my mind that I started to make all my jumps consistent. It was just self-discovery. I guess I just wanted to land these jumps so badly. It was like when you have a dream about something and you think you have actually done it."

—BRIAN ORSER, FIGURE SKATER

"If you wake up, stretch, and smile and then get out of bed, you're waking up with a positive attitude." —LORI FUNG, RHYTHMIC GYMNAST

themselves properly on the blocks before diving into the water. A great swimmer would not go up on the blocks with an empty mind; his or her imaging would be very carefully determined and would prevent other competitors, the audience, or the cameras from becoming a distraction.

INTERVIEWER: *Which is more effective: training as a "spectator" or as an "insider"?*

DURKIN: Research shows that being inside is better for learning the imaging technique, but an elite athlete will use both.

INTERVIEWER: *Are there any basic steps to follow when imaging?*

DURKIN: Yes, but people have to be trained to do imaging properly and this can take a long time. First, they have to be able to relax. They do this by physically relaxing first the feet and then the legs, or by visualizing being in a relaxing environment. Next they have to be able to concentrate. Most people have great difficulty concentrating. If asked to keep the image of an orange in their minds for ten seconds, most people couldn't do it. If they *can* concentrate on the orange, then we see if they can do things with it: pivot it in different directions, take pieces out of it. If they can do this strongly, then they can use their ability to visualize athletic activity.

INTERVIEWER: *Have you found imaging to be very successful?*

DURKIN: It tends to be as successful as regular physical practice. An elite athlete who does not visualize before an event can rarely compete successfully with an athlete whose mind is involved. All the athletes are trained so well physically, and their times are all so close, that imaging can make the difference between success and failure — every time.

"The first year I won a World Cup was in 1979. It was a mental step that allowed me to do it. I'd been on the team for some time. I knew that I was a good skier. I was racing in the first seed and I was in the top three once or twice. As I was sliding down the course one day in St. Moritz, I looked around at the other guys and they were all nervous. It was a new course and they were all pretty scared. I realized that I was not scared. I wasn't even intimidated by the course. I thought, 'Gee, I can win here. If I do everything right, I should be able to win here. I can win.' It hit me like a lightning bolt. I said, 'Well, why not?' And I just went out and did it."

—STEVE PODBORSKI, DOWNHILL SKIER

"So you have to start looking for better ways, besides drugs, to improve your performance. I guess that's where the mental aspect comes in."

— KELLY KRYCZKA. SYNCHRONIZED SWIMMER

INTERVIEWER: *I have heard that during the imaging process, heart rate changes, breathing changes, and muscles get a workout as if they were actually physically performing the activity. Can you tell me more about this?*

DURKIN: Athletes who use imaging do show heart, breathing, and muscle responses similar to those displayed during the actual activity. It's something like what happens during a nightmare: you wake up showing the same reactions as you would if the activity had really happened: accelerated heart rate, sweating, trembling. A nightmare is a visualization, an uncontrollable one for most people.

"Whenever there is a mental thing involved I usually try to mark it down in my day book. I put it in my own words and use it to instruct myself, as a reminder for the next time. I have never referred back to it but writing it down imprints it better."

—LAURIE GRAHAM, DOWNHILL SKIER

"About fifteen minutes before the race I always visualize the race in my mind and 'see' how it will go. I see where everybody else is, and then I really focus on myself. I do not worry about anybody else. I think about my own race and nothing else. I try to get those splits in my mind, and after that I am ready to go. I think a lot of swimmers don't visualize a race, and don't visualize what they really want to do."

— ALEX BAUMANN, SWIMMER

INTERVIEWER: *Can you give some examples of how imaging can be used in everyday life, for students specifically?*

DURKIN: Students can take any worrisome activity and establish positive images of doing the activity effectively. For instance, visualizing relaxation and control is an excellent way of handling exams.

INTERVIEWER: *Can you give the names of some athletes who use imaging?*

DURKIN: All the athletes I know use it: Brian Orser, Laurie Graham, Steve Podborski, Wayne Gretzky — they all use imaging.

INTERVIEWER: *So basically, all elite athletes and those planning to reach that level use imaging; they have to.*

DURKIN: Most of them are now trained to use it. All the members of the Canadian Olympic hockey team use visualization. Weightlifters use it before lifting. Most of the people I have been involved with are martial artists and tennis players. They use it constantly.

INTERVIEWER: *Do you have any comments for people who might be interested in using imaging?*

DURKIN: There are three common misconceptions. First, people tend to visualize success. I don't think it is wise for people to visualize success in terms of beating someone else. It is wiser for them to visualize doing the best they can, to image only those things over which they have control. Since they only have control over their own performance, they should not visualize their *opponent's* performance: their own personal best is the goal to achieve.

It is also unproductive to try to influence others through the visualization. For instance, people want to be liked so they may visualize people liking them. That they have no control over.

The second thing that I think is important to realize is that visualization does not make all things possible. Hard work must accompany the imaging to attain results. Elite athletes know this and work very hard physically as well as mentally.

My third concern is that people often visualize material things: money and things like that. I see these more as outcomes of activity. I think it is a waste of the technique to image in this way. It would be better for athletes to visualize themselves doing the best they can as productive and contributing people.

"It is the final piece to the puzzle. When two athletes are even-steven, the difference is in the head."

—MARTY HALL, COACH

The Finish Line

BY WALTER FARLEY

*P*am had already proved herself to her boss, Alec Ramsay. After all, she had broken and trained the young colt, Black Sand. Now she had to prove one more thing to Alec — and to Henry, the veteran trainer — and most of all, to herself: that she could ride Black Sand and win.

On Wednesday afternoon, Pam went to the post with Black Sand — the first race on the program, the first race for each of them. Alec watched her with mixed emotions and some misgivings, now that the moment of trial was at hand. But he wanted Pam to remain with him, and the thrill of racing Black Sand might be the incentive she needed.

Henry had wasted no time, once Pam had agreed to ride. He'd had Pam work Black Sand the following morning, arranging for a track steward to be there. They had watched Pam break the colt from the gate in the company of two other horses and male riders, a six-furlong* test of Pam's competence as a jockey to obtain her apprentice's licence. She had gone the distance in a good 1:14, beating one rival by five lengths and outdistancing the other.

Alec had heard the steward tell Henry, "She'll have no trouble. She has a fine pair of hands and knows what she's doing."

Henry too had been impressed by Pam's performance. Later, back at the barn, he'd asked Alec, "Where did she learn to ride like that?" And Alec had told him of the professional horsemen Pam had known who, she'd said, had taught her everything she knew.

"Not everything," Henry had replied. "She's naturally good. Yes, I like the way she rides."

Alec wondered if Henry was getting to like Pam personally as much as he liked her riding. There was no doubt that Pam was reaching him by her

---

* furlong: (in horse-racing) a distance equal to 200 m

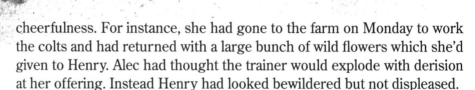

cheerfulness. For instance, she had gone to the farm on Monday to work the colts and had returned with a large bunch of wild flowers which she'd given to Henry. Alec had thought the trainer would explode with derision at her offering. Instead Henry had looked bewildered but not displeased.

"I picked them just for you," she had told him.

Alec watched the horses through his binoculars. He had found a place on the rail near the finish line, where he wanted to be when the race ended. The horses were in the chute on the far side of the track. It was a large field of two-year-old colts and fillies, all non-winners. Actually, the race was a cheap one — a six-furlong race against cheap horses, the kind Henry had wanted for their colt's first start. Except for not being race-hardened, Black Sand outclassed them all.

"If Pam only stays clear of the others and rides as I told her," he thought, "she'll win easy." Fortunately, she had the outside post position in the milling field of twelve horses.

Alec moved his binoculars along the line, passing from one jockey to another. The horses would do the running but what about the hands that guided them? Each rider had professional poise and confidence. Becky Moore was there too, riding the first of her three mounts for the afternoon. She looked as confident as any of the men.

Henry couldn't have known Becky would be in the race, but the unusual coincidence was appreciated by the crowd since it added interest to an otherwise unpredictable race among erratic two-year-olds. Never before had there been two girl jockeys in the same race at Aqueduct.

"Keep clear, Pam, just keep clear," he thought, wondering if she would remember all he'd told her over and over again these past two days. She had listened intently to him but her eyes had said, *"Talk all you like, but I must do it my way when the time comes."* And he knew she was right, for experience is the only teacher.

Now, as he watched her in the black-checkered silks of Hopeful Farm, he nervously wiped the back of his hand across his dry lips. There was nothing he could do to help her. "Okay," he said aloud, as if she could hear him. "Do it your way then. Just don't get hurt."

The starting bell rang and the grilled doors slammed open. He saw Pam slacken rein, loosen her knees, and hurl the colt forward. Black Sand came out of the gate a half-stride ahead of the others.

For a few fleeting seconds, the other horses raced beside her, running ever faster to make up the leap Black Sand had on them. But the colt was not to be caught; he was running with tremendous speed and smoothness.

"*Go, Pam, go!*" Alec shouted.

Midway down the backstretch, Black Sand was a full length in front of the jam-packed field. Pam kept him on the outside and made no attempt to move over to the rail. She was being very careful to avoid trouble.

They approached the turn and Alec watched her take Black Sand closer to the inside. She guided him with hands and body across the track, slowly, carefully toward the turn. The other horses came on and Black Sand was in closer quarters now. The colt didn't like it. His pace became rough.

Alec understood Black Sand's reluctance to move closer to the flaying whips of the oncoming riders. He saw Pam urge him on, not with her body alone but with the weight of her knowledge and understanding of what caused his fears. She was telling him with her hands, "*No whip will touch you. No one will hurt you. Just run your race, and soon we'll be clear again.*"

Black Sand lowered his head and dug in again to meet the challenge of the horses on his left. A bay horse wearing a bright-yellow hood tried to steal the lead as they curved into the turn. Beside the bay, on the inside, was another horse racing abreast. Both were trying to knife their way past still a third horse on the rail, who was tiring and bearing outward. All three

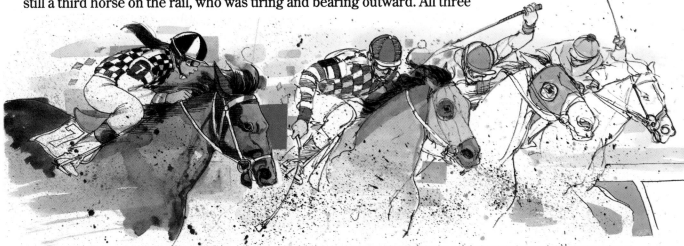

riders were making full use of their whips, Alec saw, using all the strength of their arms and shoulders. The strides of the horses lengthened under the drumming of the whips.

Pam kept Black Sand clear of them, even checking him a bit to lose more ground. Her reflexes were quick, Alec noted, and she was making split-second decisions. He knew she wanted to win but it was not as important to her as the colt's coming out of the race unscathed and free of any fear that might create greater problems later on. Black Sand seemed less afraid than he had just seconds ago, more confident in close quarters. That was to the good, Alec decided. Pam would simply keep him in stride and free of the closely crowded trio racing beside her. She would make her move again, when they came off the turn.

The horses bent around the turn, their riders whipping with either hand, scuffing and scrubbing with hands and feet, determined to get out in front for the final run down the home stretch. Becky Moore was just inside Pam, as free with her whip as the men. Too free, Alec decided; she was using it every second, leather striking hide rhythmically, switching from one hand to the other without pause in an attempt to keep her tiring mount on a steady course.

The horse with the yellow hood had surged into the lead, his jockey rocking and pushing to keep a stride ahead of the one beside him. Both horses were digging in, their hides scraping and moving over to the rail directly in front of Becky's mount.

Alec kept his binoculars on them. Becky was beaten, and must have known it. It was pointless for her to continue whipping her mount. Yet with another terrible blow, she launched her horse again. There was no place for him to go on the rail, for the two leaders left him no room. Lashed by the whip he bore out toward Black Sand!

Alec watched Pam try to stay clear of him. Black Sand's strides became ragged as Becky drove her heels into her horse's sides while lashing him with all her strength.

For the first time during the race, Alec felt the coldness of fear. Becky would stop at nothing in her determination to keep her mount going. She had switched her whip, from left hand to right, in an attempt to straighten out her mount and drive him between horses.

Pam checked Black Sand abruptly as Becky's whip came hissing down.

Whether or not it touched Black Sand on the legs, Alec couldn't see. It might have been that the colt was just frightened by it. But, suddenly, Black Sand took two quick jumps to the outside. Pam tried to stop him as he bolted crazily across the track. Alec caught a glimpse of the outer rail and knew that the colt would run full tilt into it. "*No!*" he shouted at the top of his voice.

Black Sand's hurtling body crashed into the fence and Pam was catapulted high into the air!

Alec had jumped the rail and was on the track, running for the far turn when the field of horses swept by. With the track clear, the ambulance left the infield gate. Alec flagged it down and hopped into the front seat.

A small crowd was already on the scene when they got there. Black Sand was dead, his neck twisted and broken. White-faced, Alec kneeled beside the still, silk-clad figure that was Pam. His forehead was drenched in cold sweat, his body trembling uncontrollably.

Pam's eyes were open but glazed. She tried to raise herself to an elbow but he prevented her by saying, "Lie still, Pam. You've had a bad fall." He moved aside for the ambulance attendants. They removed her helmet, and the sun shone on her hair with a violent light. Her face was grimy, with tiny rivulets of blood running through the caked dirt. He felt tenderness and gratitude that she was alive. Her eyes turned in the direction of Black Sand, and Alec knew he had no choice but to tell her. There must be no subterfuge, no phoniness. That was the way she would want it.

"The colt's dead," he said, unable to control the quaver in his voice.

She did not answer and her silence alarmed him. He touched her face.

"Please, Pam. He didn't suffer. He didn't know what happened." Alec passed his hand over her forehead. Her whole face was cold.

Then, suddenly, her hands were seeking and clutching his. He lowered his face toward hers and she pushed her head into his chest, as if hollowing out a nest. "I know," she said, swallowing noisily. "You don't have to tell me."

Alec realized that Pam had known the moment the colt had died, for she and Black Sand had been one.

From *The Black Stallion and the Girl* by Walter Farley

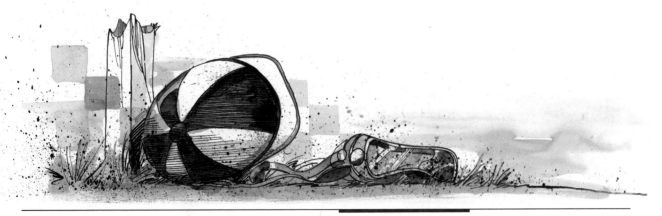

It Takes Talent...

It takes talent to fail gym three times.
It's my protest against the body beautiful.
I can't jump the side horse or climb the ropes.
Running bores me and basketball is the pits.
I can't touch my toes or do a decent sit-up.
A jumping jack looks ridiculous and parallel bars are lethal.
The gym teacher says I'm not thinking positively.
I suppose I'm not.
But what's so great about smelly bodies and wet towels?
Everyone is so into their bodies these days.
Everyone is running far ahead of me,
Jumping higher,
Scoring points,
Breaking records.
I'd rather sit here and solve equations in my head.
As long as my mind is in good shape,
I don't much care about the rest of me.

By Mel Glenn

Reggie

It's summertime
And Reggie doesn't live here anymore
He lives across the street
Spends his time with the round ball
Jump, turn, shoot
Through the hoop
Spends his time with arguments
    and sweaty friends
And not with us
He's moved away
Comes here just to eat and sleep
    and sometimes pat my head
Then goes back home
To run and dribble and jump and stretch
And stretch
And shoot
Thinks he's Kareem
And not my brother

By Eloise Greenfield

Good Sportsmanship

Good sportsmanship we hail, we sing,
    It's always pleasant when you spot it.
There's only one unhappy thing:
    You have to lose to prove you've got it.

By Richard Armour

AMAZING BUT TRUE

SPORTS STORIES

SPIT IT OUT

In the early days of lacrosse, the ball was a great deal smaller than it is today. (Modern rules state that the ball must be about 20 cm in circumference and weigh about 150 g.) Early players learned to hide the ball in their mouths as they ran toward the goal. There was only one way to find out who had the ball, and that was to smack the opposing players across the body to make the ball pop out.

GOOD BYE, REF

The referee in hockey can throw a player out of a game. Once, however, a referee took himself out of a game instead.

In the early years of the century a Montreal team was playing Winnipeg in a Stanley Cup game. Referee J. A. Findlay imposed a penalty on a Montreal player. The Montreal players complained bitterly about the decision. After referee Findlay listened for a while, he announced that he had been "insulted." Findlay went home before anyone could stop him.

Some hockey officials jumped into a sleigh and went to Findlay's house. They coaxed and pleaded, and finally the referee agreed to return to the arena. By the time he got back, however, some of the Winnipeg players had already changed into street clothes and disappeared. The game was never completed.

SUPERWOMAN!

Ever wonder who was the most versatile athlete in the history of sports? A strong contender would be Mildred "Babe" Zaharias, who won gold medals for Olympic hurdles and javelin events and a silver medal for the high jump at the 1932 Olympic Games. As if that wasn't enough, she set world records for these events.

Zaharias was also an All-American basketball player, and in her spare time set the record for throwing the baseball. She went on to win the United States Women's amateur golf title in 1946 and the United States Women's Open in 1948, 1950, and 1954.

Move over, Superman!

THE FIRST ICE HOCKEY GAME

There is evidence that a hockey-like game was first played on ice in the early sixteenth century in the Netherlands. But the game was probably first played in North America on 25 December 1855 at Kingston, Ontario. At least, that's what some Canadians believe…Others say that the first game of ice-hockey as we know it was played in Halifax.

CALLED ON ACCOUNT OF GRASSHOPPERS

A horde of grasshoppers, numbering in the millions, invaded the Texas League baseball park in Midland, Texas, during the second game of a doubleheader between Midland and Amarillo.

The grasshoppers hit in such numbers that they dimmed the lights. Fans screamed, players swung their bats, and everyone clawed at the insects covering the playing field, the stands, and the mercury vapour lights.

The umpires were forced to suspend the game.

Health Department officials said a cool weather front that had pushed into the area might have brought the invasion.

CHANNELING ONE'S LOVE

After four hours of swimming en route across the English Channel, Peter Johnson paused long enough to say, "Will you marry me?" to Julia Hughbanks. She was riding in the escort boat on August 13, 1985.

Julia, like Johnson, a geologist from Texas, nodded happily and the 26-year-old Johnson picked up his stroke as he continued the 34 km swim from Cap Gris Nez, France, to St. Margaret's Bay, near Dover, England.

It took Johnson 8 hours and 20 minutes, which trimmed 14 minutes off the previous France-to-England record for the crossing. And it marked the first time a Channel swimmer ever became engaged along the way.

Olympic Fun and Games

Moscow 1980

Rain seemed a certainty as the spectators filed into the impressive Lenin Stadium for the opening ceremony. Then, just 12 minutes after the first parade, the dark clouds cleared and a hazy sun broke through. The Russian organizers later revealed that six specially fitted airplanes had sprayed the sky with chemicals to clear the threatening clouds. Tomorrow's world is with us today!

Helsinki 1952

Jean Boiteaux had just won the Olympic 400 m swimming gold medal for France when startled officials were disturbed to see a spectator dive fully clothed into the pool. He swam to where the new champion was recovering his breath and kissed him on both cheeks. No disciplinary action was taken when it was discovered that the invader was Jean's father celebrating his son's victory.

Melbourne 1956

Russian Yvacheslav Ivanov was so excited about his victory in the single sculls that he tossed his gold medal up in a gesture of sheer delight. As he reached out to catch his prized possession, he succeeded only in knocking it into the waters of Lake Wendouree, where the rowing events were staged. The 18-year-old Muscovite dived into the water but was unable to retrieve his medal. He was later presented with a replacement medal by the International Olympic Committee. Ivanov received gold medals again in 1960 and 1964 and each time clung on tightly to the greatest reward in the world of sports.

GOOD BOOKS

Sports

Tie-Breaker/JACK BATTEN

"In the first place, it wasn't my idea to be a hot shot junior tennis player." So begins the story of Lance, a cool-headed tennis player who suddenly finds himself on the edge of stardom—to his surprise. Our unlikely hero plays against the best, *and* he gets the girl.

Fox Running/R. R. KNUDSON

On the night she meets Kathy "Sudden" Hart, Fox Running is literally running away from her life. Fox knows nothing about competitive running, and Sudden, a former Olympic runner, is eager to teach her. The two learn from each other, as Fox strives for the elusive Olympic gold.

Amazing But True
Sports Stories/PHYLLIS & ZANDER HOLLANDER

Heroes and villains, good times and bad are revealed in more than 80 true stories about sport. Funny, informative and entertaining, this book covers many unusual moments in all kinds of sports.

The Moves Make the Man/
BRUCE BROOKS

Jerome Foxworthy—the Jayfox—can *really* play basketball. Then he meets the moody and mysterious Bix Rivers. Jerome can teach Bix basketball, but Bix just won't learn to fake. Can the Jayfox convince Bix he'll never win at hoops, or anything else in his life if he doesn't learn the moves?

JOURNEYS

My friend lives in Turkey. I am going to walk until I get to him.

The Journey of Charles Wayo/88

"Keep your caps pulled down and don't raise your heads to look at anyone."

Underground to Canada/96

Hunger was now the ruling instinct in the Labrador and it drove him out to forage in the early dawn.

The Delay/108

The boy saw the giant fire-white horses being harnessed to the golden chariot.

The Horses of the Sun/114

The Journey of
CHARLES WAYO

BY CHARLES L. SANDERS

On the first day of January, 1964, a fourteen-year-old African boy set out on one of the most remarkable journeys ever recorded. His intention was to travel from his native village near Accra, in Ghana, all the way to Turkey — on foot. There he hoped to locate his "pen pal," Charles W. Simmons, a captain in the United States Air Force. The two had corresponded for two years, ever since the boy had found Simmons' name in an old magazine.

The boy, who changed his name to Charles W. Wayo after his new friend, believed that Captain Simmons would help him to study in America. Then he hoped to return and lead his fellow Africans out of poverty and oppression.

Armed with only pen and paper, a map, a calendar, two or three loaves of bread, and a bag of onions, young Charles secretly left his home and family and headed north. After walking about 70 km, he sat down and began to tell the story of his journey in his own words.

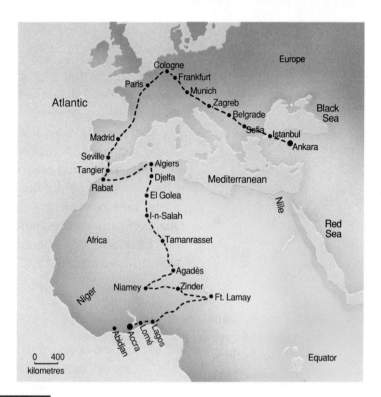

1 JANUARY 1964

This night I am going to sleep in the bush here. I have left home all alone without the knowledge of my parents to go to look for my friend Capt. Charles Wesley Simmons of the US Air Force. I am about 70 km from home (I mean Nima). My friend, the above, lives in Turkey. I am going to walk until I get to him. I must have to go to school. I am poor, I have no money, I can't get anywhere but walk. Legs were made before engines. With me are two friends — God and Death. Anyway, I am scared a little bit. God help me. Good night. Till tomorrow.

2 JANUARY 1964

Tonight, the sky is bright. I can see clearly. I have walked a lot and my legs are angry. I don't want to quarrel with them. So both of us must rest. I am about 150 km from home now. I am almost beginning to know what lies ahead. I have bread and fried fish in my bundle. The fish is smelling, so I will eat all quick. The day's walk has been interesting. I saw many creatures. God is great. Never have I seen such beautiful animals playing all over in their kingdom. They did not bother me, except one antelope which kept running in the direction I am heading. I wondered why. Well, I am sleepy, so I will climb up an orange tree and pass the night peacefully. Good night.

4 JANUARY 1964

I was nearly killed yesterday. This is how: I was asleep for about two hours when I felt something heavy on my stomach. Opened my eyes. A big black snake crawling over me, heading opposite direction. Nearly screamed. Somebody held my throat and pressed my body very strong and still till my would-be assailant towed itself away. I regained consciousness. I don't think I can sleep tonight, just sit here and continue tomorrow. I don't think I am far away from Togo now. Good night.

I got here I would not stop to tell. But it is enough to say that I have escaped death twice and escaped starvation several times. It is about 11 p.m. The weather is chilly over here. All my skin is cracking, my shirt is almost tearing. Today, I, Charles Wayo of Nima city, a little village of Ghana, am crying bitterly. Although it is cold, I have to sleep on the cold leaves. I am having a raw bird now for my supper. My hands are shaking, I can't write good. I do not think I will live long now. My situation could not be any worse. I love mankind and I am going to die for them, too.

13 JANUARY 1964

In fact, you won't believe it, but I am in Lomé. I slipped right across the border and will rest a couple of days, planning how to get to Turkey. I have much bread I picked from the marketplace, except they are hard as stones. So I want to live. Well, I have eaten them. Good day.

20 JANUARY 1964

I am going to Dahomey. I spoke to some small children begging for food and water and they laughed at me, for I was dirty and smelling. I spoke their language and told them I was one of them from the farms. They gave me water to drink and offered me two sugar canes. God bless them.

25 JANUARY 1964

I have passed through the capital of Dahomey and now I am about to enter Nigeria. There is some happiness in me, but I don't know what it's about.

28 FEBRUARY 1964

I haven't written my diary for a long time. I did not want to stop and rest. Now I am past Lagos and near Chad. Of all that befell me before

As he was wearing only a shirt and short pants Charles suffered from many cuts which had become infected. Some villagers in northern Nigeria treated him and insisted that he rest. It was five months before he wrote in his diary again.

22 JULY 1964

I begin to plan escape. I gathered much food and dried meat and hid them in the woods. Escape is not difficult. They do not hold me, but they won't be happy if I say goodbye, so run is the best.

25 JULY 1964

I got to Chad. I am very exhausted. I did not see much trouble. I went to the American Library here in Ft. Lamy, studied map, read all the newspapers I could get my hands on. Very hungry, ate my dried meat, drank some Chad water. I am heading this night for Niger. I must sleep now near the post office. I don't care.

After studying the map, Charles decided to change his route. From Chad he had to backtrack to Niger, planning to head straight from Agadès across the Sahara Desert to Algiers.

2 AUGUST 1964

This morning at 11:40 as the public clock shows, I am in Zinder, a small town in Niger. I love it. I think I will stay here for a while and rest. I will write. I am very lonely. No family and no friends. I am too young, too. I can see all the dangers I have been through now. I am crying and writing at the same time. Would you blame me? Please don't. I love mankind, and I think that with a little knowledge I could soften this world for all to live in peace. He who might find this note somewhere must not think I am silly. I have a vision right now. And so I know why, at this age, I gathered this courage to do this.

Charles rested at Zinder for several weeks while an old Moslem man treated his badly swollen feet. When he was well enough to slip away, he headed west by mistake and ended up far off-course at Niamey. Despite this setback, he set off once again for Agadès.

30 SEPTEMBER 1964

My skin is dried flat. I have had no water for the past 20 hours or so. My throat is hurting me. I am weak and dizzy. I just dug out some roots and I am chewing them raw. The sun is very high. I am still in Africa, and if I think about home and my parents, there comes such sorrow and fear in me that I feel like I should return. But I have sworn an oath that my conscience will not let me break. Death or not, I mean to push on to find Capt. Simmons, my friend. I am not going to, or can't, tell all the things that are happening to me because my hands don't feel like writing them all. Some are too fantastic.

19 OCTOBER 1964

If I don't keep on saying I am suffering, you may not be able to guess how terrible I look. Imagine you, a human like me, with flesh and blood, walking thousands of kilometres and without much food or water, eating leaves and roots, no bath for about a month and sweating from the heat and you are only 15 or 16 years old. Well, just make the picture of it. Facing wild animals who could devour you in a minute, or tribesmen who might kill you just for the fun of it. Well, there is nothing I can do except put my trust in Providence and ask Him for the salvation of my soul.

Charles was passing a small house near Agadès when he grabbed a chunk of goat meat and wrapped it up in his shirt. He arrived at the once-important city extremely ill. Although the goat meat had spoiled in the heat, he had eaten it, and his old sores had reopened as well. He would probably have died if one of the tall, proud Tuaregs, a desert tribe, had not found him.

4 NOVEMBER 1964

Well, I told you that God stays right beside me and His work is wonderful. A native found me yesterday and seeing my condition did not like it at all. He carried me on his shoulders to his hut and put me down. Tomorrow a native doctor will come and see me. Maybe this is my end and I am going to die as a brave man. I am lying on my back, for my stomach is bitter and my sides are filled with sores. Pray for my poor soul.

6 DECEMBER 1964

A thousand Amens to God. The sun is high and thick. I must have been asleep for a month. Now I can talk to the man who saved me, Mallam Abudu. I understand I fainted so many times.

I had fever. They wanted to know my father's house, but I told them I was an orphan child without home. Agreement to work for them. I said yes, but my brain said no. I must escape.

18 DECEMBER 1964

I am over 300 km away from Mallam Abudu, the man who has been nice to me. May God forgive me if I have been mean to him. I did not mean to do it, but I must keep going until I fall dead and the world hears me no more.

26 DECEMBER 1964

On Christmas Day, yesterday, I sat down all day, cried and prayed and cursed. My eyes are swollen now. I think I have eye-ache. For the first time I have fully understood my dangers and my isolation. I am crying because I know I am thousands of kilometres away from home and may never see it again. But every time I let out a breath, I let it out with hope.

Christmas has gone without me. Happy New Year will come for many and they will live a better life. I will stay here in this place and look at the birds. I wish I were a bird. I would fly away and go to Capt. Simmons for the New Year. But it is impossible. Oh God help my soul. If you help me I will just sit here and nurse my legs. If my eyes get fine I will head right across the Sahara toward Turkey.

Month after month Charles followed the south-north route across the Tropic of Cancer and through the desert to Algiers. It took him weeks to cross the Ahaggar, the mountain range which is one of the most cruel of all Sahara areas. The intense sun made him fear his brains would boil. He took to walking at night and hiding in the shade of rocks and dunes during the day.

29 MARCH 1965

I am right in the sandy Sahara, and I think no man in the world has done this before. Am I crazy? I can see death walking hand-in-hand with me, for there is sand, sand, sand. I have never been so scared in my life. I can't stand the sun too long I think. Even my oranges are boiled. But I suck them and the water wets my throat. Am I really Wayo in this place? Who brought me here? The sun is merciless. It seems to come low and sit right on my head. I wish I had a hat.

30 MARCH 1965

My trip is hard and rugged and very, very slow. My oranges are 10 now, my bananas 2, pineapples 0, some dried meat, and eight birds. They will run out soon. I will be without water and food and will die here. I will hide this notebook near my left armpit, and if my body is found, look for it there. I will put a note on my mouth telling you.

Charles laughs now when he says that he awoke the following morning, felt himself to see if he was dead, then got up and walked on.

9 JUNE 1965

From time to time, for one week, I have seen dwarf trees and I sit under them and look at the sun and watch it rule the Sahara with no mercy. I walk in the night and even here on the Sahara it becomes more cold than any other cold I ever felt. My teeth rattle, my body shakes, and believe me if I see fire somewhere one of these nights I will jump in.

12 JULY 1965

This story is too miraculous to tell you here. But I will say it in short. Some French army men riding on the Sahara picked me up while dying. So, after all, God has taken mercy on my youth and granted me another pardon. Now the Frenchmen have left me with two months' supply of food after treating me for three days. They can't keep anyone longer than that. They brought me somewhere and said I should sit here and a truck will come soon and pick me up. I have sardines, some strange long bread which could be used to spank someone. I have a water can, etc. May the Lord guard, guide, and protect those men. And I was picked up again by some Arabs yesterday, and I am riding on top of a truck now. It is about 8 m long and well packed with goods. I am enjoying it. The two men are sitting in front and I am right at the back. I am moving much faster now....

Within two months, Charles had reached El Golea in north-central Algeria. At the town of Djelfa, the Sahara ended, and he began seeing signs pointing to Algiers and the sea.

I am well glad to see such a fantastic city as Algiers. It is beautiful, and being here means that Wayo has conquered the Sahara. I am now halfway to Turkey, and only God knows that this is really me. I will not write anymore in my diary, for I am cold and still have a long way to go. Maybe I will write again when I reach my goal. Now I am going to Morocco, for someone has told me it is better to get to Turkey from there. Good-bye.

From Algiers, Charles made his way to Tangier, Morocco, where he hid aboard a ferry going to Spain. He had reached Europe at last! In Spain, Charles was amazed to see poor white people, beggars whose clothes were as ragged as his. The only whites he had known in Africa were all wealthy. For a while he hated the white people for what seemed like deception, but after a while his feelings softened. As he continued to travel, he realized that white and black people could be just the same — rich or poor, kind or indifferent.

Heading east through France, Germany, Austria, and Yugoslavia, Charles had many more adventures. When he finally reached Ankara, Turkey, he says he couldn't believe his journey was over.

It was the end of May, 1966, nearly two and a half years since Charles had left his village. In the streets of Ankara, he stopped airman after airman to ask for the address of Captain Charles W. Simmons. When at last he arrived at the apartment door, he knocked again and again. There was no answer.

"I sat right down on the steps and cried," Charles says. But an airman, the last in the long chain of rescuers, took him to his home to wait for Simmons. Sure enough, after a few hours Simmons returned home with his wife and children. Charles knocked again on the apartment door. This time it opened. Charles was so frightened he couldn't say a word. But a very kind-faced man shouted, "You're Charles Wayo, aren't you?" Charles managed to say, "Yes, sir, it's me," and the man grabbed him, almost too amazed to believe what he saw. Charles' friend had been found.

IN CONTEXT
FOLLOW UP

Charles Wayo has accomplished much during the twenty-four years since he came to the United States to enter Boy's Town School in Omaha, Nebraska. He was dissatisfied with the strict discipline at the famous school and home for orphaned young men, so he ran away and found refuge with a family in the southern United States. He finished high school, then enrolled at a university in Michigan. Before graduation, he met and married a fellow student, and they are parents of a daughter.

After college, Charles began working for a Chicago-area firm that exports agricultural equipment to countries around the world. For many years, Charles has travelled on his sales missions, and he became such a successful salesman that he was named president of his company.

Charles Wayo has become a successful man, but he is also a generous one. He often makes gifts to his close friends, and for many years has sent money back home to Ghana.

—Charles L. Sanders

Bike Trail

By Myra Stillborn

The path
down the slope
is a zipper,
sand-coloured
in cloth of green.

I on my bike
am the tab,
gleaming in sunlight of May.
Poised at the top
I wait
and then
in a smooth descent
I glide through the soft, spring air
unzipping the coat of green.

Underground to Canada

BY BARBARA SMUCKER

"*There's a place the slaves been whisperin' around called Canada. The law don't allow no slavery there. They say you follow the North Star, and when you step onto this land you are free. Don't forget that place.*"

When Julilly and Liza stole away one night from the Riley cotton plantation, they knew that the slave-hunters would soon be after them with their dogs. The girls travelled by dark, secretly aided by friends. They knew Julilly's mother was right — they couldn't rest until they reached that promised land where slavery had been abolished.

"**I** don't like bein' tied up in a sack, Julilly." Liza scowled and there was a look of terror in her eyes. But she pulled the harsh cloth over her head and sat waiting in the carriage seat. Julilly did the same.

The driver opened the door and crawled inside. He tied each sack tightly at the top. Then he picked up Liza and handed her to his waiting helper outside.

"Make yourself as small as possible," he told Julilly, "and I will carry you over my shoulder."

Julilly knew if she stretched out she would be twice as long as Liza. She huddled together as best she could.

A swirling sound of people and train noises, together with the drip of steady rain, surrounded Julilly. She felt the arms of the driver tighten about her.

A voice cried out above the confusion:

"Search all those cars for runaway slaves."

Julilly's heart pounded. She was glad for the sack and glad for the protecting arms around her.

"Two packages of dry goods go in this car," she heard another voice call.

She was lifted into the car and carried far back into what must have been a dark corner. She was placed next to the sack that was Liza.

"Don't move and don't talk until the train starts," the driver said softly. "You're going to Cleveland. A friend of the Underground Railway will meet you there. It's best you stay in the sacks until you reach your destination. But I'll loosen the top so you can stick your heads out for the trip."

He pulled the cloth down from the girls' heads, but it was so dark they could barely see each other. The car began to move and the man left quickly.

There was a screech and the banging of a door. Wheels creaked and rolled beneath them. The car jerked and the girls fell against each other. A bell clanged. The train was frightening with its strange urgency. The wheels turned fast and then faster, clicking over the long, silver track. Julilly pictured it in her mind. It would look like the track they had walked along in the state of Kentucky. The sound and speed of the wheels began

humming inside Julilly's head. She felt dizzy. Liza groaned each time the big empty freight car rattled and jerked.

Julilly grew thirsty. Her mouth was dry and her tongue felt thick. She began to think about the rain outside and how she wanted it to pound through the car and wash down over her. She leaned against Liza.

"Julilly," Liza mumbled, "I think my own bones has come loose, and is rattlin' around in this sack."

Julilly had no answer. The train rattled on and on. It was going on forever, she began to think, and with all this speed it might fly right off the tracks. Julilly forgot about a destination and that sometime the train would have to stop.

She dozed off to sleep for a time, and was surprised when their freight car banged into the car ahead of them and the rhythm of the wheels became slower and slower and then stopped.

"Liza!" Julilly cried out in alarm, feeling her friend's body slumped against her legs.

"I'm not dead," Liza groaned. "I just can't sit up."

In the middle of the car a light appeared. The door of their car slowly opened and a wild whip of cold fresh air blew in around them.

"I am seeking two parcels of dry goods shipped to me from Cincinnati," a familiar voice called out. "I will take care of their transfer aboard the schooner *Mayflower* personally." Julilly remembered. The voice belonged to Massa Ross from Canada! He must have escaped from jail. He had come, as he promised, to take them into the land of freedom.

"Ah, here they are!" he cried. He leaned over the girls without speaking and quickly tied the sacks over their heads. Then he picked up a girl in each strong arm and strode from the car. Within minutes he lifted them into a carriage with heavy drawn curtains. He untied the sacks at once and pulled the girls free from them.

Liza fell onto the floor. She was too twisted and bent to sit on the seat. Julilly stooped to lift her and came face to face with Massa Ross. But was it Massa Ross? He had no beard; his hair was dark red but shorter; his chest and stomach were puffed out round and full as before, but the clothes that covered them were plain. The ruffled shirt was gone.

He rubbed his smooth chin and his eyes crinkled with laughter.

"Julilly and Liza." His voice was muffled but still lofty as though he might be preaching a sermon. "Praise God that you have overcome innumerable hardships and are now on the very brink of freedom."

"A drink, Massa Ross." Julilly could barely manage the words. Her mouth had the dryness of dust on the road to the cotton fields.

"My dear children." The large man heaved himself down to a bag at his feet. He pulled out a bottle and unscrewed a cap. Water gurgled into a cup.

"Liza first," Julilly said.

Mr. Ross held Liza upright and lifted the cup to her lips.

"Drink slowly, child," he said. "When your body has been drained of moisture, it cannot stand the shock of unlimited amounts."

Soon the cup came to Julilly. The moisture cooled her lips. She held the liquid in her mouth. It trickled down her throat and she swallowed twice, greedily.

"There will be more when you board the *Mayflower*." Mr. Ross bent down and returned the bottle to the leather bag.

Now that her mind was released from the dreadful thirst, Julilly realized that the carriage was moving. She could see only the outlines of Mr. Ross's face in the seat opposite her and Liza. Liza clutched the seat with both hands, struggling painfully to straighten her back.

"Freedom ain't easy, Massa Ross." Liza sounded again like the sullen, angry girl of the long-ago slave cabin on the Riley plantation. "Even you got put in jail, and your face don't look so well."

Mr. Ross was weary. He leaned his back against the carriage seat.

"They had to release me when the slave whose disappearance caused my trial returned. He came into the courtroom just when I was about to be condemned."

Mr. Ross spoke again, but quieter this time: "Injustice is the weapon of evil men. But there are always brave and noble souls who proceed on the course of right and are impervious to the consequences. I feel rewarded for all my efforts, just to free the two of you."

Julilly was pleased with the ring of his words. Whatever Massa Ross was saying, it helped her lift her head and straighten her back and think of Mammy Sally, who never bent low to anyone.

Julilly thought back to the hot day in the cotton fields, when Massa Ross marched down the rows and chose Lester and then Adam to be his guides. Lester and Adam! Why hadn't she and Liza asked about them right away? Massa Ross would know where they were.

"Massa Ross," Julilly blurted out in a jumble of fear and hope, "did Lester and Adam get to Canada?"

Mr. Ross leaned forward slowly.

"They reached Canada, all right," he said. "They both knew freedom."

He paused. "Lester has a job in the town of St. Catharines. He wants both of you to come there.... Adam died."

There was a shocked moment of silence.

Kind, gentle Adam. Julilly felt the dryness again in her throat, but this time there was throbbing pain. Liza bent forward, straining her crippled back. Her eyes filled with tears, which ran freely over her scarred black cheeks.

"How did he die, Massa Ross?" she asked.

Mr. Ross's shoulders slumped. "It was the chains." His voice was husky. "They were too tight and cut through the flesh. When we filed them off, there was blood poisoning. Adam lived in Canada only one day. We buried him under a tall pine tree."

There was nothing more to say. The evil chains. Julilly felt herself wanting to pry them apart for ever — to strain every muscle in her body to pull every chain loose from the legs, and arms, and necks of every slave.

The carriage stopped and Julilly wiped the tears from her face with the sleeve of her newly knitted sweater. Before she heard about Adam, Julilly was going to ask Massa Ross if he had seen a tall, black-skinned woman with a proud walk who went by the name of Mammy Sally. Now she was afraid to know.

The carriage jolted. The door opened and the girls with Mr. Ross stepped into a dusky, lead-grey street. It was evening. To be safe, they pulled their new hats far down over the blackness of their faces. They tucked their hands under the warmth of the wisteria-blue sweaters.

Before them was a vast, grey stretch of water. It didn't have the sound of the rolling Mississippi. The water heaved and pushed towards the shore and then splashed in one long row of waves. Great hulks of boats, anchored along its sides, rocked with the rhythm of the moving water. On one of the largest, the sails were being pulled aloft.

"That one is the *Mayflower* — the Abolition* Boat," Mr. Ross said. "It will take you across Lake Erie to Canada under its waving sails."

"Then you aren't comin' with us?" Julilly faced him soberly.

Mr. Ross heaved his great shoulders and breathed long and full into the vastness of his chest. "I must return again to the South and free more of your people," he said. He picked up the skimpy bundles from the carriage floor and walked towards the boat.

"Keep your caps pulled down and don't raise your heads to look at anyone," Mr. Ross turned and whispered to the girls. "With those new clothes a passer-by would think you were my children. It's fortunate the day is grey and cloudy."

---

* abolition: doing away with something — in this case, slavery

It was only a few steps to the boat and at once Mr. Ross began shaking the hand of a man he called "the Captain." Mr. Ross didn't raise his voice with his usual flourish but spoke quietly.

"A friend with friends," he said at first. The magic password of the Underground Railway. Julilly felt warm and excited each time she heard it.

"These are my children," Mr. Ross continued. "Take them safely to Fort Malden."

The Captain was a jolly man with a hat cocked to one side of his head.

"Aye, that I will." He hung onto each word with peals of laughter. "Come with me, lads, to your bunks below."

Mr. Ross patted each girl gently on the shoulder and bade them good-bye. He disappeared into the grey evening dusk. Julilly and Liza wanted to call out to thank this big, kind man. But both of them knew the need for silence. It would be dangerous, too, for them and for Mr. Ross if they lifted their heads and showed their black faces.

The girls walked aboard the *Mayflower* with the Captain. Julilly felt the boat must be breathing and that she was walking over its body. It went up and down with each rise and fall of the waves beneath it. They followed the Captain down a narrow flight of stairs and then walked along a corridor with tiny doors on either side. At one of them they stopped. The Captain opened the door to a little room. It was hardly big enough for the three of them to stand inside. Two beds seemed to hang on the side of the wall and a small round window looked out on the water.

"I know ye are lassies," the Captain laughed again, "but for this trip ye will be laddies to me and me mates."

He showed the girls how to lock their door and warned them to open it only when they heard three knocks and then the words "a friend with friends." He would bring them food and water at once. Then they were to crawl into their beds and sleep with all their clothing on.

"If all goes well" — the Captain smiled broadly beneath his thick black mustache — "we will reach the banks of Canada in the early morning light." The r's in his speech trilled together like the song of a bird, Julilly thought. She would have no trouble recognizing his voice behind a door that was closed.

The Captain bent down and walked out of the little door. The girls locked it behind him.

There was barely time for Julilly and Liza to look about the cabin, when three raps were heard on the door, and the Captain's voice whispered, "A friend with friends. Open the door, lassies, there's trouble aboard."

Julilly turned the lock. The Captain's face puffed with anger.

"I've had word there's a slave-hunter and sheriff coming aboard, with a warrant to search the schooner before we set sail." He peered closely at the girls.

"I've a notion that ye're the lassies they're making all the stir about."

He picked up their bundles and hurried them out of the door. They ran down the narrow corridor and up the winding stairs. It was nearly dark on the open deck. Firefly-looking lanterns bobbed here and there. The wind was full of the smell of fish, and it was cold.

The girls ran with the Captain across the deck to the far side of the schooner where a little lifeboat, covered with canvas, hung against the side. The Captain pulled back the canvas and helped Julilly and Liza inside.

"Ye'll find blankets, water, and a bite of food in there. Take care and pray that the Good Lord will protect ye." He pulled down the canvas and left them alone.

The girls shivered. They felt about for the blankets and crawled under them, partly for warmth and partly for protection.

"We're gonna jump into the water," Julilly said solemnly, "if that sheriff comes near this little boat and takes the canvas off the top."

Liza clutched Julilly's shoulder.

"We're never goin' back to bein' slaves again."

It was a pledge between them. They were near the end of their journey. Massa Ross had said that Canada and freedom were on the other side of Lake Erie. There was no more walking through the woods, or climbing mountains, or hiding in wet swamp water.

"After all our trials, Liza," Julilly said slowly, "anythin' is better than goin' back to slavery."

There was a small opening between the canvas and the top of their little boat, and the girls found that by looking through it they could see onto the deck.

People walked aboard with baskets and bundles in their arms. Sailors pulled at ropes and lifted rolls of heavy white cloth. Near the plank where the people came on board, the Captain stood scowling — his cap still pulled down over one eye and his mustache looking stiff and forbidding.

The girls kept their eyes on him. Two large men shoved their way up the plank and approached him. They could be the sheriff and the slave-hunter. Julilly and Liza didn't know. They had never seen them before. The men spoke to the Captain, waving their arms in his face and pacing impatiently up and down beside him. They seemed like horses pawing the ground, wanting some kind of action. But the words they spoke were lost to Liza and Julilly in the wind and the splashing noise of lapping water.

The Captain shook his head. He threw his arms into the air as though in despair. He walked towards the thin stairway. The big men followed.

"They are going to search the cabins, Liza!" Julilly gasped, realizing just how lucky their escape had been. "We're gonna get to Canada, if we've got to hang onto the bottom of this boat and get pulled across Lake Erie." Julilly was angry now. What right had these men to keep chasing them right up to the border, as if they were two runaway dogs? She and Liza were not going to be slaves no more.

It was night now. The grey fringes of daylight had slipped from the sky. Dark clouds formed and raced above the *Mayflower*. Then they parted and a half-moon dazzled the schooner with yellow light. The North Star shone above with radiant steadiness. A bell clanged and the boat swayed impatiently as though eager to break away from the shore.

The Captain and the two large men popped out of the stairway. They heaved and puffed and ran to the entrance plank. They shook their fists in the Captain's face, but he shoved them onto the plank and waved good-bye.

The *Mayflower* turned. It swung around into the wind. The sails high above began cutting through the sky.

"I feel that I'm flyin' through the sky just like those sails." Liza hugged Julilly as they both pushed a wider opening in the canvas so they could see more of the outside.

The joy that Julilly felt was so intense that there was pain around her heart.

"Liza," Julilly said finally, "Mammy Sally is watchin' that same North Star. I've got to keep myself from hopin' too much, but I'm hopin' that it's led her to freedom, too."

Liza began feeling about for the bundle of food and the flask of water. The girls ate and drank all of it. They drew the blankets close around them and watched the billowing sails catch the rushing wind.

Without wanting to, they slept in the hollow shelter of the small lifeboat. When the Captain found them later, peaceful and warm, he left them to rock through the night and be refreshed for the morning.

A crisp, bright morning came quickly with thin, white frost powdering the deck. The air was strong with fresh fish smells. They mixed with the land smells of pine and pungent walnut bark and fertile earth still warm from summer. The waves on Lake Erie lapsed into gentle ripples. Sails were pulled in and the *Mayflower* drifted ashore.

Julilly and Liza woke with the sudden stillness of the schooner's landing. They grasped each other's hand for comfort, at once remembering the *Mayflower*, Lake Erie, and their nearness to Canada.

They pushed up the canvas on their little boat and the bright sun showered over them. The Captain ran towards them shouting with his trilling r's and upturned sentences.

"Ahoy." He waved for the girls to join him. "All passengers ashore."

He grabbed the girls by their arms and ushered them down the plank to the shoreline. He pointed to rows of tall, silent trees and the long, bleak shore.

"See those trees?" he shouted. "They grow on free soil."

Julilly and Liza ran down the plank and jumped to the ground.

"Canada?" they cried together.

The Captain nodded.

Liza dropped to her knees. She spread out her arms and kissed the ground. "Bless the Lord, I'm free!" she cried.

Julilly stood as tall and straight as she could. She pulled the cap from her head and held her head high. There was no longer any need to hide her black skin. She was Julilly, a free person. She was not a slave.

From *Underground to Canada* by Barbara Smucker

The Underground Railroad

It was called the Underground Railroad, but it didn't have any tracks and it ran only one way: north to freedom for the slaves of the American South. The Underground Railway was named by the slave-catchers because the runaways they hunted often seemed just to disappear under the ground.

Unscrupulous bounty-hunters were eager to gain the rewards offered for returning runaway slaves to their owners, so escape plans had to be made as secretly as possible. Often codes were used. After the Underground Railroad was constructed, a spiritual called "The Gospel Train" took on a whole new meaning for slaves looking for ways to escape: "Get on board little children / There's room for many a more." The lyrics of traditional songs often announced news too dangerous to be spoken. The song "Deep River" signalled slaves to meet after dark at a river, and "Wade in the Water" warned a runaway to walk in the river, for the blood hounds had picked up the scent.

On the Underground Railroad, train terms also took on new meaning. After receiving a message such as, "By tomorrow's mail you will receive several volumes bound in black. Please read and forward," a "conductor" would keep a watch for the expected "freight." This slave "freight" would then follow the roads and paths, or "tracks," that led on to each "station," where a conductor would hide them until it was safe to move on.

Many of the conductors went to great lengths to ensure the safety of their passengers. Barns and houses often had secret cellars, a woodpile might have a secret inner chamber, as might a haystack , corncrib, or smokehouse. In some houses, secret passageways were built into the walls. Carriages had false bottoms, and boxcars on trains had false ends. Padlocked trunks carried runaways instead of merchandise. And, for each clever hiding place, there was a clever conductor who knew how to keep his or her eyes open and mouth closed.

From the Deep South to the Canadian border, resourcefulness, bravery, and sheer luck kept the Underground Railroad running and set thousands of people free.

WHAT DO I REMEMBER OF THE EVACUATION

What do I remember of the evacuation?
I remember my father telling Tim and me
About the mountains and the train
And the excitement of going on a trip.
What do I remember of the evacuation?
I remember my mother wrapping
A blanket around me and my
Pretending to fall asleep so she would be happy
Though I was so excited I couldn't sleep.
(I hear there were people herded
Into the Hastings Park like cattle
Families were made to move in two hours
Abandoning everything, leaving pets
And possessions at gun point.
I hear families were broken up
Men were forced to work. I heard
It whispered late at night
That there was suffering) and
I missed my dolls.
What do I remember of the evacuation?

Japanese-Canadian fishing boats are rounded up in Vancouver harbour.

Joy Kogawa's Memories

Joy Kogawa had just finished Grade One when she and her family were taken from their Vancouver home to a detention camp for Japanese Canadians. Decades later, Kogawa reached back to that six-year-old girl and wrote her story.

Even after so much time, Kogawa's memories were alive, vibrant, and knife-sharp. Time had, in fact, polished them, while experience picked them up and saw in them things a younger person might have missed. What Kogawa re-

I remember Miss Foster and Miss Tucker
Who still live in Vancouver
And who did what they could
And loved the children and who gave me
A puzzle to play with on the train.
And I remember the mountains and I was
Six years old and I swear I saw a giant
Gulliver of *Gulliver's Travels* scanning the horizon
And when I told my mother she believed it too.
And I remember how careful my parents were
Not to bruise us with bitterness
And I remember the puzzle of Lorraine Life
Who said "Don't insult me" when I
Proudly wrote my name in Japanese
And Tim flew the Union Jack
When the war was over but Lorraine
And her friends spat on us anyway
And I prayed to the God who loves
All the children in his sight
That I might be white.

By Joy Kogawa

membered of the evacuation became brilliant poetry and award-winning prose. Kogawa's novel *Obasan* was the first work of fiction to lay bare the ordeal of thousands of Japanese Canadians who were rounded up, stripped of their property, and confined for the duration of World War II.

As Kogawa told the story of five-year-old Naomi Nakane, Naomi told the story of Joy Kogawa. In both *Obasan* and a simpler version meant for younger readers, *Naomi's Road*, Kogawa explored what happened to her, opening doors that would let her readers make their own kinds of discoveries.

Families are sent by train to internment camps in the interior of British Columbia and Alberta.

The Delay

BY SHEILA BURNFORD

An old bull terrier, a young Labrador retriever, and a tough little Siamese cat: this remarkable trio couldn't have known that their journey to rejoin the family they loved would become a harrowing trek through 400 km of northern wilderness.

Hunger was now the ruling instinct in the Labrador and it drove him out to forage in the early dawn. He was desperate enough to try some deer droppings, but spat them out immediately in disgust. While he was drinking from a marsh pool still covered with lily pads, he saw a frog staring at him with goggle eyes from a small stone; measuring the distance carefully, he sprang and caught it in the air as it leaped to safety. It disappeared down his throat in one crunch and he looked around happily for more. But an hour's patient search rewarded him with only two, so he returned to his companions. They had apparently eaten, for there were feathers and fur scattered around and both were licking their lips. But something warned him not to urge his old companion on. The terrier was still utterly exhausted, and in addition had lost a lot of blood from the gashes suffered at the cub's claws the day before. These were stiff and black with blood, and had a tendency to open and bleed slightly with any movement, so all that day he lay peacefully in the warm autumn sunshine on the grass, sleeping, eating what the cat provided, and wagging his tail whenever one of the others came near.

The young dog spent most of the day still occupied with his ceaseless foraging for food. By evening he was desperate, but his luck turned when a rabbit, already changing to its white winter coat, suddenly started up from the long grass and swerved across his path. Head down, tail flying, the young dog gave chase, swerving and turning in pursuit, but always the rabbit was just out of reach of his hungry jaws. At last, he put all his

strength into one violent lunge and felt the warm, pulsating prize in his
mouth. The generations fell away, and the years of training never to sink
teeth into feathers or fur; for a moment the Labrador looked almost wolf-
like as he tore at the warm flesh and bolted it down in ravenous gulps.

They slept in the same place that night and most of the following day,
and the weather mercifully continued warm and sunny. By the third day
the old dog seemed almost recovered and the wounds were closed. He
had spent most of the day ambling around and sleeping, so that by now he
seemed almost frisky and quite eager to walk a little.

So, late in the afternoon, they left the place which had been their home
for three days and trotted slowly along the track together again. By the
time the moon rose they had come to the edge of a small lake which the
track skirted.

A moose was standing in the water among the lily pads on the far shore,
his great antlered head and humped neck silhouetted clearly against the
pale moon. He took no notice of the strange animals across the water but
thrust his head again and again under the surface, raising it high in the air
after each immersion, and arching his neck. Two or three water hens swam
out from the reeds, a little crested grebe popped up like a jack-in-the-box in
the water beside them, and the spreading ripples of their wake caught the
light of the moon. As the three sat, ears pricked, they watched the moose
squelch slowly out of the muddy water, shake himself, and turn cantering

up the bank out of sight.

The young dog turned his head suddenly, his nose twitching, for his keen scent had caught a distant whiff of wood smoke, and of something else — something unidentifiable…Seconds later, the old dog caught the scent too, and started to his feet, snuffing and questioning with his nose. His thin whippy tail began to sweep to and fro and a bright gleam appeared in the slanted black-currant eyes. Somewhere, not too far away, were human beings — his world. He could not mistake their message — or refuse their invitation: they were undoubtedly cooking something. He trotted off determinedly in the direction of the tantalizing smell. The young dog followed somewhat reluctantly, and for once the cat passed them both; a little moon-mad perhaps, for he lay in wait to dart and strike, then streaked back into the shadows, only to reappear a second later in an elaborate stalk of their tails. Both dogs ignored him.

The scent on the evening breeze was a fragrant compound of roasting rice, wild-duck stew, and wood smoke. When the animals looked down from a hill, tantalized and hungry, they saw six or seven fires in the clearing below, their flames lighting up a semicircle of tents and conical birch bark shelters against a dark background of trees; flickering over the canoes drawn up on the edge of a wild rice marsh and dying redly in the black waters beyond; and throwing into ruddy relief the high, flat planes of brown Ojibwa faces gathered around the centres of warmth and brightness.

The men were a colourful lot in jeans and bright plaid shirts, but the women were dressed in sombre colours. Two young boys, the only children there, were going from fire to fire shaking grain in shallow pans and stirring it with paddles as it parched. One man in long soft moccasins stood in a shallow pit trampling husks, half his weight supported on a log frame. Some of the band lay back from the fires, smoking and watching idly, talking softly among themselves, while others still ate, ladling the fragrant contents of a black iron pot onto tin plates. Every now and then one of them would throw a bone back over a shoulder into the bush, and the watching animals gazed hungrily after it. A woman stood at the edge of the clearing pouring grain from one bark platter to another, and the loose chaff drifted off on the slight wind like smoke.

The old dog saw nothing of this, but his ears and nose supplied all he needed to know; he could contain himself no longer and picked his way carefully down the hillside, for his shoulder still pained him. Halfway down he sneezed violently in an eddy of chaff. One of the boys by the fire looked up at the sound, his hand closing on a stone, but the woman nearby spoke sharply, and he waited, watching intently.

The old dog limped out of the shadows and into the ring of firelight, confident, friendly, and sure of his welcome, his tail wagging his whole stern ingratiatingly, his lips laid back in his nightmarish grimace. There was a stunned silence — broken by a wail of terror from the smaller boy, who flung himself at his mother — and then a quick excited chatter from the Indians. The old dog was rather offended and uncertain for a moment, but he made hopefully for the nearest boy, who retreated, nervously clutching his stone. But again the woman rebuked her son, and at the sharpness of her tone the old dog stopped, crestfallen. She laid down her basket then, and walked quickly across the ring of firelight, stooping down to look more closely. She spoke some soft words of reassurance, then patted his head gently and smiled at him. The old dog leaned against her and whipped his tail against her black stockings, happy to be in contact with a human being again. She crouched down beside him to run her fingers lightly over his ears and back, and when he licked her face appreciatively, she laughed. At this, the two little boys drew nearer to the dog and the rest of the band gathered around. Soon the old dog was where he most loved to be — the centre of attention among some human beings. He made the most of it and played to an appreciative audience; when one of the men tossed him a chunk of meat he sat up painfully on his hindquarters and begged for more, waving one paw in the air. This sent the Indians into paroxysms of laughter, and he had to repeat his performance time and time again, until he was tired and lay down, panting but happy.

The Indian woman stroked him gently in reward, then ladled some of the meat from the pot onto the grass. The old dog limped toward it; but before he ate he looked up in the direction of the hillside where he had left his two companions.

A small stone rebounded from rock to rock, then rolled into the sudden silence that followed.

When a long-legged, blue-eyed cat appeared out of the darkness, paused, then filled the clearing with a strident plaintive voice before walking up to the dog and calmly taking a piece of meat from him, the Indians laughed until they were speechless and hiccupping. The two little boys rolled on the ground, kicking their heels in an abandonment of mirth, while the cat chewed his meat unmoved; but this was the kind of behaviour the bull terrier understood, and he joined in the fun. But he rolled so enthusiastically that the wounds reopened; when he got to his feet again his white coat was stained with blood.

All this time the young dog crouched on the hillside, motionless and watchful, although every driving, urgent nerve in his body fretted and strained at the delay. He watched the cat, well-fed and content, curl himself on the lap of one of the sleepy children by the fire; he heard the faint note of derision in some of the Indians' voices as an ancient woman addressed them in earnest and impassioned tones before hobbling over to the dog to examine his shoulder as he lay peacefully before the fire. She threw some cattail roots into a boiling pot of water, soaked some moss in the liquid, and pressed it against the dark gashes. The old dog did not move; only his tail beat slowly. When she had finished, she scooped some more meat onto a piece of birchbark and set it on the grass before the dog; and the silent watcher above licked his lips and sat up, but still he did not move from his place.

But when the fires began to burn low and the Indians made preparations for the night, and still his companions showed no signs of moving, the young dog grew restless. He skirted the camp, moving like a shadow through the trees on the hill behind, until he came out upon the lake's shore a half-kilometre upwind of the camp. Then he barked sharply and imperatively several times.

The effect was like an alarm bell on the other two. The cat sprang from the arms of the sleepy little Indian boy and ran toward the old dog, who was already on his feet, blinking and peering around rather confusedly. The cat gave a guttural yowl, then deliberately ran ahead, looking back as he paused beyond the range of firelight. The old dog shook himself resignedly and walked slowly after — reluctant to leave the warmth of the fire. The Indians watched impassively and silently and made no move to stop him. Only the woman who had first befriended him called out softly, in the tongue of her people, a farewell to the traveller.

The dog halted at the treeline beside the cat and looked back, but the commanding, summoning bark was heard again, and together the two passed out of sight and into the blackness of the night.

That night they became immortal, had they known or cared, for the ancient woman had recognized the old dog at once by his colour and companion: he was the White Dog of the Ojibwa, the virtuous White Dog of Omen, whose appearance heralds either disaster or good fortune. The Spirits had sent him, hungry and wounded, to test tribal hospitality; and for benevolent proof to the skeptical they had chosen a cat as his companion — for what *mortal* dog would suffer a cat to rob him of his meat? He had been made welcome, fed and succoured; the omen would prove fortunate.

From *The Incredible Journey* by Sheila Burnford

Wandering Time

A Copper Inuit Poem

Glorious it is to see
The caribou flocking down from the forests
And beginning
Their wanderings to the north.
Timidly they watch
For the hunters' pitfalls.
Glorious it is to see
The great herds from the forests
Spreading out over plains of white.
Glorious to see.

Glorious it is to see
Early summer's short-haired caribou
Beginning to wander.
Glorious to see them trot

To and fro
Across the promontories,
Seeking a crossing place.

Glorious it is
To see long-haired winter caribou
Returning to the forests.
Fearfully they watch
For the hunting people,
While the herd follows the ebb-mark of the sea
With a storm of clattering hooves.
Glorious it is
When wandering time is come.

Anonymous

The Horses of the Sun

A GREEK MYTH RETOLD
BY BERNARD EVSLIN,
DOROTHY EVSLIN AND NED HOOPES

Long ago, when the world was very new, two boys were racing along the edge of a cliff that hung over a deep blue sea. They were the same size; one boy had black hair; the other had yellow hair. The race was very close. Then the yellow-haired one spurted ahead and won the race. The loser was very angry.

"You think you're pretty good," he said. "But you're not so much. My father is Zeus."

"My father is Apollo," said the yellow-haired boy, whose name was Phaethon.

"My father is the chief god, king of the mountain, lord of the sky."

"My father is lord of the sun."

"My father is called the thunderer. When he is angry, the sky grows black and the sun hides. His spear is a lightning bolt, and that's what he kills people with. He hurls it a thousand kilometres and it never misses."

"Without *my* father there would be no day. It would always be night. Each morning he hitches up his horses and drives the golden chariot of the sun across the sky. And that is daytime. Then he dives into the ocean stream, and boards a golden ferryboat and sails back to his eastern palace. That time is called night."

"Sometimes I visit my father," said Epaphus, the other boy. "I sit on Olympus with him, and he teaches me things, and gives me presents. Know what he gave me last time? A little thunderbolt just like his — and he taught me how to throw it. I killed three vultures, scared a fishing boat, and started a forest fire. Next time I go, I'll throw it at more things. Do you visit your father?"

Phaethon never had. But he could not bear to tell Epaphus. "Certainly," he said. "Very often. I go to the eastern palace, and he teaches me things, too."

"What kind of things? Has he taught you to drive the horses of the sun?"

"Oh, yes. He taught me to handle their reins, and how to make them go, and how to make them stop. And they're huge horses. Tall as this mountain.

They breathe fire."

"I think you're making it all up," said Epaphus. "I can tell. I don't even believe there is a sun chariot. There's the sun, look at it. It's not a chariot."

"Oh, what you see is just one of the wheels," said Phaethon. "There's another wheel on the other side. The body of the chariot is slung between them. That is where the driver stands and whips his horses. You cannot see it because your eyes are too small, and the glare is too bright."

"Well," said Epaphus. "Maybe it is a chariot, but I still don't believe your father lets you drive it. In fact, I don't believe you've been to the palace of the sun. I doubt that Apollo would know you if he saw you. Maybe he isn't even your father. People like to say they're descended from the gods, of course. But how many of us are there, really?"

"I'll prove it to you," cried Phaethon, stamping his foot. "I'll go to the palace of the sun right now and hold my father to his promise. I'll show you."

"What promise?"

"He said I was getting to be so good a charioteer that next time he would let me drive the sun chariot *alone*. All by myself. From dawn to night. Right across the sky. And this time is next time."

"Poof—words are cheap," said Epaphus. "How will I know it's you driving the sun? I won't be able to see you from down here."

"You'll know me," said Phaethon. "When I pass the village I will come down close and drive in circles around your roof. You'll see me all right. Farewell."

"Are you starting now?"

"Now. At once. Just watch the sky tomorrow, son of Zeus."

And he went off. He was so stung by the words of his friend, and the boasting and lying he had been forced to do, that he travelled night and day, not stopping for food or rest, guiding himself by the morning star and the evening star, heading always east. Nor did he know the way. For, indeed, he had never once seen his father, Apollo. He knew him only through his

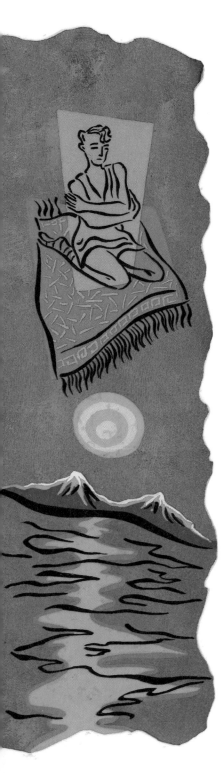

mother's stories. But he did know that the palace must lie in the east, because that is where he saw the sun start each morning. He walked on and on, until, finally, he lost his way completely. Weakened by hunger and exhaustion, he fell swooning in a great meadow by the edge of a wood.

Now, while Phaethon was making his journey, Apollo sat in his great throne room on a huge throne made of gold and rubies. This was the quiet hour before dawn when night left its last coolness upon the earth. And it was then, at this hour, that Apollo sat on his throne, wearing a purple cloak embroidered with the golden signs of the zodiac. On his head was a crown given him by the dawn goddess, made of silver and pearls. A bird flew in the window and perched on his shoulder and spoke to him. This bird had sky-blue feathers, golden beak, golden claws, and golden eyes. It was one of Apollo's sun hawks. It was this bird's job to fly here and there gathering gossip. Sometimes she was called the spy bird.

Now she said, "Apollo, I have seen your son!"

"Which son?"

"Phaethon. He's coming to see you. But he has lost his way and lies exhausted at the edge of the wood. The wolves will surely eat him. Do you care?"

"I will have to see him before I know whether I care. You had better get back to him before the wolves do. Bring him here in comfort. Round up some of your companions, and bring him here as befits the son of a god."

The sun hawk seized the softly glowing rug at the foot of the throne and flew away with it. She summoned three of her companions, and they each took a corner of the rug. Over a desert and a mountain and a wood they flew and came to the field where Phaethon lay. They flew down among the howling of wolves, among burning eyes set in a circle about the unconscious boy. They pushed him onto the rug, and each took a corner in her beak, and flew away.

Phaethon felt himself being lifted into the air. The cold wind of his going revived him, and he sat up. People below saw a boy sitting with folded arms on a carpet rushing through the cold, bright moonlight far above their heads. It was too dark, though, to see the birds, and that is why we hear tales of flying carpets even to this day.

Phaethon was not particularly surprised to find himself in the air. The last thing he remembered was lying down on the grass. Now, he knew, he was dreaming. A good dream—floating and flying—his favourite kind. And when he saw the great cloud castle on top of the mountain, all made of snow and rosy in the early light, he was more sure than ever that he was dreaming. He saw sentries in flashing golden armour, carrying golden spears. In the courtyard he saw enormous woolly dogs with fleece like cloud-drift guarding the gate. These were Apollo's great sun hounds, ancestors of our own Skye terriers.

Over the wall flew the carpet, over the courtyard, through the tall portals. And it wasn't until the sun hawks gently let down the carpet in front of the throne that he began to think that this dream might be very real. He raised his eyes shyly and saw a tall figure sitting on the throne. Taller than any man, and appallingly beautiful to the boy — with his golden hair and stormy blue eyes and strong laughing face. Phaethon fell on his knees.

"Father," he cried. "I am Phaethon, your son!"

"Rise, Phaethon. Let me look at you."

He stood up, his legs trembling.

"Yes, you may well be my son. I seem to see a resemblance. Which one did you say?"

"Phaethon."

"Oh, Clymene's boy. I remember your mother well. How is she?"

"In health, sire."

"And did I not leave some daughters with her as well? Yellow-haired girls — quite pretty?"

"My sisters, sire. The Heliads.*"

"Yes, of course. Must get over that way and visit them all one of these seasons. And you, lad — what brings you to me? Do you not know that it is courteous to await an invitation before visiting a god — even if he is in the family?"

"I know, Father. But I had no choice. I was taunted by a son of Zeus, Epaphus. And I would have flung him over the cliff and myself after him if I had not resolved to make my lies come true."

"Well, you're my son, all right. Proud, rash, accepting no affront, refusing no adventure. I know the breed. Speak up, then. What is it you wish? I will do anything in my power to help you."

"Anything, Father?"

"Anything I can. I swear by the river Styx, an oath sacred to the gods."

"I wish to drive the sun across the sky. All by myself. From dawn till night."

Apollo's roar of anger shattered every crystal goblet in the great castle.

"Impossible!" he cried. "No one drives those horses but me. They are tall as mountains. Their breath is fire. They are stronger than the tides,

---

* Heliads: daughters of Helios, another name for the sun god

stronger than the wind. It is all that *I* can do to hold them in check. How can your puny grip restrain them? They will race away with the chariot, scorching the poor earth to a cinder."

"You promised, Father."

"Yes, I promised, foolish lad. And that promise is a death warrant. A poor charred cinder floating in space — well, that is what the oracle* predicted for the earth, but I did not know it would be so soon…so soon."

"It is almost dawn, Father. Should we not saddle the horses?"

"Will you not withdraw your request — allow me to preserve my honour without destroying the earth? Ask me anything else, and I will grant it. Do not ask me this."

"I have asked, sire, and you have promised. And the hour for dawn comes, and the horses are unharnessed. The sun will rise late today, confusing the wise."

"They will be more than confused when this day is done," said Apollo. "Come."

Apollo took Phaethon to the stable of the sun, and there the boy saw the giant fire-white horses being harnessed to the golden chariot. Huge they were. Fire-white with golden manes and golden hooves and hot yellow eyes. When they neighed, the trumpet call of it rolled across the sky — and their breath was flame. They were being harnessed by a Titan, a cousin of the gods, tall as a tree, dressed in asbestos armour with helmet of tinted crystal against the glare. The sun chariot was an open shell of gold. Each wheel was a flat round disc, like the sun as it is seen in the sky. And Phaethon looked very tiny as he stood in the chariot. The reins were thick as bridge cables, much too large for him to hold, so Apollo tied them around his waist. Then Apollo stood at the head of the team gentling the horses, speaking softly to them, calling them by name — Pyroeis, Eous, Aethon, Phlegon.

"Good lads, good horses, go easy today, my swift ones. Go at a slow trot and do not leave the path. You have a new driver today."

The great horses dropped their heads to his shoulder and whinnied softly, for they loved him. Phaethon saw the flame of their breath play about his head, saw Apollo's face shining out of the flame. But he was not harmed, for he was a god, and could not be hurt by physical things.

He came to Phaethon, and said, "Listen to me, son. You are about to start a terrible journey. Now, by the obedience you owe me as a son, by the faith you owe a god, by my oath that cannot be broken, and your pride that

---

* oracle: a person who delivers spoken messages about the future from a god

will not bend, I put this rule upon you: Keep the middle way. Too high and the earth will freeze, too low and it will burn. Keep the middle way. Give the horses their heads; they know the path, the blue middle course of day. Drive them not too high, nor too low, but above all, do not stop. Or you will fire the air about you where you stand, charring the earth and blistering the sky. Do you heed me?"

"I do, I do!" cried Phaethon. "Stand away, sire! The dawn grows old and day must begin! Go, horses, go!"

And Apollo stood watching as the horses of the sun went into a swinging trot, pulling behind them the golden chariot, climbing the first eastern steep of the sky.

At first things went well. The great steeds trotted easily along their path across the high blue meadow of the sky. And Phaethon thought to himself, "I can't understand why my father was making such a fuss. This is easy. For me, anyway. Perhaps I'm a natural-born coachman, though…"

He looked over the edge of the chariot. He saw tiny houses down below, and specks of trees. And the dark blue puddle of the sea. The coach was trundling across the sky. The great sun wheels were turning, casting light, warming and brightening the earth, chasing all the shadows of night.

"Just imagine," Phaethon thought, "how many people now are looking up at the sky, praising the sun, hoping the weather stays fair. How many people are watching me, me, me…?" Then he thought, "But I'm too small to see. They can't even see the coach or the horses — only the great wheel. We are too far and the light is too bright. For all they know, it is Apollo making his usual run. How can they know it's me, me, me? How will my

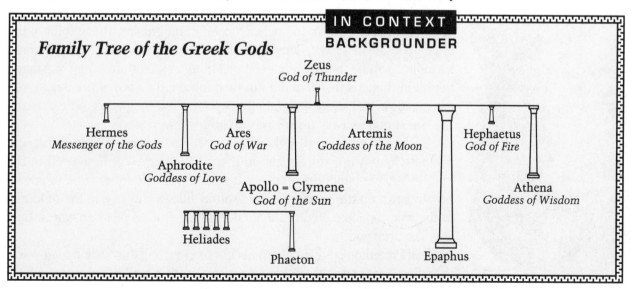

mother know, and my sisters? They would be so proud. And Epaphus—above all, Epaphus—how will *he* know? I'll come home tomorrow after this glorious journey, and tell him what I did, and he will laugh at me, and tell me I'm lying, as he did before. And how shall I prove it to him? No, this must not be. I must show him that it is I driving the chariot of the sun—I alone. Apollo said not to come to close to earth, but how will he know? And I won't stay too long—just dip down toward our village and circle his roof three times—which is the signal we agreed upon. After he recognizes me, I'll whip up the horses and resume the path of the day."

He jerked on the reins, pulled the horses' heads down. They whinnied angrily, and tossed their heads. He jerked the reins again.

"Down!" he cried. "Down! Down!"

The horses plunged through the bright air, golden hooves twinkling, golden manes flying, dragging the great glittering chariot after them in a long flaming swoop. When they reached his village, he was horrified to see the roofs bursting into fire. The trees burned. People rushed about screaming. Their loose clothing caught fire, and they burned like torches as they ran.

Was it his village? He could not tell because of the smoke. Had he destroyed his own home? Burned his mother and his sisters?

He threw himself backward in the chariot, pulling at the reins with all his might, shouting, "Up! Up!"

And the horses, made furious by the smoke, reared on their hind legs in the air. Then they leaped upward, galloping through the smoke, pulling the chariot up, up.

Swiftly the earth fell away beneath them. The village was just a smudge of smoke. Again he saw the pencil-stroke of mountains, the inkblot of the seas. "Whoa!" he cried. "Turn now! Forward on your path!" But he could no longer handle them. They were galloping, not trotting. They had taken the bit in their teeth. They did not turn toward the path of the day across the meadow of the sky, but galloped up, up. And the people on earth saw the sun shooting away until it was no larger than a star.

Darkness came. And cold. The earth froze hard. Rivers froze, and oceans. Boats were caught fast in the ice in every sea. It snowed in the jungle. Marble buildings cracked. It was impossible for anyone to speak; breath froze on the speaker's lips. And in village and city, in the field and in the wood, people died of the cold. And the bodies piled up where they fell, like firewood.

Still Phaethon could not hold his horses, and still they galloped upward, dragging light and warmth away from the earth. Finally, they went so high that the air was too thin to breathe. Phaethon saw the flame of their breath which had been red and yellow burn blue in the thin air. He himself was gasping for breath; he felt the marrow of his bones freezing.

Now the horses, wild with change, maddened by the feeble hand on the reins, swung around and dived toward the earth again. Now all the ice melted, making great floods. Villages were swept away by a solid wall of water. Trees were uprooted and whole forests were torn away. The fields were covered by water. Lower swooped the horses, and lower yet. Now the water began to steam — great billowing clouds of steam as the water boiled. Dead fish floated on the surface. Naiads* moaned in dry riverbeds.

Phaethon could not see; the steam was too thick. He had unbound the reins from his waist, or they would have cut him in two. He had no control over the horses at all. They galloped upward again — out of the steam — taking at last the middle road, but racing wildly, using all their tremendous speed. Circling the earth in a matter of minutes, smashing across the sky from horizon to horizon, making the day flash on and off like a child playing with a lamp. And the people who were left alive were bewildered by the light and darkness following each other so swiftly.

Up high on Olympus, the gods in their cool garden heard a clamour of grief from below. Zeus looked upon earth. He saw the runaway horses of the sun and the hurtling chariot. He saw the dead and the dying, the burning forests, the floods, the weird frost. Then he looked again at the chariot and saw that it was not Apollo driving, but someone he did not know. He stood up, drew back his arm, and hurled a thunderbolt.

It stabbed through the air, striking Phaethon, killing him instantly, knocking him out of the chariot. His body, flaming, fell like a star. And the horses of the sun, knowing themselves driverless, galloped homeward toward their stables at the eastern edge of the sky.

Phaethon's yellow-haired sisters grieved for the beautiful boy. They could not stop weeping. They stood on the bank of the river where he had fallen, until Apollo, unable to comfort them, changed them into poplar trees. Here they still stand on the shore of the river, weeping tears of amber sap.

Since that day, no one has been allowed to drive the chariot of the sun except the sun god himself. But there are still traces of Phaethon's ride. The ends of the earth are still covered with icecaps. And mountains still rumble, trying to spit out the fire started in their bellies by the diving sun.

---

* Naiads: in Greek myth, water nymphs, female spirits of oceans, lakes, and streams

Stopping by Woods on a Snowy Evening

Whose woods these are I think I know,
His house is in the village though;
He will not see me stopping here
To watch his woods fill up with snow.

My little horse must think it queer
To stop without a farmhouse near
Between the woods and frozen lake
The darkest evening of the year.

He gives his harness bells a shake
To ask if there is some mistake.
The only other sound's the sweep
Of easy wind and downy flake.

The woods are lovely, dark and deep,
But I have promises to keep,
And miles to go before I sleep,
And miles to go before I sleep.

By Robert Frost

Sailing in on 5 years of Memories

BY JACK CAHILL

When the little nine-metre sloop *Lorcha* dropped its single, funny, faded Chinese-junk sail and docked in New York a few weeks ago, a lot of people saw the Canadian flag on the stern and remarked to the crew that they were a long way from home.

"Which way did you come?" the friendly New Yorkers constantly asked Fiona McCall. "Did you come all the way down the east coast or down the Hudson River?"

"No," Fiona always replied, "we came the long way."

Most people didn't understand her. Some didn't seem to want to ask further questions in case they displayed an ignorance of Canadian-American geography. The faces of a few lit up with surprise.

"You mean you've come all the way around the world," they said, "in that little boat with those little kids? You've got to be kidding."

Fiona McCall, 47, former director of communications for Toronto's Harbourfront, Paul Howard, 44, a social worker, sailor and handyman, and their two children, Penny, 12, and Peter, 9, were not kidding. They had come from Toronto to New York the long way.

After five years, 64 000 km, one new sail, a few hundred dollars worth of diesel fuel, a few coats of anti-fouling paint, an expenditure of about $50 000, twenty-nine countries and many experiences, the McCall-Howard family have completed the circumnavigation they began in July 1983.

Only the *Lorcha* looks a bit worn. Down below she is cluttered and a bit musty, although everything has its place from toys to books, spare diesel oil and sourdough yeast to make bread and pancakes. The paint (twenty coats of it on deck) is peeling from parts of the sturdy steel hull and there are small patches of rust here and there. The Canadian flag on the stern is frayed and faded now and some stitches are broken on the luff of that strange, single sail. But Paul Howard says that with a bit of sanding and new paint she'll be just as strong and seaworthy and shining as when they left.

I sailed on the *Lorcha* on one of the last, short legs of its journey on Lake Ontario from Wilson to Youngstown, New York, while photographer Dick Loek took photographs from his own, much more modern and sophisticated nine-metre sloop, *Infinity*.

On the way the family chatted about their experiences:

THE BIGGEST WAVE "was a rogue wave on our first Atlantic crossing," Fiona says. "We were in 40 to 45 knots of wind on the edge of the Gulf Stream where the waves tend to build up because of the turbulence of the Gulf Stream meeting the colder waters. You get unusual waves there. We were about 700 km off Newfoundland and I was in the cockpit and Paul was below with the children.

"This wave was a huge sheet of white water that came out of nowhere. It wasn't as though you saw it on the horizon. It came from the port side and it just absolutely creamed towards us. The sound was like an express train. And then there was this enormous crash and then it went on past and was gone.

"It hit us on the beam and the boat obviously rode up with it and there was no problem. But I felt like the breath had been knocked out of me. It hadn't, but I was so stunned, surprised and awed by this sheet of water that had come out of nowhere. I mean you can see 360 degrees around you so how can it suddenly appear? And yet these odd things happen at sea. I've never been really frightened and I didn't have time to be frightened then. But I'm often amazed or awestruck or dumbfounded by the power of the sea. I know it in my head, how powerful it is. And yet when you see it time and time again, doing something you don't expect it to do, you're pretty impressed. And I was impressed by that rogue wave."

THE MOST BEAUTIFUL SIGHT "was at Madagascar," Fiona says. "Not many yachts go to Madagascar, but we try to get to at least some of the out-of-the-way places just because they are more interesting than the usual route. So we went and camped in the country for a few days in Madagascar and there was one morning when we were camped just outside a market town and we got up at first light which was about five o'clock and washed ourselves in a little stream that was near a road. And as we were washing the sun suddenly came up over the road and the people were walking to market with all their goods on their heads and with their cattle in front of them and the sun suddenly broke through the clouds. The sun came up red. And then there was this light in front of the red sun and the dust rose up and mingled with the light. And the people were walking through this dawnlight

and the lighted dust in a constant stream for about ten minutes or so. It was breathtaking. And everybody was so interested and so polite, everybody pointing to our tent. I'm not sure they'd ever seen white people camping before and they were so human and nice and the light around them was so eerie and beautiful. That was a lovely moment."

THE MOST HOSPITABLE PEOPLE "are at Palmerston Island in the Cook Islands," says twelve-year-old Penny. "There's only about sixty people there but a long time ago (in 1937) there was a very big hurricane and all the coconut trees were blown down so there was no copra to trade. And the trade boats which brought their supplies didn't come any more and their houses and boats were gone and they were hungry. And in the first year after the hurricane the only boats that stopped were three yachts. And the people on the yachts gave the people on the island everything they had, and they have never forgotten that.

"So now if these island people see a passing yacht, they get in big aluminum boats with engines and they zoom out over the reefs to try to get them to come in. And they said we had to come in to have lunch. They practically kidnapped us. It's very shallow and they practically dragged *Lorcha* over the reefs and cooked us a lunch with eighteen courses. There was pork and taro and rice and fish and they made us eat it while they stood around and watched. They kept saying 'help yourself, help yourself,' until we were really full and it was good. And they didn't want anything from us. They just wanted to be nice to us."

THE ODDEST BOAT NAME on the long-distance cruising yacht circuit "was a catamaran named *Dog* sailed by an Australian couple," Paul recalls. His own little junk-rigged sloop *Lorcha* was named after a type of 18th century Portuguese vessel, used in trade from Portugal to the Orient, which had a western hull and a Chinese sail.

THE HAPPIEST TIME "was at a little atoll in the Solomons," says Fiona. "I forget its name. It was the first port in the Solomons we went into and not many sailors go there so lots of dugout canoes came out with kids in them to trade shells and we invited the kids on board. The kids were as black as can be. They probably have the blackest skin pigment in the world although some have blond, fuzzy hair. In the end there must have been twenty or twenty-five on board and they were so well-mannered and so polite and our kids got on so well with them. We cooked up a batch of popcorn and when we handed it around the Solomon Island kids would take one piece each. They were so happy, these kids, and our kids were so happy to have them on board, so we were happy too. We've had a lot of visitors on *Lorcha* and a lot of good times, but I think that was the happiest time of all."

The McCall-Howard family have now returned home from their epic voyage, and Fiona and Peter have gone back to school in a regular classroom. What did they look forward to most about going home? Penny couldn't wait to find a library so she could get some new books. Peter wanted to go fishing…but he was expecting to catch the same exotic fish as he had from Lorcha.

GOOD BOOKS

Journeys

Exit Barney McGee/CLAIRE MACKAY
How would you feel if your mother married your Grade 6 teacher? Suddenly you are expected to call him Dad instead of Sir. When this happens to Barney McGee he decides it's time to leave home and find his real Dad.

Slave Dancer/PAULA FOX
Kidnapped and imprisoned on a slave ship, Jessie must play his flute to "dance the slaves", for their morning exercise. After four months of fear and hazardous sailing, Jessie's ordeal comes to an enthralling climax.

The Endless Steppe/E. HAUTZIG
Esther and her family are used to a life of comfort and security. World War II begins and they are forced from their home in Poland, and into exile in Siberia. Esther must help her family endure the cruel climate and desperate poverty.

Days of Terror/BARBARA SMUCKER
Peter Neufeld and his family must flee the anarchy and famine of the Russian revolution. The Neufelds decide to join the mass exodus of Mennonites to North America. But will they survive the dangers of the long journey?

IT'S A MYSTERY

The Arctic trails have
their secret tales/That
would make your
blood run cold.

*The Cremation of Sam
McGee*/136

"You are disappointed.
You were told that I
was a secret agent, a
spy, dealing in
espionage and
danger."

*The Midnight
Visitor*/139

Brian shrank back
farther and farther
into his hiding place.

A Crime Fanatic/142

Sherlock Holmes picked up the hat and gazed at it intensely.

The Adventure of the Blue Carbuncle/152

131

The Listeners

By Walter De La Mare

"Is there anybody there?" said the Traveller,
    Knocking on the moonlit door;
And his horse in the silence champed the grasses
    Of the forest's ferny floor.
And a bird flew up out of the turret,
    Above the Traveller's head:
And he smote upon the door again a second time;
    "Is there anybody there?" he said.
But no one descended to the Traveller;
    No head from the leaf-fringed sill
Leaned over and looked into his grey eyes,
    Where he stood perplexed and still.
But only a host of phantom listeners
    That dwelt in the lone house then
Stood listening in the quiet of the moonlight
    To that voice from the world of men:
Stood thronging the faint moonbeams on the dark stair
    That goes down to the empty hall,
Hearkening in an air stirred and shaken
    By the lonely Traveller's call.
And he felt in his heart their strangeness,
    Their stillness answering his cry,
While his horse moved, cropping the dark turf,
    'Neath the starred and leafy sky;
For he suddenly smote on the door, even
    Louder, and lifted his head:—
"Tell them I came, and no one answered,
    That I kept my word," he said.
Never the least stir made the listeners,
    Though every word he spake
Fell echoing through the shadowiness of the still house
    From the one man left awake:
Aye, they heard his foot upon the stirrup,
    And the sound of iron on stone,
And how the silence surged softly backward,
    When the plunging hoofs were gone.

Johanna

BY JANE YOLEN

The forest was dark and the snow-covered path was merely an impression left on Johanna's moccasined feet. If she had not come this way countless daylit times, Johanna would never have known where to go. But Hartwood was familiar to her, even in the unfamiliar night. She had often picnicked in the cool, shady copses and grubbed around the tall oak trees. In a hard winter like this one, a family could subsist for days on acorn stew.

Still, this was the first night she had ever been out in the forest, though she had lived by it all her life. It was tradition — no, more than that — that members of the Chevril family did not venture into the midnight forest. "Never, never go to the woods at night," her mother said, and it was not a warning as much as a command. "Your father went though he was told not to. He never returned."

And Johanna had obeyed. Her father's disappearance was still in her memory, though she remembered nothing else of him. He was not the first of the Chevrils to go that way. There had been a great-uncle and two girl cousins who had likewise "never returned." At least, that was what Johanna had been told. Whether they had disappeared into the maw of the city that lurked over several mountains to the west, or into the hungry jaws of a wolf or bear, was never made clear. But Johanna, being an obedient girl, always came into the house with the setting sun.

For sixteen years she had listened to that warning. But tonight, with her mother pale and sightless, breathing brokenly in the bed they shared, Johanna had no choice. The doctor, who lived on the other side of the wood, must be fetched. He lived in the cluster of houses that rimmed the far side of Hartwood, a cluster that was known as the "Village," though it was really much too small for such a name. The five houses of the Chevril family that clung together, now empty except for Johanna and her mother, were not called a village though they squatted on as much land.

Usually the doctor himself came through the forest to visit the Chevrils.

Once a year he made the trip. Even when the grandparents and uncles and cousins had been alive, the village doctor came only once a year. He was gruff with them and called them "strong as beasts," and went away never even offering a tonic. They needed none. They were healthy.

But the long, cruel winter had sapped Johanna's mother's strength. She lay for days silent, eyes cloudy and unfocussed, barely taking in the acorn gruel that Johanna spooned for her. And at last Johanna had said: "I will fetch the doctor."

Her mother had grunted "no" each day, until this evening. When Johanna mentioned the doctor again, there had been no answering voice. Without her mother's no, Johanna made up her own mind. She *would* go.

If she did not get through the woods and back with the doctor before dawn, she felt it would be too late. Deep inside she knew she should have left before, even when her mother did not want her to go.

And so she ran as quickly as she dared, following the small, twisting path through Hartwood by feel.

At first Johanna's guilt and the unfamiliar night were a burden, making her feet heavier than usual. But as she continued running, the crisp night air seemed to clear her head. She felt unnaturally alert, as if she had suddenly begun to discover new senses.

The wind moulded her short dark hair to her head. For the first time she felt graceful and light, almost beautiful. Her feet beat a steady tattoo on the snow as she ran, and she felt neither cold nor winded. Her steps lengthened as she went.

Suddenly a broken branch across the path tangled in her legs. She went down heavily on all fours, her breath caught in her throat. As she got to her feet, she searched the darkness ahead. Were there other branches waiting?

Even as she stared, the forest seemed to grow brighter. The light from the full moon must be finding its way into the heart of the woods. It was a comforting thought.

She ran faster now, confident of her steps. The trees seemed to rush by. There would be plenty of time.

She came at last to the place where the woods stopped, and cautiously she ranged along the last trees, careful not to be silhouetted against the sky. Then she halted.

She could hear nothing moving, could see nothing that threatened. When she was sure, she edged out onto the short meadow that ran in a downward curve to the back of the village.

Once more she stopped. This time she turned her head to the left and right. She could smell the musk of the farm animals on the wind, blowing faintly up to her. The moon beat down upon her head and, for a moment, seemed to ride on her broad, dark shoulder.

Slowly she paced down the hill toward the line of houses that stood like teeth in a jagged row. Light streamed out of the rear windows, making threatening little earthbound moons on the greying snow.

She hesitated.

A dog barked. Then a second began, only to end his call in a whine.

A voice cried out from the house furthest on the right, a woman's voice, soft and soothing. "Be quiet, Boy."

The dog was silenced.

She dared a few more slow steps toward the village, but her fear seemed to precede her. As if catching its scent, the first dog barked lustily again.

"Boy! Down!" It was a man this time, shattering the night with authority.

She recognized it at once. It was the doctor's voice. She edged toward its sound. Shivering with relief and dread, she came to the backyard of the house on the right and waited. In her nervousness, she moved one foot restlessly, pawing the snow down to the dead grass. She wondered if her father, her great-uncle, her cousins had felt this fear under the burning eye of the moon.

The doctor, short and too stout for his age, came out of the back door, buttoning his breeches with one hand. In the other he carried a gun. He peered out into the darkness.

"Who's there?"

She stepped forward into the yard, into the puddle of light. She tried to speak her name, but she suddenly could not recall it. She tried to tell why she had come, but nothing passed her closed throat. She shook her head to clear the fear away.

The dog barked again, excited, furious.

"My God," the doctor said, "it's a deer."

She spun around and looked behind her, following his line of sight. There was nothing there.

"That's enough meat to last the rest of this cruel winter," he said. He raised the gun, and fired.

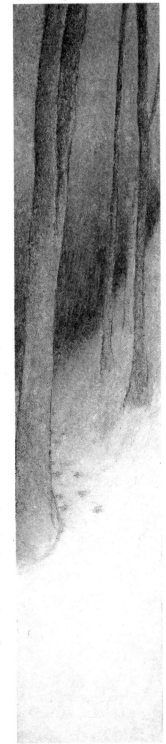

The Cremation of Sam McGee

By Robert Service

There are strange things done in the midnight sun
By the men who moil for gold;
The Arctic trails have their secret tales
That would make your blood run cold;
The Northern Lights have seen queer sights,
But the queerest they ever did see
Was that night on the marge of Lake Lebarge
I cremated Sam McGee.

Now Sam McGee was from Tennessee,
    where the cotton blooms and blows.
Why he left his home in the South to roam
    'round the Pole, God only knows.
He was always cold; but the land of gold
    seemed to hold him like a spell;
Though he'd often say in his homely way
    that he'd "sooner live in Hell."

On a Christmas Day we were mushing our way
    over the Dawson trail.
Talk of your cold! Through the parka's fold
    it stabbed like a driven nail.
If our eyes we'd close, then the lashes froze
    till sometimes we couldn't see,
It wasn't much fun, but the only one
    to whimper was Sam McGee.

And that very night, as we lay packed tight
    in our robes beneath the snow,
And the dogs were fed, and the stars o'erhead
    were dancing heel and toe,
He turned to me, and "Cap," says he,
    "I'll cash in this trip, I guess;
And if I do, I'm asking that you
    won't refuse my last request."

Well, he seemed so low that I couldn't say no;
    then he says with a sort of moan,
"It's the cursed cold, and it's got right hold
    till I'm chilled clean through to the bone.
Yet 'taint being dead—it's my awful dread
    of the icy grave that pains;
So I want you to swear that, foul or fair,
    you'll cremate my last remains."

A pal's last need is a thing to heed,
    so I swore I would not fail;
And we started on at the streak of dawn;
    but God! he looked ghastly pale.
He crouched on the sleigh, and he raved all day
    of his home in Tennessee;
And before nightfall a corpse was all
    that was left of Sam McGee.
There wasn't a breath in that land of death,
    and I hurried, horror-driven,
With a corpse half hid that I couldn't get rid,
    because of a promise given;
It was lashed to the sleigh, and it seemed to say:
    "You may tax your brawn and brains,
But you promised true, and it's up to you
    to cremate these last remains."

Now a promise made is a debt unpaid,
  and the trail has its own stern code.
In the days to come, though my lips were dumb,
  in my heart how I cursed that load!
In the long, long night, by the lone firelight,
  while the huskies, round in a ring,
Howled out their woes to the homeless snows —
  Oh God, how I loathed the thing!

And every day that quiet clay
  seemed to heavy and heavier grow;
And on I went, though the dogs were spent
  and the grub was getting low.
The trail was bad, and I felt half mad,
  but I swore I would not give in;
And I'd often sing to the hateful thing,
  and it hearkened with a grin.

Till I came to the marge of Lake Lebarge,
  and a derelict there lay;
It was jammed in the ice, but I saw in a trice
  it was called the *Alice May*.
And I looked at it, and I thought a bit,
  and I looked at my frozen chum;
Then "Here," said I, with a sudden cry,
  "is my cre-ma-tor-eum!"

Some planks I tore from the cabin floor,
  and I lit the boiler fire;
Some coal I found that was lying around,
  and I heaped the fuel higher;
The flames just soared, and the furnace roared —
  such a blaze you seldom see,
And I burrowed a hole in the glowing coal,
  and I stuffed in Sam McGee.

Then I made a hike, for I didn't like
   to hear him sizzle so;
And the heavens scowled, and the huskies howled,
   and the wind began to blow.
It was icy cold, but the hot sweat rolled
   down my cheeks, and I don't know why;
And the greasy smoke in an inky cloak
   went streaking down the sky.

I do not know how long in the snow
   I wrestled with grisly fear;
But the stars came out and they danced about
   ere again I ventured near;
I was sick with dread, but I bravely said,
   "I'll just take a peep inside.
I guess he's cooked, and it's time I looked."
   Then the door I opened wide.

And there sat Sam, looking cool and calm,
   in the heart of the furnace roar;
And he wore a smile you could see a mile,
   and he said, "Please close that door.
It's fine in here, but I greatly fear
   you'll let in the cold and storm—
Since I left Plumtree, down in Tennessee,
   it's the first time I've been warm."

There are strange things done in the midnight sun
   By the men who moil for gold;
The Arctic trails have their secret tales
   That would make your blood run cold;
The Northern Lights have seen queer sights,
   But the queerest they ever did see
Was that night on the marge of Lake Lebarge
   I cremated Sam McGee.

The Creation of Sam McGee

Robert Service was born in 1874 in England, an island known for its rose gardens and mild, foggy climate. Thirty years later, he was a happy resident of the High North—the Yukon—where winter is "long, lonely and cruelly cold, but to the sourdough is the season best beloved."

After leaving England at the age of twenty, Robert Service wandered for ten years before winding up as a bank teller in British Columbia. It was when the bank transferred him to Whitehorse in 1904 that Service set out to become a true sourdough. He loved the cold wilderness of the Yukon winters and spent his time working, walking, and absorbing the spectacular beauty of the north.

A month later, Service was at a party where a "portly and important" mining man from Dawson "spun a yarn of a man who cremated his pal." In a flash of inspiration, Service knew that he had the makings for his next ballad. He quickly left the party and walked out into the moonlit woods. "As I started in: *There are strange things done in the midnight sun*, verse after verse developed with scarcely a check. As I clinched my rhymes I tucked the finished stanza away in my head and tackled the next. For six hours I tramped those silver glades, and when I rolled happily to bed, my ballad was cinched."

The Midnight Visitor

BY ROBERT ARTHUR

Ausable did not fit any description of a secret agent Fowler had ever read. Following him down the musty corridor of the gloomy French hotel where Ausable had a room, Fowler felt let down. It was a small room, on the sixth and top floor, and scarcely a setting for a figure of romantic adventure. But Ausable, in his wrinkled business suit badly in need of cleaning, could hardly be called a romantic figure.

He was, for one thing, fat. Very fat. And then there was his accent. Though he spoke French and German passably, he had never altogether lost the New England twang he had brought to Paris from Boston twenty years before.

"You are disappointed," Ausable said wheezily over his shoulder. "You were told that I was a secret agent, a spy, dealing in espionage and danger. You wished to meet me because you are a writer, young and romantic. You envisioned mysterious figures in the night, the crack of pistols, drugs in the wine.

"Instead, you have spent a dull evening in a French music hall with a sloppy fat man who, instead of having messages slipped into his hand by dark-eyed beauties, gets only a prosaic telephone call making an appointment in his room. You have been bored!"

The fat man chuckled to himself as he unlocked the door of his room and stood aside to let his discomfited guest enter.

"You are disillusioned," Ausable told him. "But take cheer, my young friend. Presently you will see a paper, a quite important paper for which several men have risked their lives, come to me in the next-to-the-last step of its journey into official hands. Some day soon that paper may well affect the course of history. In that thought there is drama, is there not?"

As he spoke, Ausable closed the door behind him. Then he switched on the light.

And as the light came on, Fowler had his first authentic thrill of the day. For halfway across the room, a small automatic in his hand, stood a man. Ausable blinked a few times.

"Max," he wheezed, "you gave me a start. I thought you were in Berlin. What are you doing here in my room?"

Max was slender, a little less than tall, with features that suggested slightly the crafty, pointed countenance of a fox. There was about him — aside from the gun — nothing especially menacing.

"The report," he murmured. "The report that is being brought to you tonight on Russia's new missiles. I thought it would be safer in my hands than in yours."

Ausable moved to an armchair and sat down heavily.

"I'm going to raise the devil with the management this time, and you can bet on it," he said grimly. "This is the second time in a month somebody has gotten into my room off that confounded balcony!"

Fowler's eyes went to the single window of the room. It was an ordinary window, against which now the night was pressing blackly.

"Balcony?" Max said, with a rising inflection. "No, a passkey. I did not know about the balcony. It might have saved me some trouble had I known."

"It's not my balcony," Ausable said with extreme irritation. "It belongs to the next apartment."

He glanced at Fowler by way of explanation.

"You see," he said, "this room used to be part of a large unit, and the next room — through the door there — used to be the living room. *It* had the balcony, which extends under *my* window now.

"You can get onto it from the empty room two doors down — and somebody did, last month. The management promised me to block it off. But they haven't."

Max glanced at Fowler, who was standing stiffly not far from Ausable, and waved the gun with a commanding gesture.

"Please sit down," he suggested. "We have a wait of half an hour at least, I think."

"Thirty-one minutes," Ausable said moodily. "The appointment was for twelve-thirty. I wish I knew how you learned about that report, Max."

The other smiled without mirth.

"And we wish we knew how it was gotten out of Russia," he replied. "However, no harm has been done. I will have it back — what is that?"

Unconsciously Fowler, who was still standing, had jumped at the sudden rapping on the door. Ausable yawned.

"The gendarmes," he said. "I thought that so important a paper as the one we are waiting for might well be given a little extra protection tonight."

Max bit his lip in uncertainty. The rapping was repeated.

"What will you do now, Max?" Ausable asked. "If I do not answer, they will enter anyway. The door is unlocked. And they will not hesitate to shoot."

The man's face was black as he backed swiftly toward the window; with his hand behind him he flung it up to its full height, and swung a leg over the sill.

"Send them away!" he rasped. "I will wait on the balcony. Send them away or I'll shoot and take my chances!"

The rapping on the door became louder. And a voice was raised.

"M'sieu! M'sieu Ausable!"

Keeping his body twisted so that his gun still covered the fat man and his guest, the man at the window grasped the frame with his free hand to support himself as he rested his weight on one thigh, then swung his other leg up and over the sill.

The doorknob turned. Swiftly Max pushed with his left hand to free himself from the sill and drop to the balcony outside. And then, as he dropped, he screamed once, shrilly.

The door opened and a waiter stood there with a tray, a bottle, and two glasses.

"M'sieu, the cognac you ordered for when you returned," he said, and set the tray upon the table, deftly uncorked the bottle, and retired.

White-faced, Fowler stared after him.

"But —" he stammered, "the police —"

"There were no police…" Ausable sighed. "Only Henri, whom I was expecting."

"But won't that man out on the balcony —" Fowler began.

"No," Ausable said, "he won't return. You see, my young friend, there is no balcony."

A Crime Fanatic

BY H. R. F. KEATING

There are football-fact fanatics. There are car-make fanatics. There are train-number fanatics. But Brian was a crime fanatic.

He couldn't remember what had first made him interested in crimes and the detectives who solved them, but by the time he was twelve — which was nearly a year ago — he had used every book token he had received for his birthday, and all the money, buying paperbacks about the way crooks operated and the way the police caught them.

He could tell you all about the great Brink's robbery, which happened in Boston, Massachusetts. And the trouble was, really, that he often did.

The football-fact fans had other football-fact fans to swap facts with. And so did the car-make nuts. And the train-number idiots. But no one that Brian knew shared his interest, and so when he started to talk about it they were usually rude.

"Well, Brian," they would say after he had produced some interesting piece of information, like how if someone comes into a store twice in an evening asking whether they've got the latest edition of the paper it means they're casing it out for a holdup. "Well, Brian, suppose they just wanted the paper?"

And that made it all the more annoying once when he was in the paper shop near the school with Mike and a girl called Felicity. A funny-looking old man had come in and asked for the evening paper, and the proprietor had said, "No, I told you before, I haven't got one." So he had felt that he had to warn him that his shop was going to be robbed. But the proprietor had just laughed and said, "No, lad, that's only old Bones. A bit batty he is, and always coming in wanting a paper. So I always tell him I haven't got one. No harm in him."

"Well, Brian," Mike had said outside, "got any more sure and certain signs of a crime?"

And Felicity had giggled so much that she had spit out her bubble gum. Served her right.

So Brian never asked anybody to come with him on Friday mornings in the summer when he used to stake out the pedestrian bridge over the canal. He was afraid that nothing would happen, though he felt certain in his heart of hearts that one day it would. He had worked the whole thing out: it was bound to be the place.

Long, long ago — when he was eight — he had seen more than once on television, on "Junior Police Five," the route that a bank-robbery gang took after they had done a job.

They would come up to whichever bank it was in a car they had stolen especially. Generally that would be quite soon after the bank had opened, when it was nice and quiet. And most often it would be on a Friday, when there was a lot of money in the banks for people to draw out for the weekend. Then, once they had grabbed the loot, they would race out to the stolen car and drive away fast — till they got to someplace like the pedestrian bridge over the canal, a place where any chasing cars couldn't follow. They would leap out there, run across the bridge with the bags of cash, and jump into a different car that another member of the gang would have waiting.

And there was nowhere better for this trick than the bridge over the canal. The banks on High Street were about a half a kilometre away. There was a good road running from there to the near side of the narrow bridge, and on the far side of the bridge lay a nice quiet side street leading nowhere, just right for a second getaway car to wait in without any trouble.

It was the ideal situation. And one Friday morning, Brian knew, some gang was going to take advantage of it. He just hoped it wouldn't be during school, because he was determined he was going to be there to see it happen if he could. And to get the car licence number and good descriptions of the gang members. Then when he told the police, perhaps they'd show him through the station or let him ride in a cruiser. They could pretend he'd got lost and they were taking him home. By a sort of roundabout way.

On the Friday that was different from all the others he had arrived at the special hiding place he had found on the far side of the bridge even earlier than usual. It had been raining hard all night and looked as if it were going to start again soon, so he had hurried off while he could still make his way there without getting wet. He'd once spent an hour after he'd got caught in a shower hidden in his place — it was a narrow space between two of the big iron girders that held up the bridge — and he thought it must have been doing that which had given him such a stinking awful cold.

This Friday, almost as soon as he had settled in, a car drove up — a car with just one man in it, who didn't get out and walk away when he had parked but just sat there with the car engine running, pretending to look at a newspaper.

This is it, Brian said to himself. *I knew it would happen one day, and now it's going to.*

For just a moment he wished he'd never come. What if he got something wrong — say, he couldn't remember the car licence number or something? He ought to have brought a pencil to write it down with. Only he hadn't brought any paper.

But he repeated and repeated the number to himself — EJJ 238J, EJJ 238J, EJJ 238J — and hoped it would be all right whatever happened.

Then he looked at his watch. It was important to know the time of arrival of the suspicious vehicle.

It was only a quarter of nine. The banks didn't open till nine-thirty. The getaway driver was going to have a long time to wait.

It was then that he had his great idea. He'd always imagined the second car arriving only just before the men with the stolen cash came thundering across the bridge. But if this one had come so early, there would be masses of time to get to the nearest phone box and tell the police about it before the others came. Then the police could be waiting for them on the spot, and he would actually see the arrests.

He slid out of his hiding place and went quickly down the quiet side road, on the opposite side from the parked getaway car, to where on previous expeditions he had located a phone box just in case. And he knew the number of the police station and the number of the car — EJJ 238J.

He got through without any trouble. It was all going like a dream.

"I want to report some suspicious circumstances," he said.

"Yes, madam."

It took him a moment to recover from that. But he did. "I'm not a madam. I'm a boy, and I want to tell you about a getaway car that's parked on Hillingdon Road. Car number EJJ 238J."

The man at the police station listened to everything he had to say. In silence. Brian rather wished he would interrupt. Or say, "Just a moment, I'd better put out an all-stations call."

But he didn't. He just listened right to the end, and then he said, "All right, sonny. You've had your bit of fun. Now hop off the line quick, like a good lad. It might be wanted for a real emergency."

Brian thought of telling him that this was the real emergency, but he didn't think he'd be able to convince him. And then the line might be wanted for an emergency as well—a road accident, say, or some old lady losing her cat. He hung up.

Slowly and sadly he went back to the bridge, really because he couldn't think of anything else to do. He went right past the man in the car this time—he was still reading his paper—but he didn't bother to look at him. He reached his hiding place and settled down in it.

What's the good of crime? he thought. *S'pose I'll have to try and get interested in football.*

And then, round the corner at the end of Hillingdon Road, there came a police car, going rather fast, taking the corner with a squeal of tires.

It's them. It's the police. They listened. I was right.

The thoughts flashed through Brian's head. He jumped up from his squatting position and peered out along the road.

The police car drew up sharply just beside EJJ 238J. The cop who wasn't driving got out and approached the man with the newspaper.

Golly, suppose he pulls out a gun and starts firing.

But the man didn't. He just lowered his paper, switched off the car engine, and listened to what the policeman had to say. Then he pulled out something from his pocket—it was probably his driver's license—and talked for a bit while the policeman examined it. And finally the policeman gave it back to him and returned to the cruiser. It drove away.

The man in the car sat staring in front of him. Brian could see the look of annoyance on his face even through the windshield. He dodged back into hiding.

And that was what must have given his position away. Because the next moment the man flung the car door open, bounced out, and came walking fast, straight toward him.

Oh, golly, Brian thought.

But that wasn't the worst of it. All the rain in the night had created a huge sticky patch of mud just to the side of the path going up to the bridge, and as the man came up to the place between the two tall girders his feet went right into it. His shoes sank in till the mud squelched over their tops.

So by the time he reached Brian, he was in a doubly tearing rage.

"You — you little sneak!" he shouted. "What do you mean poking your little nose in where it's not wanted, getting a good honest man quietly reading his paper in the warm because he's too early for an appointment into trouble with the police? And my license out of date, too! I've got a good mind to haul you out of there and give you what you deserve!"

Brian just shrank back farther and farther into his hiding place and wished some black doors would open behind him and let him fall into a sort of nothingness where nothing ever happened and nothing you did ever did anything to any other person ever. But at last the man ran out of nasty things to say and turned back and squished his way through the mud again to his car. When he got into it he started up the motor once more and drove away fast.

Brian sat where he was, wishing he'd never got interested in crime, that he had never learned how most bank raids happen, that it had rained all morning and stopped him coming out.

So deep was his misery that it was some time before he took it in that heavy steps, three or four sets of them, were coming thundering along the bridge above him. And that just where car EJJ 238J had been waiting another car had drawn up, plunging into its place as if it were on the point of being late.

It was it.

It was happening.

And this time it really was the right thing. Brian quickly squirmed out of his hiding place and looked up at the bridge. Yes, there were three men running along it, and each of them was lugging a pair of bulky black polyethylene sacks. The loot. The stolen cash. And the driver of the car that had just pulled up had jumped out and was flinging open its trunk ready for the others to throw in the sacks.

It was it. It really, really was.

Brian hopped up and down in sheer delight.

And that was when the driver of the getaway car saw him.

"A kid!" he yelled. "There's a blooming kid there!"

Which was when Brian made his big mistake. If he had pretended just to have been playing the men might have left him to it. But he didn't pretend he didn't understand exactly what was going on. He knew he had been spotted, and he ran.

But there was only one way to go — down Hillingdon Road. He started to get over to the opposite side from the car, but it was no good. The driver was very fast on his feet, and before Brian had gone ten metres he had him firmly gripped by his T-shirt and a moment later he was pushing him painfully by the neck down onto all fours on the ground just at the edge of that sea of mud.

"Gawd," Brian heard him say, "what are we gonna do? Little bleeder's sure to have seen the car licence number. I told you we ought ter 'ave stolen one for this part of it, too. What are we gonna do?"

"Aw, give 'im a good kick and let 'im go," another voice said. "Little kid like that'll never be able ter describe us."

Oh, that's right, too, Brian thought, his face near the slimy mud. *I couldn't describe them. I never really looked at them. And the car licence number, I didn't even look at that!*

But then a sudden realization came to him.

If he hadn't been able to see the number of this car in the short time it had been there and with all the excitement of the men coming pounding over the bridge, he could see it now, despite his face being held down so close to the muddy puddle. He could see it quite clearly through his legs. JPD 269N.

Yes, but would he remember that? Would he be able to remember it with all the things that might happen to him in the next few minutes? Would he — he suddenly felt as if his stomach weren't there — would he even be around to remember it? If these men were as tough as some bank robbers, the ones who had sawed-off shotguns and used them —

But, though he felt so empty inside that he was almost not there at all, his brain still seemed to be working. Working and whirring. And coming up with an extraordinary idea. He didn't have anything to write a car number on, and held face-down the way he was, he couldn't have written anything if he had. But there was, bang in front of him, a marvellous writing surface. And he had just the thing to write on it with. His finger.

Heaving himself up a tiny bit, he got his right hand off the ground. Stretching forward just a few inches, he found a smooth area of mud that was just right. And there, digging deep into the firm sticky stuff, he traced out the number JPD 269N.

He was lucky the driver didn't notice him because something else had been distracting his attention. "Blimey," he was saying, "that's a police siren. This side of the canal. Come on — run!"

"Yeah. Push the kid in the mud and let's go."

Brian felt himself hurtled forward into the squelching muck, hoping he had flung himself enough to the side to have missed those letters inscribed in its sticky surface, and then with mud in his mouth and in his eyes and all up his nose he didn't know what was happening for some time.

The first thing he knew was the feel of a hand on his shoulder pulling him upward. Then he realized he was hearing a voice. "It might be the kid who phoned in when we came round here earlier," it said.

Brian rolled over. Yes, it was a policeman. And the cruiser he had seen before was drawn up at the curb a few metres away.

"Listen, sonny," the policeman said. "Did you by any chance see some men get into a car here a few minutes ago?"

"JPD 269N," Brian said.

"You did? And that's the number? Hey, that's pretty good!"

"Oh, come on," said the driver of the car, who had come up, too. "The kid can't be sure of that, not after being out cold here in a puddle and all. He's making it up."

"No," said Brian. And he pointed to the sticky, firm mud at the puddle's edge, where, plain to see, the car number JPD 269N was still clearly inscribed.

"I'll get on the radio. Car computer. We could be lucky."

The driver wasn't gone very long, and when he came back his face was wreathed in smiles. "They did it," he said. "Old box o'tricks turned up trumps. Vehicle registered in the name of Arthur Blagrove."

"Awful Arthur," said his mate. "Awful Arthur Blagrove. Well, this time we've got him dead to rights." Then the two of them took down Brian's name in their notebooks, because they said he'd be a necessary witness when it came to the trial. And after that they took him home in the police car. So he did get a ride in one, and without anybody having to make excuses, either. But the nicest thing of all was what happened when they let him out.

He was walking up the garden path, a bit worried about all the mud on his clothes, when he just heard through the cruiser's open window what the driver said to his mate. "You know, that boy'll make a jack one of these days, see if he doesn't."

Brian wasn't quite sure that he remembered what a "jack" was, but he thought he had read in one of his paperbacks that it was police slang for a detective.

Mysteries to Solve

BY GEORGE SHANNON

THE STICKS OF TRUTH

Long ago in India judges travelled from village to village. One day a judge stopped at an inn to rest, but the innkeeper was very upset. Someone had just that day stolen his daughter's gold ring. The judge told him not to worry and had all the guests gather so that he could question them. When he could not figure out from their answers who the thief was, the judge decided to use some old magic. He told them all he was going to have to use the sticks of truth.

"These are magic sticks," he explained, "that will catch the thief."

He gave each guest a stick to keep under their bed during the night.

"The stick belonging to the thief will grow five centimetres during the night. At breakfast we will all compare sticks and the longest stick will be the thief's."

The next morning the judge had all the guests come by his table and hold their sticks up next to his to see if they had grown. But one after another all were the same. None of them had grown any longer. Then suddenly the judge called, "This is the thief! Her stick is shorter than all the rest."

Once caught, the woman confessed and the ring was returned. But all the guests were confused about the sticks of truth. The judge had said the longest stick would be the thief's, but instead it had been the shortest stick.

Why?

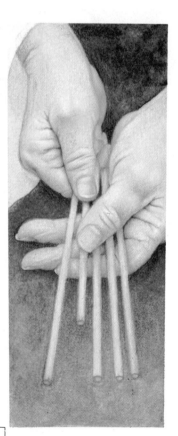

HOW IT WAS DONE

None of the sticks were magical. The only one to worry about being caught, the thief had cut off five centimetres of her stick during the night in an effort to hide its growth. But since the sticks were not magical, her stick ended up the only short one.

THE GUILTY STONE

One day as he was walking near the edge of town, a judge saw a little boy crying at the side of the road.

"What's wrong?" asked the judge.

"I've been selling pastries all day long and someone has stolen my money," cried the boy. "I was so tired I put the money in my basket under the last of the pastries while I took a nap. But someone took all the pastries and my money."

"Well," said the judge, "since you and this stone were the only ones near the basket after you put the money inside, it is quite clear that the stone is the thief."

The judge quickly had the stone arrested, chained, and taken into the centre of town for its trial. People were soon gathering around to see if the judge was really going to be silly enough to have a trial for a stone. He did, and when the stone refused to answer questions, the judge said, "Guilty!" and sentenced the stone to a public whipping.

The villagers had thought it was strange enough, but when he ordered the servants to beat the stone, everyone burst out laughing.

"Silence," yelled the judge. "How dare you mock my judgement? Each of you must pay a ten-coin fine right now!"

As people searched their pockets for coins, the judge had a big jar of water brought near his chair.

"File by and drop your money into the jar," he ordered.

Being nervous for fear he might increase the fine if they laughed again, people quickly filed by, dropping their coins into the jar of water.

Suddenly the judge said, "This man is the real thief. Arrest him!"

Once caught, the man confessed and was taken off to jail. The people went home and the judge gave the boy all the coins in the jar to replace what the thief had stolen. Everyone was happy, but no one could figure out how the judge had discovered the thief. Can you?

> ### HOW IT WAS DONE
> *The thief's coins were those he had stolen from the bottom of the greasy pastry basket. When his coins were dropped into the jar of water, bits of grease and frosting floated to the surface.*

ONE WORD SOLVES A MYSTERY

A local merchant was preparing to go on a selling trip. After loading his boat, he waited on board for his servant. Seeing the merchant waiting alone, the boatman decided it would be easy to kill him and steal his goods. The boatman quickly attacked and drowned the merchant and took the goods to his own house. And then to create an alibi, he went to the merchant's house and asked why he had not come to the boat.

The merchant's wife had all her servants go looking, but they could find no trace of him. In time the investigation reached the magistrate, who sent everyone out of the room except the merchant's wife. He asked her for an exact description of events at the time that the boatman first came to ask about her husband.

"My husband had already been gone quite a while," said the wife, "when the boatman came to our gate and called, 'Mistress, why hasn't the master come down yet?'"

Next the magistrate talked with the boatman who repeated exactly what he had said when he went to the merchant's house.

"That's it!" the magistrate told the boatman. "The merchant was killed and you are the killer. You just confessed."

"What confession?" protested the boatman.

Do you know what confession?

HOW IT WAS DONE

When he came to the merchant's house, he called only for the mistress. He called for her because he knew, having killed the merchant, that he wasn't there.

The Adventure of the Blue Carbuncle

BY ARTHUR CONAN DOYLE

I called upon my good friend Mr. Sherlock Holmes on the second morning after Christmas. I wanted to wish him the compliments of the season. I found Holmes lounging on the sofa. A huge pile of newspapers lay beside him. Next to the couch was a wooden chair. On its back hung a rather worn black felt hat and on its seat was a large magnifying glass…a tool which suggested Sherlock had been closely examining the hat.

"You are engaged," I said. "Perhaps I interrupt you…"

"Not at all! I am glad to have a friend with whom I can discuss my results. The matter is a small one," Sherlock said, pointing to the hat. "But it is interesting in its own way."

I seated myself in his armchair and warmed my hands before his crackling fire. Outside a sharp frost had set in and the windows were thick with icicles.

"I suppose," I remarked, "this hat has some deadly story linked to it. Is it the one clue that will guide you to solve some mystery and punish some criminal?"

"No, no! No crime," answered Sherlock Holmes, laughing. "Do you know Peterson, the commissionaire?"

"Yes," I replied.

"He found this hat. Its owner is unknown. It arrived on Christmas morning in the company of a good fat goose — which is now roasting in front of Peterson's fire. The facts are these: about four o'clock on Christmas morning, Peterson was walking home. The street was well-lit by a nearby gaslight. A tallish man was walking in front of him. He carried a white goose over his shoulder. At the corner stood a small gang of young ruffians. As the stranger approached, they began to bother him. One knocked off his hat. In defense, the stranger swung his walking stick over his head. The stick accidentally broke a shop window behind him. Peterson rushed forward to protect the stranger, but the man was shocked at having broken

the window. On seeing an official-looking person rush toward him, he dropped his goose and took to his heels. The gang also fled. Peterson was left with this battered hat and a beautiful Christmas goose."

"Why didn't he return them to their rightful owner?" I asked.

"My dear fellow, there lies the problem. A small card was attached to the bird's left leg. On it was printed: FOR MRS. HENRY BAKER. The initials H. B. are written on the lining of the hat. But there are thousands of Bakers and hundreds of Henry Bakers in London. It is not easy to return property to any one of them."

"What did Peterson do?"

"He brought the hat and the goose to me. He knew such problems are of interest to me. We kept the goose till this morning when we realized, despite the slight frost, it should be eaten without unnecessary delay. Its finder took it home while I have the hat of the unknown gentleman who lost his Christmas dinner."

"Did he not advertise?"

"No."

"Then what clues could you have to his identity?"

"Only as much as we can deduce," answered Holmes.

"From his hat?" I asked.

"Precisely."

"But you are surely joking. What can you gather from this old battered felt hat?"

"Here is my lens." Sherlock said as he handed me his magnifying glass. "You know my methods. What can you learn from this hat about its owner?"

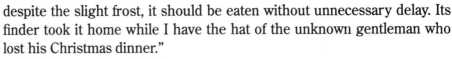

I took the tattered hat in my hands and turned it over. It was a very ordinary round felt hat—very much the worse for wear. There was no maker's name. However, the initials H. B. were written on one side. It was cracked, exceedingly dusty, and spotted in several places. Ink had been smeared on some of the spots to hide them.

"I can see nothing out of the ordinary," I said and handed Sherlock back the hat.

"On the contrary, Watson. You can see everything. However, you fail to reason from what you see."

"Then tell me what you can find from this hat," I responded.

Sherlock Holmes picked up the hat and gazed at it intensely. "The owner was highly intelligent. He was fairly well-to-do within the last three years and has fallen on bad times. However he has not lost his self-respect. These are the most obvious facts that can be deduced from this hat."

"You are certainly joking, Holmes!" I exclaimed.

"Not in the least. Can it be that even after I have given you these facts you cannot see how I deduced them?"

"I must confess I cannot follow you. For example, how did you deduce that this man was intelligent?"

Holmes placed the hat on his head. It came right down over his forehead and settled on the bridge of his nose.

"It is a question of cubic capacity," he said. "A man with so large a brain must have something in it."

"The decline of his fortune then?" I asked.

"This hat is three years old. These flat brims were popular then. It is a hat of the very best quality. Look at the band of ribbed silk and the excellent lining. This man could afford to buy an expensive hat three years ago. However he has had no new hat since. His fortunes have assuredly gone down. But he has tried to conceal some of the stains with ink. He has certainly not lost his pride."

"Your deductions are remarkable," I said. "But you said no crime has been committed and no harm done. It seems a waste of your energy."

Sherlock had just opened his mouth to answer, when the door was flung open. Peterson, the commissionaire, rushed into the room. His cheeks were flushed and he seemed dazed.

"The goose, Mr. Holmes! The goose, sir!" he gasped.

"What of it?" Sherlock asked. "Has it returned to life and flapped off through the kitchen window?"

"See here, sir! See what my wife found in its belly." He held out an open hand. A small but brilliant blue stone dazzled in its palm.

Sherlock Holmes sat up with a whistle. "By Jove, Peterson!" he exclaimed. "This is a treasure! Do you know what you have there?"

"A diamond, sir! A precious stone! It cuts into glass as though through putty."

"It's more than a precious stone. It is *the* precious stone!"

"Not the Countess of Morcar's blue carbuncle?" I exclaimed.

"Precisely so. I ought to know its size and shape," said Holmes. "I have read about it every day in the *Times*. The stone is absolutely unique. Its value can only be guessed at. The reward of one thousand pounds is certainly not a twentieth its market price."

"A thousand pounds! Great Lord of mercy!" gasped the commissionaire. He plumped himself down into a chair and stared at us in disbelief.

"It was lost, if I remember correctly, at the Hotel Cosmopolitan," I said.

"On the twenty-second of December, just five days ago," said Holmes. "John Horner, a plumber, was charged with stealing it from the Countess' jewel case." Holmes began to rummage through his pile of newspapers. At last he found the page he was looking for. He smoothed it out, doubled it over, and read the following paragraph:

HOTEL COSMOPOLITAN JEWEL ROBBERY
John Horner, 26, plumber, was charged with the robbery of the Countess of Morcar's valuable gem known as the Blue Carbuncle. The hotel manager, Mr. James Ryder, stated that he had taken Horner up to the Countess' room to mend the bathroom grate. He remained with Horner for some time, but was finally called away. On returning, he found that Horner had disappeared. The bureau had been forced open and the jewel case lay empty on the dressing table. Ryder instantly gave the alarm. The Countess' maid, Miss Catharine

Cusack, heard Ryder's cry. She rushed into the room and found matters exactly as described by the hotel manager. Horner was found that same evening. The stone was neither on his person nor in his rooms. Since he had been convicted of a similar crime once before, he was arrested. Proceedings were started against him immediately. The accused man protested his innocence.

"Hum!" said Holmes. "We must now figure out the sequence of events that lead a precious stone from a Countess' jewel case to the belly of a Christmas goose! You see, Watson, our little deductions suddenly take on meaning. Here is the stone. The stone came from the goose...and the goose came from Mr. Henry Baker. We must now find him and learn what part he played in this mystery. To do this, we must try the simplest means first...an advertisement in the evening newspapers. If this fails, I shall have to resort to other methods."

"What will you say?" I asked.

"Give me a pencil and that slip of paper. Now then:

Found: *A goose and a black felt hat. Mr. Henry Baker can have the same by applying at 6:30 this evening at 221B Baker Street.*

"I believe that will do. Peterson, please run down to the advertising agency and have this printed in the evening papers. I shall keep the stone here and shall drop the Countess a note telling her that we have found it. On your way back buy a goose. We must have one to give to Mr. Baker in place of the one your family is devouring right now!"

That evening at half-past six I returned to Baker Street. Holmes and I had agreed to have dinner together after our visitor left. As I approached the house I saw a tall man waiting outside. Just as I arrived the door was opened. We were both shown up to Sherlock Holmes' rooms.

"Ah, Watson, you have come at the right time," said Holmes. He turned to the tall man, "Mr. Henry Baker, I believe. Pray take this chair by the fire." He handed the man the hat and added, "Is this your hat, Mr. Baker?"

"Yes, sir," replied Baker. He was a large man with rounded shoulders, a massive head, and a broad, intelligent face. His black frock coat was buttoned high in front with the collar turned up. There was no sign of either cuff or shirt beneath.

"Why didn't you advertise your loss?" Holmes asked.

Our visitor gave a rather shame-faced laugh. "Shillings have not been as plentiful with me as they once were," he remarked. "I assumed the gang of ruffians carried off both my hat and the bird. I did not care to spend money in a hopeless attempt to recover them."

"Naturally. By the way, about the bird—we were compelled to eat it."

"To eat it!" exclaimed our visitor. He half rose from his chair in agitation.

"Yes, it would have been no use to anyone had we not done so. But I presume this other goose on the sideboard will do. It is about the same weight and perfectly fresh."

"Oh, certainly, certainly!" answered Mr. Baker with a sigh of relief.

"Of course, we still have the feathers, legs, belly and so on of your own bird. So if you wish…"

"They might be useful to me as relics of my adventure," said Baker, "but beyond that I can hardly see what use they would be."

Sherlock glanced sharply across at me. He shrugged his shoulders.

"There is your hat and there is your bird. By the way," Sherlock said, "would it bore you to tell me where you got the other one from? I am somewhat of a fowl fancier and I have seldom seen a better-grown goose."

"Certainly, sir. A number of my friends and I often visit the Alpha Inn near the museum. This year our good host, Mr. Windigate, started a goose club. We were to pay a few pennies each week and in exchange receive a goose at Christmas. I paid my weekly pennies and was taking home the bird the other night. You know what followed." Mr. Henry Baker took up his bird and hat, thanked us, and departed.

"So much for Mr. Henry Baker," said Holmes. "It is quite certain that he knows nothing about the matter. Shall we turn our dinner into a late supper and follow up our clue while it is hot?"

"By all means!" I agreed enthusiastically.

We bundled up and went outdoors. It was a bitter night and the breath of passersby hung in the air like smoke. Our footsteps rang out crisply as we walked. In a quarter of an hour we were at the Alpha Inn. Holmes immediately ordered two glasses of beer from the ruddy-faced landlord.

"Your beer should be excellent if it is as good as your geese!" Holmes told the landlord.

"My geese!" exclaimed the landlord, Windigate.

"Yes. I was speaking only half an hour ago to Mr. Henry Baker. He is a member of your goose club."

"Ah yes, I see. But they weren't my geese."

"Indeed!" said Holmes. "Whose then?"

"Well, I got the two dozen from a salesman in Covent Garden Market."

"I know some of them!" exclaimed Holmes. "Which salesman was it?"

"Breckinridge is his name."

"Ah! I don't know him. Well, here's to your good health and to the prosperity of your inn." Sherlock drank his beer, rose from his seat,

and motioned for me to follow. In a moment we were standing outside once again.

"Now for Mr. Breckinridge," Holmes said. "Remember, Watson, a man may get seven years imprisonment if we cannot prove his innocence. Our only clue is a Christmas goose that somehow had a gem in its belly. Our inquiry may lead to Horner's guilt, but we must follow it through to the bitter end."

By the time we reached Covent Garden Market it was near closing time. There were still many people milling about. One of the largest stalls bore the name of Breckinridge. Beneath the sign stood the man himself. He had a rather sharp face and trim side whiskers and was helping a boy shut up the shutters.

"Sold out of geese, I see," Holmes commented, pointing at the bare slabs of marble.

"Let you have five hundred tomorrow morning," muttered Breckinridge.

"That's no good," Holmes answered.

"Well, there are still some at the next stall," replied the salesman.

"Ah, but I was recommended to you."

"Who by?" he asked.

"The landlord of the Alpha."

"Ah yes, I sent him a couple of dozen," Breckinridge answered.

"Fine birds they were too," Holmes replied. "Where did you get them from?"

To my surprise the question provoked a burst of anger from the salesman.

"What are you driving at?" he asked. "Let's have it straight now."

"It is straight enough," said Sherlock. "I should like to know who sold you the geese which you then sold to Alpha."

"Well, I shan't tell you!" responded Breckinridge.

"Oh! It is a matter of no importance. But I don't know why you should be so hot over such a small thing."

"Hot! You'd be hot, if you were as pestered as I am. When I pay good money for a good article that should be an end to the business. But it's 'Where are the geese?' and 'What will you take for the geese?' and 'Who did you sell the geese to?' One would think they were the only geese in the world to hear the fuss that is made over them."

"Well, I have no connection with any other people," Holmes said carelessly. "But I bet five pounds that the bird I ate was country bred."

"Well then, you've lost your money. It was town bred," snapped the salesman.

"It was nothing of the kind!" insisted Sherlock.

"I say it was!"

"I don't believe it."

"Do you think you know more about birds than I do?" asked Breckinridge. "I've been handling them since I was a child. I tell you all the birds that went to the Alpha were town bred."

"Will you bet then?" prodded Holmes.

"It's merely taking your money, for I know I am right. But I'll bet just to teach you not to be so stubborn." The salesman chuckled grimly. "Bring me my books, Bill," he ordered.

The boy brought back a small ledger and a large greasy one. He placed them both on a slab of marble beneath a hanging lamp.

"You see this little book," said Breckinridge. "It contains a list of the people from whom I buy. Here on this page are the country folk and the numbers after their names are where their accounts are in the big ledger. You see this other page in red ink? Well, this is a list of my town suppliers. Now, look at the third name. Just read it out to me."

"Mrs. Oakshott, 117 Brixton Road — page 249," read Holmes.

"Quite so. Now turn to page 249 in the large ledger."

Holmes turned to that page. On it was written: "Mrs. Oakshott, 117 Brixton Road, egg and poultry supplier."

"Now what is the last entry?" asked the salesman.

"December 22, twenty-four geese."

"Quite so. There you are…and underneath?"

"Sold to Mr. Windigate of the Alpha."

"What have you to say now?" asked Breckinridge triumphantly.

Sherlock looked deeply upset. He drew a coin out of his pocket and threw it down onto the slab. Then he turned away in disgust. A few yards off he stopped under a lamppost and laughed in a hearty, noiseless fashion. "Well, Watson," he said to me. "I fancy we are nearing the end of our quest. The only question that remains is whether we should go on to this Mrs. Oakshott's tonight or tomorrow. It is clear there are others who are anxious about the matter, and I should…"

Just then a commotion broke out at the stall we had just left.

"I've had enough of you and your geese!" Mr. Breckinridge was shouting at a little cringing man. "If you come pestering me anymore with your silly talk I'll set the dog on you. You bring Mrs. Oakshott here and I'll answer her, but what have you to do with it? Did I buy the geese off you?"

Detectives in Literature

"It looks like The Cobra's M.O. all right. But we've got suspects coming out of our ears — it could be any one of them."

"You're right, Lieutenant. Are you thinking what I'm thinking?"

"Right. We need some top-drawer help on this one. Check the card catalogue...see who's around."

"Detectives. Detectives. Ah, here we are. *Liz* and *Tom Austen*. Created by Eric Wilson out in Vancouver."

"Boy oh boy, that guy's typewriter must be smokin'. Every time I turn around he's got those kids solving another crime. Couple of smart ones, they are. Kidnapping is their specialty, but they're into all sorts of stuff. Gotta have those two. Maybe they could hop on *The Canadian* and get out here by the weekend. Who else have you got?"

"*Nancy Drew.* Specializes in spooky crimes — of secret passages and underground caves. Very bright, very brave — runs with a clean-cut crowd. I've heard she's available right now."

"Who's her author?"

"Carolyn Keene."

"Okay. Next."

"Wimsey. *Lord Peter Wimsey.* A duke no less. Wears a monocle. Very sharp. Very reckless. A real gent. London's leading amateur detective, he is. And a big hit on the silver screen, too. Dorothy Sayers turned out a real lady's man when she invented him."

"A handsome devil I hear. Is that everyone?"

"Just the tip of the iceberg. Should I go on?"

"Hey, what about Spade? Is Sam around?"

"I'll have to check. Dashiell Hammet had him awfully busy with that Maltese Falcon business. But you know *Sam Spade* — always up for a little action."

"*Sherlock Holmes* is probably tied up though, I'll bet. Conan Doyle barely gives the poor man time to breathe. Good thing Watson's around as backup."

"Who else have you got?"

"*Charlie Chan* just made Inspector with Honolulu P.D. Charming fellow. Clever as a fox. Busy though. His creator, guy named Earl Biggers, landed him with *eleven* kids. Then he hands him one tough case after another. Don't know how he does it. And we've got to have *Miss Marple.*"

"Jane! Of course! Do you think Agatha Christie would send her over with the other Brits?"

"I certainly hope so. She's one shrewd lady. Fools everyone with her 'have-another-cookie-dear' act. No better detective on either side of the Atlantic."

"Speaking of Agatha Christie — what's she got *Hercule Poirot* doing these days?"

"You name it — that's one cop turned private eye who can handle everything you can throw at him. A little weird if you ask me. But quite a brain. Sharp dresser, great moustache. Maybe he and Miss Marple can travel together."

"What are you, a matchmaker? Hey! What about Benny? Do you think he could give us a hand?"

"*Benny Cooperman*? Great private eye. Isn't Howard Engel his creator? Yeah, I thought so. Hmmm. He was in Niagara for *The Suicide Murders*. Handled The *Ransom Game* case and solved *Murder on Location*. Couple of others since. Could be free at the moment."

"Let's hope so."

"So there you have it. There are others, but they're all tied up at the moment. Which ones should I call?"

"All of them. This case is a real killer. We're going to need all the help we can get."

"No, but one of them was mine just the same," whined the little man.

"Well, then ask Mrs. Oakshott for it!"

"She told me to ask you."

"You can ask the King of Prussia for all I care! I've had enough. Get out!!!" He rushed fiercely forward. The little man ran quickly into the darkness.

"Ha, this may save us a visit to Brixton Road," whispered Holmes. My companion speedily overtook the man and touched him on the shoulder. The man sprang around nervously. I could see by the gaslight that his face was deathly pale.

"Who are you? What do you want?" he asked in a shaken voice.

"My name is Sherlock Holmes. It is my business to know what other people don't know."

"But you know nothing of this," the man insisted.

"Excuse me, I know everything of it," Holmes replied. "You are trying to trace some geese. They were sold by Mrs. Oakshott of Brixton Road to a salesman named Breckinridge. They were in turn sold to Mr. Windigate of the Alpha and by him to Mr. Henry Baker."

"Oh sir, you are the very man whom I have longed to meet," cried the little fellow.

Sherlock Holmes hailed a cab. "In that case we had better discuss the matter in the privacy of my rooms. Who do I have the pleasure of assisting?"

"My name is John Robinson," he answered.

"No, no. The real name," said Holmes, sweetly. "It is always awkward doing business with an alias."

The stranger's cheeks turned red, "Well, then," he said, "my real name is James Ryder."

"Precisely so! Manager of the Hotel Cosmopolitan! Step into the cab and I shall be able to tell you everything you wish to know presently." Holmes motioned toward the waiting cab.

The little man stood glancing from one of us to the other. His eyes were half frightened and half hopeful. Then he stepped into the cab. In half an hour we were back at Baker Street. Nothing had been said during the drive. But our companion's heavy breathing told us how nervous he was.

"Here we are!" said Sherlock cheerfully as we filed into the room. "The fire looks very seasonable in this weather. You look cold, Mr. Ryder. Take this basket-chair. I will just put on my slippers before we settle this little matter of yours. Now then! You want to know what became of those geese? Or rather, of that goose. It was one bird, I imagine, which interests you — white with a black bar across its tail."

Ryder quivered with emotion. "Oh, sir," he cried, "can you tell me where it went?"

"It came here."

"Here?"

"Yes and a most remarkable bird it proved to be. I don't wonder that you should take an interest in it. It laid an egg after it was dead — the brightest little blue egg that ever was seen. I have it right here."

Our visitor staggered to his feet and steadied himself against the mantelpiece. Holmes unlocked his strongbox and held up the blue carbuncle. It shone out like a star. Ryder glanced at it, uncertain whether to claim it or disown it.

"The game's up, Ryder," Holmes said quietly. Ryder staggered, nearly falling into the fire. I helped him into his chair and gave him a dash of brandy. He sat staring at his accuser.

"I have deduced most of the facts of this case. There is little for you to tell me," said Holmes. "Still, that little may as well be cleared up. How did you first learn of the Countess' stone?"

"It was Catherine Cusack who told me of it," he said.

"I see. Her ladyship's maid. And the temptation of easy wealth was too much for you. You knew the plumber Horner had once been involved in a similar matter. He would immediately be suspected. So what did you do? You created a job for him in the Countess' room. When he was done, you stole the gem, raised the alarm and had him arrested. You then…"

Ryder threw himself on the rug. "For God's sake, have mercy," he shrieked. "Think of my father! Of my mother! It would break their hearts. I never went wrong before! I never will again. I swear it. I'll swear it on a Bible. Oh don't bring it into court!"

"Get back into your chair!" said Holmes sternly. "It is all very well for you to cringe and crawl now. You thought little of poor Horner in prison for your crime."

"I will flee, Mr. Holmes. I will leave the country. Then the charge against him will be dropped."

"Hum! We will talk about that later. And now let us hear the true account of the next act. How did the stone come to be in the goose and the goose come to be in the market? Your safety depends on you telling us the truth."

Ryder passed his tongue over his parched lips. "I will tell you just as it happened, sir," he said. "I had to hide the stone. There was no safe hiding place in the hotel. After Horner was arrested, I went to my sister's house. She is married to a man named Oakshott. She lives on Brixton Road and breeds birds in her backyard. Along the way I suspected each man I saw

of being a policeman or detective. By the time I got to Brixton Road sweat was pouring down my face. My sister asked me what was the matter. I told her the jewel robbery at the hotel had upset me. Then I went into the back yard, smoked a pipe and wondered what to do next.

"I remembered a friend called Maudsley. He knew the ways of thieves and how they got rid of what they stole. I made up my mind to go to Kilburn where he lived. He would show me how to turn the stone into money. But how to get it to him?…At any moment I could be seized and searched. And there was the stone in my pocket. I looked down at the geese waddling about me feet. Suddenly an idea came into my head — one which would stump the best detective that ever lived!

"My sister had promised me a goose for Christmas. I would take my goose now and in it I would carry my stone to Kilburn. I spotted a fine white bird with a distinctive tail. I caught the bird and pried open its bill.

Then I thrust the stone down its throat. The bird gave a gulp. I felt the stone pass along its gullet and into its belly. The bird flapped and struggled. Out came my sister. As I turned to speak to her, the bird broke loose and joined the others.

"'Whatever were you doing with that bird, Jim?' she asked.

"'Well, you said you'd give me one for Christmas. I was feeling to see which one was the fattest.'

"'Oh! We've set yours aside for you. Jim's bird, we call it. It's the big, white one over yonder. There's twenty-six of them, which makes one for you and one for us and two dozen for the market.'

"'Thank you, Maggie,' says I. 'But if it is all the same to you, I'd rather have that one I was handling just now.'

"'The other is much heavier,' she said. 'We fattened it expressly for you.'

"'Never mind, I'll have the other and I'll take it now.'

"'Oh, very well,' she answered. 'Kill it and take it with you.'

"Well, I did what she said, Mr. Holmes, and I carried the bird all the way to Kilburn. I told my pal what I had done and he laughed until he nearly choked. We got a knife and opened the goose. But there was no stone. I immediately knew there had been some terrible mistake. I left the bird and rushed back to my sister's. But there was not one bird to be seen.

"'Where are they all, Maggie?' I cried.

"'Gone to the dealer's, Jim.'

"'Which dealer's?'

"'Breckinridge of Covent Garden.'

"'But was there another with a barred tail?' I asked. 'The same as the one I chose?'

"'Yes, Jim,' she answered. 'There were two barred-tailed ones. I could never tell them apart.'

"Well, then I realized what had happened. I ran off as fast as my feet would carry me to Breckinridge. He had sold them and wouldn't tell me where they had gone. You heard him yourselves. My sister thinks I am going mad. Sometimes I think I am, too! And now—and now I am myself a branded thief. Without ever having touched the wealth for which I sold my character! God help me!" He burst into sobs and buried his face in his hands.

There was a long silence broken only by Ryder's sobs and Sherlock's fingers tapping on the table beside him. Finally my friend rose and threw open the door.

"Get out!" he told the man.

"What, sir?" Ryder exclaimed in disbelief. "Oh, heaven bless you!"

"No more words. Get out!"

And no more words were needed. There was a sudden rush to the door, a clatter on the stairs, the bang of the front door, and the rattle of running footsteps from the street.

"After all, Watson," said Holmes, reaching for his clay pipe, "I am not employed by the police. If Horner were in danger it would be another thing. But this fellow will not testify against him. The case will collapse. I suppose I should turn him in. But perhaps by setting him free I am saving his soul. This fellow will not go wrong again. He is too frightened. Send him to jail now and you make him a jailbird for life. Besides, it is the season of forgiveness. Chance put a curious mystery in our hands. Our solution is our reward."

"And now, Dr. Watson. Please ring Mrs. Hudson, the housekeeper…It is time to investigate yet another bird — one which she has kindly prepared for our supper."

DARK WATER, DEEP WATER

There have never been any guarantees of safety for those who boat or swim above Niagara Falls.
Niagara Daredevils/170

Waves bow before the shore.
Waves/175

What danger could a few pieces of ice present to an unsinkable ship?
The Fateful Night/178

Our hunt was almost over.
The Discovery of the
Titanic/190

ISLAND

River

Take the clothes to the river
beat them on the stones
Sing some songs to the river
praise its deep green face
But don't go where river meets sea
there's a fight going on.
The fight is blue and green and gold,
the current is strong and foamy
'Cause river wants to go to sea
but sea won't be her boat.

POEMS

Fisherman

He is dark and wiry,
his bones, thin and sharp,
like the bones of the fish
in his net.
It seems as if
webbing grows on his fingers
and feet,
a starfish is his heart,
a seagull is his voice,
an oyster's pearl his eye,
he juts out of the sand
like a rock or some coral,
so long he has lived in the sea.

By Dionne Brand

NIAGARA DAREDEVILS

BY LINDA GRANFIELD

DRAMA — OR DEATH?

There have never been any guarantees of safety for those who boat or swim above Niagara Falls. But some people seem to have *courted* death as they performed amazing stunts above the Falls or threw themselves over the edge. People have judged some of the stunters to be fools who were greedy for money or fame. But many of the stunters were quite intelligent men and women who could never explain why they took such chances. Some lived; some died terrible deaths.

In the summer of 1985, two men attempted at different times to go over the Falls in barrels. Such stunts have been illegal since 1912. Although both men were fined for their illegal escapades, one tried it again and was successful. The treacherous waters kept him from being rescued for more than an hour; it might have taken days. The manager of the *Maid of the Mist* company said to reporters: "These people who say they have studied the Falls and the river are fools. I have worked the river for 32 years and it's always unpredictable and dangerous. There is no guarantee of that barrel coming out [from under the Falls] at any time."

The unpredictability of nature is what has lured people to see the stunters. Some of the daredevils became sacrifices to mighty Hinu* while others lived to tell their tales.

A SHIP FULL OF ANIMALS

Stunts at Niagara Falls occurred as early as 1827. In September of that year, a partially dismantled schooner, the *Michigan*, was filled with a menagerie of animals and sent over the Falls. Some claimed only a goose survived. This senseless gimmick was organized by William Forsyth, the owner of the Pavilion, one of the most popular hotels on the Canadian side. William Lyon Mackenzie was an eyewitness and wrote about the stunt for his newspaper, elaborating on the details for added sensationalism. He estimated

---

* Hinu: the Neutrals, an Indian tribe of the Niagara region, believed the god Hinu — the Great Thunderer — lived in a cave under the Falls

Bobby Leach and his barrel after his perilous trip over Niagara Falls, July 25th, 1911

that 8 000 to 10 000 people were there, hanging from every branch and rooftop, "including show men with wild beasts, gingerbread people, cake and beer stalls, wheel of fortune men, etc." Bands played, people cheered…and a boatload of animals lost their lives.

SAM PATCH

Two years later, even greater crowds came to witness Sam Patch's much-advertised leap into the Falls. The 23-year-old mill worker from Rhode Island was quite a braggart, and he knew how to get the most out of newspaper publicity. He announced he was going to leap nearly 30 m into the Falls from a tiny platform on Goat Island on October 7, 1829.

The crowds grew still as he paused on the platform. Then, in a patriotic gesture, Sam kissed the American flag and leaped feet first, arms straight by his side. He hit the water at an estimated 96 km per hour, surfaced and swam to the nearby rocks. "There's no mistake in Sam Patch," he said as he climbed from the water. As

Sam Patch became more famous, this expression became well known and often used.

A month later, Sam Patch tried another daring leap — this time at the Genesee Falls in New York State. Some observers thought he was a bit shaky before the leap. He seemed in a panic when he fell; he lost control and failed to surface. His body was not found until the next spring and he was buried in a grave near Rochester.

Sam Patch's dramatic death gave America a new folk hero and gave Niagara Falls a stunter to be outdone. Fifteen years after his death, children still skipped rope in the schoolyard to a popular jingle:

Poor Sam Patch — a man
 once world renowneded,
Much loved the water,
 and by it was drownded.
He sought for fame,
 and as he reached to pluck it,
He lost his ballast, and
 then kicked the buck-it.

Bold Blondin balanced
bravely above the boiling breach.

BLONDIN THE FUNAMBULIST

In 1859, Jean François Gravelet, a well-known French tightrope walker (funambulist), tried an even more amazing stunt. Gravelet was better known as Blondin, or the Prince of Manila. (Manila rope, 5 centimetres thick, was his tightrope material.) On June 30, before a crowd of about 100 000 people, Blondin set out to walk from the American to the Canadian side of the Niagara Gorge across a rope stretched over it. Guy wires attached to the shore helped keep the rope from swaying too much. But the rope, strung 46 m above the water, sagged in the

middle. This meant that part of Blondin's trip would be uphill. The band played the French national anthem as Blondin, carrying his 11 m balancing pole, stepped onto the rope.

The crowd of watchers on the shore were speechless as Blondin surefootedly scampered across the rope. But many gasped as he sat down on the rope halfway across. To the amazement of all, he lowered a rope to the *Maid of the Mist* below and brought back up a bottle of something to drink. Then he continued his trip across. The entire crossing took only 15 minutes. After celebrating in Canada, he crossed the river, by rope again, but the return trip only took seven minutes!

Blondin made more trips across the gorge during the next year. Each time he thrilled larger crowds with more exciting acts. He balanced a chair on the rope and stood on it. He took pictures of the crowd while he balanced on the rope. He cooked a meal on a small portable cooker and lowered it to amazed passengers on the boat below. He crossed while shackled in chains. He crossed carrying his manager on his back, and when the Prince of Wales visited in 1860, Blondin, on stilts, carried his assistant across and performed antics on the way. The Prince, like the other spectators, was left breathless and asked Blondin never to do it again. Imagine the Prince's reaction when Blondin offered to carry *him* across on his back or in a wheelbarrow!

This French daredevil lived to be 73 years old and died peacefully in his bed, no mean feat for the funambulist who kept crowds gasping as he performed until he was 68.

Annie Edson Taylor
being helped from her barrel after
successfully plunging over Horseshoe Falls

A FEMALE STUNTER

Women as well as men attempted to make themselves famous by challenging the Falls. On October 24, 1901, Annie Edson Taylor became the first person to go over the Horseshoe Falls in a barrel. Mrs. Taylor was a 43-year-old schoolteacher from Bay City, Michigan, who hoped to become rich and famous by "barrelling" over the Falls. Her escapade was all the more unusual because she couldn't swim. Her oak barrel measured 137 cm high and was held together with iron hoops. She was strapped in with leather loops, cushions were placed around her for protection, and air was pumped in to keep her alive.

Launched from the American side, her barrel went over the Falls in ten seconds and drifted to the Canadian side. Rescuers pulled the barrel to shore and opened the lid. There sat Mrs. Taylor, asking if she'd gone over the Falls yet! She had been knocked unconscious and was bleeding from a head wound. She was quick to tell people she wouldn't do it again.

Mrs. Taylor began to call herself "the Queen of the Mist" and started out on a lecture tour to earn money from her stunt. But she did not take her barrel with her, and that's what people wanted to see. The barrel lay rotting in the river. Not many people attended her lectures, so Mrs. Taylor got another barrel and sat beside it in the town of Niagara Falls. She was a sorry sight, trying to tell tourists her story — for a fee, of course.

When she died in 1921, Mrs. Taylor was a pauper without a home. She was buried in Niagara Falls, New York, and her gravestone proclaims her feat, as she did:

Annie Edson Taylor
First to Go Over
The Horseshoe Fall
In a Barrel and Live
October 24, 1901

Other barrel-stunters followed Mrs. Taylor over the Falls, some taking turtles and dogs with them. Sometimes the pets survived and the owners were killed.

Even powerful swimmers were overcome by the raging waters. Captain Matthew Webb of England, who in 1875 became the first swimmer to cross the English Channel, could not succeed at Niagara. Webb's attempt to swim the rapids on July 24, 1883, ended in death when he was sucked into the swirling centre of the whirlpool.

Few stunters enjoyed the fame or success they expected after their stunts. If they survived, they returned to the life they had before or died during later stunts. Today people are still unable to explain why they feel they must conquer the mighty, unpredictable, deadly Niagara Falls.

I Shall Wait and Wait

As I stand alone on the middle of the ice,
the sky above gets darker by the minute.
The seal has not yet come.
It must be somewhere out there where I cannot see it.
It must be playing in the water below the ice,
or searching for food as I am doing now.
He has his life too, as I do.

I came here to bring food to my family,
so it is most important I stay and wait.
Wait till the seal comes up to the hole below me.
A hole that is filled with salted water.
Food is waiting there.

My children are waiting for me too.
Waiting to be fed from the seal that has not come.

The long wait is worth every single length of time.
I shall wait until the seal arrives to breathe for life.
Then I shall push my spear down into the hole
as hard as I can and let the blood appear.
Then I shall pull the seal out, smiling with the wonderful
feeling that food is on its way to my family;
to my wife, to my children.

They are still waiting for the moment
when fresh meat will touch their tongues
and visit their tummies,
when they can enjoy the taste of the seal
that hasn't made an appearance yet through the hole below.

I shall wait and wait until it comes.

By Alootook Ipellie

Waves

Waves
bow
before
the shore

courtiers
to their king

and then
withdraw.

From the Arabic
Anonymous

THE TITANIC STORY

~

The estimated 2 200 people aboard the Titanic on an April night in 1912 considered themselves lucky to be on its maiden voyage.

In size the Titanic was as long as four city blocks — 265 m — and as high as an eleven-storey building.

But propellers as big as windmills, a rudder as big as an elm tree, and stokers who worked constantly feeding coal into the giant boilers to create the steam for the Titanic's huge engines were no match for the giant icebergs that lay in the ship's path.

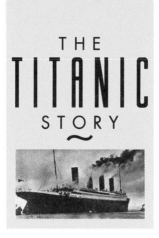

THE TITANIC STORY

THE FATEFUL NIGHT

BY ROBERT D. BALLARD

Jack Phillips, the first wireless operator on the *Titanic*, quickly jotted down the message coming in over his headphones. "It's another iceberg warning," he said wearily to his young assistant, Harold Bride. "You'd better take it up to the bridge." Both men had been at work for hours in the *Titanic*'s radio room, trying to get caught up in sending out a large number of personal messages. In 1912, passengers on ocean liners thought it was a real novelty to send postcard-style messages to friends at home from the middle of the Atlantic.

Bride picked up the iceberg message and stepped out onto the Boat Deck. It was a sunny but cold Sunday morning, the fourth day of the *Titanic*'s maiden voyage. The ship was steaming at full speed across a calm sea. Harold Bride was quite pleased with himself at having landed a job on such a magnificent new ship. After all, he was only twenty-two years old and had just nine months' experience at operating a "wireless set," as a ship's radio was then called. As he entered the bridge area, he could see one of the crewmen standing behind the ship's wheel steering her course toward New York.

Captain Smith was on duty in the bridge, so Bride handed the message to him. "It's from the *Caronia*, sir. She's reporting icebergs and pack ice ahead." The captain thanked him, read the message, and then posted it on the bulletin board for other officers on watch to read. On his way back to the radio room, Bride thought the captain had seemed quite unconcerned by the message. But then again, he had been told that it was not unusual to have ice floating in the sea lanes during an April crossing. Besides, what danger could a few pieces of ice present to an unsinkable ship?

Elsewhere on board, passengers relaxed on deck chairs, reading or taking naps. Some played cards, some wrote letters, while others chatted with friends. As it was Sunday, church services had been held in the morning, the first-class service led by Captain Smith. Jack Thayer spent most of the day walking about the decks getting some fresh air with his parents.

At 12:45 a.m. the ship was well down at the bow and the first white distress flares were fired.

Two more ice warnings were received from nearby ships around lunch time. In the chaos of the radio room, Harold Bride only had time to take one of them to the bridge. The rest of the day passed quietly. Then, in the late afternoon, the temperature began to drop rapidly. Darkness approached as the bugle call announced dinner.

Jack Thayer's parents had been invited to a special dinner for Captain Smith, so Jack ate alone in the first-class dining room. After dinner, as he was having a cup of coffee, he was joined by Milton Long, another passenger going home to the States. Long was older than Jack, but in the easygoing atmosphere of shipboard travel, they struck up a conversation and talked together for an hour or so.

At 7:30 p.m., the radio room received three more warnings of ice about 80 km ahead. One of them was from the steamer *Californian* reporting three large icebergs. Harold Bride took this message up to the bridge and it was again politely received. Captain Smith was attending the dinner party being held for him when the warning was delivered. He never got to see it. Then, around 9:00 p.m., the captain excused himself and went up to the bridge. He and his officers talked about how difficult it was to spot icebergs on a calm, clear, moonless night like this with no wind to kick up white surf around them. Before going to bed, the captain ordered the lookouts to keep a sharp watch for ice.

After trading travel stories with Milton Long, Jack Thayer put on his coat and walked around the deck. "It had become very much colder," he said later. "It was a brilliant, starry night. There was no moon and I have never seen the stars shine brighter…sparkling like diamonds…It was the kind of night that made one feel glad to be alive." At eleven o'clock, he went below to his cabin, put on his pajamas, and got ready for bed.

In the radio room, Harold Bride was exhausted. The two operators were expected to keep the radio working twenty-four hours a day, and Bride lay down to take a much-needed nap. Phillips was so busy with the passenger messages that he actually brushed off the final ice warning of the night. It was from the *Californian*. Trapped in a field of ice, she had stopped for the night about 28 km north of the *Titanic*. She was so close that the message literally blasted in Phillips' ears. Annoyed by the loud interruption, he cut off the *Californian*'s radio operator with the words, "Shut up, shut up. I'm busy."

The radio room had received a total of seven ice warning messages in one day. It was quite clear that floating icebergs lay ahead of the *Titanic*.

High up in the crow's nest on the forward mast, Fred Fleet had passed a quiet watch. It was now 11:40 p.m., and he and his fellow lookout were waiting to be relieved so they could head below, perhaps for a hot drink before hopping into their warm bunks. The sea was dead calm.

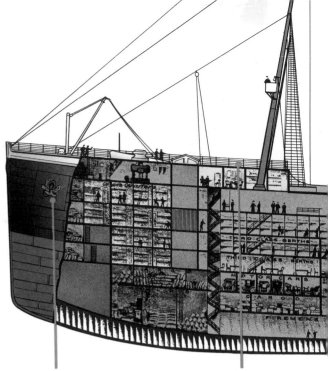

A team of 20 horses was needed to pull the huge anchor made for the *Titanic*.

The deck of the forecastle area of the ship held the giant anchor chains and large round bollards to which ropes were tied when the ship was in port.

The air was bitterly cold.

Suddenly, Fleet saw something. A huge, dark shaped loomed out of the night directly ahead of the *Titanic*. An iceberg! He quickly sounded the alarm bell three times and picked up the telephone.

"What did you see?" asked the duty officer.

"Iceberg right ahead," replied Fleet.

Immediately, the officer on the bridge ordered the wheel turned as far as it would go. The engine room was told to reverse the engines, while a button was pushed to close the doors to the watertight compartments in the bottom of the ship.

The lookouts in the crow's nest braced themselves for a collision. Slowly the ship started to turn. It looked as though they would miss it.

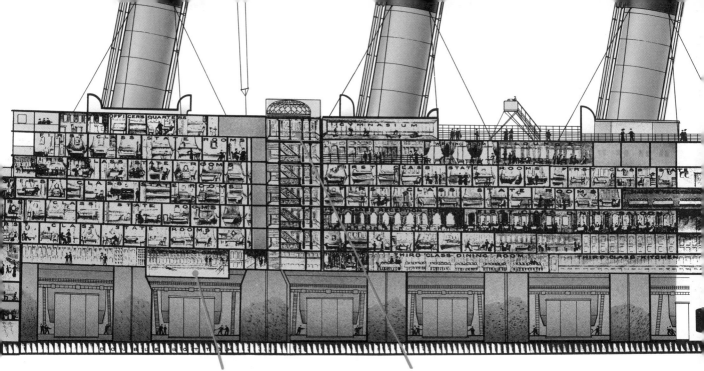

The *Titanic's* swimming pool was one of the first ever seen on an ocean liner.

This elegant foyer stood below the wrought-iron and glass dome over the first-class staircase.

But it was too late. They had avoided a head-on crash, but the iceberg had struck a glancing blow along the *Titanic*'s starboard bow. Several tonnes of ice fell on the ship's decks as the iceberg brushed along the side of the ship and passed into the night. A few minutes later, the *Titanic* came to a stop.

Many of the passengers didn't know the ship had hit anything. Because it was so cold, almost everyone was inside, and most people had already gone to bed. Ruth Becker and her mother were awakened by the dead silence. They could no longer hear the soothing hum of the vibrating engines from below. Jack Thayer was about to step into bed when he felt himself sway ever so slightly. The engines stopped. He was startled by the sudden quiet.

Sensing trouble, Ruth's mother looked out

of the door of the second-class cabin and asked a steward what had happened. He told her that nothing was the matter, so Mrs. Becker went back to bed. But as she lay there, she couldn't help feeling that something was very wrong.

Jack heard running feet and voices in the hallway outside his first-class cabin. "I hurried into my heavy overcoat and drew on my slippers. All excited, but not thinking anything serious had occurred, I called in to my father and mother that I was going up on deck to see the fun."

On deck, Jack watched some third-class passengers playing with the ice that had landed on the forward deck as the iceberg had brushed by. Some people were throwing chunks at each other, while a few skidded about playing football with pieces of ice.

Down in the very bottom of the ship, things

The boilers of the *Titanic* were over 4.5 m high.

Stokers worked day and night shoveling coal into boilers that created the steam that drove the giant reciprocating engines.

were very different. When the iceberg had struck, there had been a noise like a big gun going off in one of the boiler rooms. A couple of stokers had been immediately hit by a jet of icy water. The noise and the shock of cold water had sent them running for safety.

Twenty minutes after the crash, things looked very bad indeed to Captain Smith. He and the ship's builder, Thomas Andrews, had made a rapid tour below decks to inspect the damage. The mail room was filling up with water, and sacks of mail were floating about. Water was also pouring into some of the forward holds and two of the boiler rooms.

Captain Smith knew that the *Titanic*'s hull was divided into a number of watertight compartments. She had been designed so that she could still float if only the first four compartments

were flooded, but not any more than that. But water was pouring into the first five compartments. And when the water filled them, it would spill over into the next compartment. One by one all the remaining compartments would flood, and the ship would eventually sink. Andrews told the captain that the ship could last an hour, an hour and a half at the most.

Harold Bride had just awakened in the radio room when Captain Smith stuck his head in the door. "Send the call for assistance," he ordered.

"What call should I send?" Phillips asked.

"The regulation international call for help. Just that." Then the captain was gone. Phillips began to send the Morse code "CQD" distress call, flashing away and joking as he did it. After all, they knew the ship was unsinkable.

Five minutes later, the captain was back.

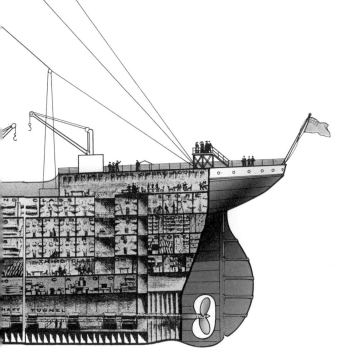

The *Titanic* had three propellers. The middle one was 5 m across and the other two were over 7 m.

"What are you sending?" he asked.

"CQD," Phillips answered. Then Bride cut in and suggested that they try the new SOS signal that was just coming into use. They began to send out the new international call for help—it was one of the first SOS calls ever sent out from a ship in distress.

Ruth and her family had stayed in their bunks for a good fifteen minutes or so after the room steward had told them nothing was wrong. But Ruth's mother couldn't stop worrying as she heard the sound of running feet and shouting voices in the hallway. Poking her head out of the cabin, she found a steward and asked what the matter was.

"Put on your things and come at once," said the steward.

"Do we have time to dress?" she asked.

"No, madam. You have time for nothing. Put on your lifejackets and come up to the top deck."

Ruth helped her mother dress the children quickly. But they only had time to throw their coats over their nightgowns and put on their shoes and stockings. In their rush, they forgot to put on their lifejackets.

Just after midnight, Captain Smith ordered the lifeboats uncovered. The ship's squash court, which was ten metres above the keel, was now completely flooded. Jack Thayer and his father came into the first-class lounge to try to find out exactly what the matter was. When Thomas Andrews, the ship's builder, passed by, Mr. Thayer asked him what was going on. He replied in a low voice that the ship had not much more than an hour to live. Jack and his father couldn't believe their ears.

The iceberg brushing past the *Titanic*. In the picture one can see that the largest part of the iceberg was underwater.

The *Titanic* was divided into 16 so-called "watertight" compartments. Because they were not sealed at the top, water from one full compartment could spill over into the next one until the ship eventually sank.

From the bridge of the *Titanic*, a ship's lights were observed not far away, possibly the *Californian's*. Captain Smith then ordered white distress rockets fired to get the attention of the nearby ship. They burst high in the air with a loud boom and a shower of stars. But the rockets made no difference. The mystery ship in the distance never answered.

In the radio room, Bride and Phillips now knew how serious the accident was, and were feverishly sending out calls for help. A number of ships heard and responded to their calls, but most were too far away to come to the rescue in time. The closest ship they had been able to reach was the *Carpathia*, about 83 km away. Immediately, the *Carpathia* reported that she was racing full steam to the rescue. But could she get there in time?

Not far away, the radio operator of the *Californian* had gone to bed for the night and turned off his radio. Several officers and crewmen on the deck of the *Californian* saw rockets in the distance and reported them to their captain. The captain told them to try to contact the ship with a Morse lamp. But they received no answer to their flashed calls. No one thought to wake up the radio operator.

On board the *Titanic*, almost an hour after the crash, most of the passengers still did not realize the seriousness of the situation. But Captain Smith was a very worried man. He knew that the *Titanic* only carried lifeboats for barely half the estimated 2 200 people on board. He would have to make sure his officers kept order to avoid any panic among the passengers. At 12:30 a.m. Captain Smith gave the orders to start loading the lifeboats — women and children first. Even though the *Titanic* was by now quite noticeably down at the bow and listing slightly to one side, many passengers still didn't want to leave the huge, brightly lit ship. The ship's band added to a kind of party feeling as the musicians played lively tunes.

About 12:45 a.m., the first lifeboat was lowered. It could carry sixty-five people, but left with only twenty-eight aboard. Indeed, many of the first boats to leave were half empty. Ruth Becker noticed that there was no panic among the crowds of passengers milling about on the decks. "Everything was calm, everybody was

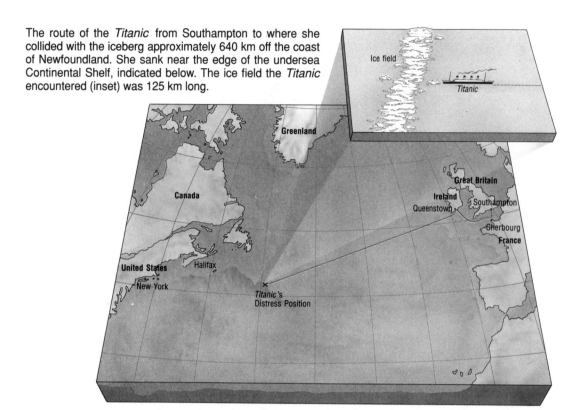

The route of the *Titanic* from Southampton to where she collided with the iceberg approximately 640 km off the coast of Newfoundland. She sank near the edge of the undersea Continental Shelf, indicated below. The ice field the *Titanic* encountered (inset) was 125 km long.

orderly." But the night air was now biting cold. Ruth's mother told her to go back to their cabin to get some blankets. Ruth hurried down to the cabin and came back with several blankets in her arms. The Beckers walked toward one of the lifeboats, and a sailor picked up Ruth's brother and sister and placed them in the boat.

"That's all for this boat," he called out. "Lower away!"

"Please, those are my children!" cried Ruth's mother. "Let me go with them!"

The sailor allowed Mrs. Becker to step into the lifeboat with her two children. She then called back to Ruth to get into another lifeboat. Ruth went to the next boat and asked the officer if she could get in. He said, "Sure," picked her up, and dumped her in.

Boat No. 13 was so crowded that Ruth had to stand up. Metre by metre it was lowered down the steep side of the massive ship. The new pulleys shrieked as the ropes passed through them, creaking under the weight of the boat and its load of sixty-four people. After landing in the water, Ruth's lifeboat began to drift. Suddenly Ruth saw another lifeboat coming down right on top of them! Fearing for their lives, the men in charge of her boat shouted, "Stop!" to the sailors up on the deck. But the noise was so great that nobody noticed. The second lifeboat kept coming down, so close that they could actually touch the bottom of it. All of a sudden, one of the men in Ruth's boat jumped up, pulled out a knife and cut them free of their lowering ropes. Ruth's boat pushed away from the *Titanic* just as boat No. 15

The final moments of the *Titanic*.

hit the water centimetres away from them.

Below, in the third-class decks of the ship, there was much more confusion and alarm. Most of these passengers had not yet been able to get above the decks. Some of those who did finally make it out had to break down the barriers between third and first class.

By 1:30 a.m. the bow was well down, and people were beginning to notice the slant in the decks. In the radio room, Bride and Phillips were still desperately sending out calls for help: "We are sinking fast...women and children in boats. We cannot last much longer." The radio signal gradually got weaker and weaker as the ship's power faded out. Out on the decks, most passengers now began to move toward the stern area, which was slowly lifting out of the water.

By 2:05 a.m. there were still over 1 500 people left on the sinking ship. All the lifeboats were now away, and a strange stillness took hold. People stood quietly on the upper decks, bunching together for warmth, trying to keep away from the side of the tilting ship.

Captain Smith now made his way to the radio room and told Harold Bride and Jack Phillips to save themselves. "Men, you have done your full duty," he told them. "You can do no more. Abandon your cabin. Now it's every man for himself." Phillips kept working the radio, hanging on until the very last moment. Suddenly Bride heard water gurgling up the deck outside the radio room. Phillips heard it too, and cried, "Come on, let's clear out."

Near the stern, Father Thomas Byles had heard confession and given absolution to over one hundred passengers. Playing to the very end, the members of the ship's brave band finally had to put down their instruments and try to save themselves. In desperation, some of the passengers and crew began to jump overboard as the water crept up the slant of the deck.

Jack Thayer stood with his friend Milton Long at the railing to keep away from the crowds. He had become separated from his father in the confusion on deck. Now Jack and his friend heard muffled thuds and explosions deep within the ship. Suddenly the *Titanic* began to slide into the water. The water rushed up at them. Thayer and Long quickly said goodbye and good luck to each other. Then they both jumped.

As he hit the water, Jack Thayer was sucked down. "The cold was terrific. The shock of the water took the breath out of my lungs. Down and down I went, spinning in all directions." When he finally surfaced, gasping for air and numbed by the water, the ship was about 12 m away from him. His friend Milton Long was nowhere to be seen. Jack would never see him again.

Jack Thayer was lucky. As he struggled in the water, his hand came to rest on an overturned lifeboat. He grabbed hold and hung on, barely managing to pull himself up out of the water. Harold Bride had been washed overboard and now also clung to this same boat.

Both Jack and Harold witnessed the mighty ship's last desperate moments. "We could see groups of…people aboard, clinging in clusters or bunches, like swarming bees; only to fall in masses, pairs or singly, as the great part of the ship…rose into the sky…" said Thayer. "I looked upwards — we were right under the three enormous propellers. For an instant, I thought they were sure to come right down on top of us. Then…she slid quietly away from us into the sea."

Out in the safety of her lifeboat, Ruth Becker also witnessed the end of the *Titanic*. "I could look back and see this ship, and the decks were just lined with people looking over. Finally, as the *Titanic* sank faster, the lights died out. You could just see the stern remaining in an upright position for a couple of minutes. Then…it disappeared."

Then, as Ruth recalled, "there fell upon the ear the most terrible noise that human beings ever listened to — the cries of hundreds of people struggling in the icy cold water, crying for help with a cry we knew could not be answered." In Thayer's words, they became "a long continuous wailing chant." Before long this ghastly wailing stopped, as the freezing water took its toll.

Jack Thayer and Harold Bride and a number of other survivors clung to their overturned lifeboat, centimetres away from an icy death in the North Atlantic. Numb from the cold and not daring to move in case the boat sank under their weight, they prayed and waited for help. Then, as the first light of dawn crept on the horizon, a rocket was seen in the distance. The *Carpathia* had come to their rescue.

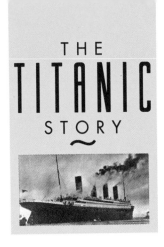

THE TITANIC STORY

SURVIVOR!
AN EYEWITNESS ACCOUNT OF THE SINKING OF THE TITANIC

BY MAGGIE GOH

Eva Hart was only seven years old when she boarded the Titanic *with her parents. She survived the disaster and grew up in England. Before retiring, she was a music teacher, an industrial welfare officer, and a magistrate. Now in her eighties, Miss Hart still travels widely making speeches about her experiences on that memorable night.*

INTERVIEWER: *Can you tell me how you came to be on the* Titanic — *where were you going and why were you going there?*

EVA: My father was a master builder and business was not very good in England in 1911. One day a friend of his, who had emigrated to Winnipeg and was doing a lot of building there, came back for a visit. In one evening, this man succeeded in persuading my father to move to Winnipeg and join him in a business. So we were actually on our way to New York, to visit an aunt who was living there, before taking the train to Winnipeg.

INTERVIEWER: *How did you and your mother feel about this move?*

EVA: I was only seven and terribly excited about the whole thing. My father spent a lot of time telling me all about Canada and I was absolutely fascinated. Even the long names, like Saskatchewan, fascinated me…I had never heard such words before.

Things were totally different for my mother. From the moment she heard of my father's plans, she was gripped with a terrible premonition of danger. Over and over again, she told my father, "I know we must not go. If only I knew why we must not do this, but I cannot explain it. I only know it is so." Unfortunately, Father's mind was made up, and there was no arguing with him. As a result, the atmosphere at home in the months before we left was very tense. Mother was dreadfully unhappy.

INTERVIEWER: *Why did your father choose the* Titanic?

EVA: Actually, he didn't. Once his mind was made up, he sold the business and booked our passage on a ship called the *Philadelphia*. Unfortunately, a coal strike started before we could sail, and because ships in those days were powered by coal, we couldn't go. Mother, naturally, was most relieved and tremendously pleased. But Father was grimly determined to go. He had made a business commitment to be in Winnipeg by a certain time. He kept journeying into London, bugging the shipping lines for tickets. Finally, he came home one day and announced that he had managed to get us tickets for what he described as the largest ship in the world, the unsinkable *Titanic*.

INTERVIEWER: *Tell me about the voyage and the memorable night.*

EVA: Once we were on board the ship, my mother, who was still convinced of impending doom, told my father that she would only sleep during the day and keep watch at night. So, she stayed awake at night from Wednesday to Saturday.

On Sunday night, when the ship struck the iceberg, Mother was wide awake. Later, she described the moment of impact as "just a tiny jolt, like when a train pulls into a station."

The moment she felt the impact, Mother woke up Father and insisted that he go up to find out what was happening. After a while, he came back and admitted that the ship was indeed in trouble. They roused me and carried me up to the decks well before the lifeboats were launched. Father put Mother and me into lifeboats. He made no attempt to get into one himself, and that was the last I ever saw of him.

In the dark and in the confusion — people were shouting, "Got room for four in this boat!" "No more room here!" — I was separated from Mother. We were put on different lifeboats! I was terrified and I screamed for her all night long. We were finally picked up by the *Carpathia*, a ship that had picked up the *Titanic's* distress signals and come to the rescue. But Mother and I did not find each other until the next day, so you can imagine what a frightful night I had.

INTERVIEWER: *Do you have vivid memories of the actual sinking of the* Titanic?

EVA: Yes. It's as if it just happened. I never ever look at pictures, I don't need to. I watched the ship sink from the lifeboat. There are many debates about whether or not the *Titanic* broke into two before it sank. I tell you as sure as I am sitting here, I saw it break before it went under. Bob [Dr. Robert Ballard, the man who found the wreck of the *Titanic*] agrees with me.

INTERVIEWER: *I read that many of the passengers were either not aware of the disaster or were too confident of the ship's capabilities to be worried even when they heard what had happened.*

EVA: That's right. Many passengers were asleep, and many others simply did not believe that the ship could sink. After all, it had been widely described as one of the most incredible ships to have been built. So many people died in it who should not have. If no one had perished in the tragedy, people would have forgotten about the *Titanic* less than two years later. But 1 500 people lost their lives. And those people should not have died.

Eva Hart two weeks before setting sail on the *Titanic*.

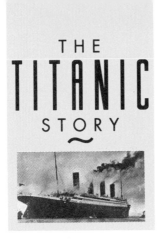

THE DISCOVERY
OF THE TITANIC

BY ROBERT D. BALLARD

"Lifeboats!" I said excitedly to Jean-Louis, pointing at the map on the plotting table. "We know that the *Carpathia* picked up the lifeboats right about here. The *Titanic* must be north of that point. If we start there and work north, we're bound to find her." My French partner and friend Jean-Louis Michel and I huddled over the maps and charts spread out before us. We were aboard the Woods Hole research ship, *Knorr*. Out in the middle of the Atlantic Ocean, in August 1985, we were plotting a new strategy in our search for the *Titanic*. After six weeks, we had found nothing. Now some new thinking was called for. I was also praying that our luck would finally turn.

In the dangerous stretch of the northwest Atlantic where the *Titanic* sank, there are only a few months during the year when the weather is likely to be good. Even then, terrible storms are possible. Now we had barely five weeks to complete our difficult mission. Five weeks not only to find the *Titanic* kilometres down in the middle of nowhere, but to bring back photographs of the wreck for the waiting world to

see. My dream of finding the *Titanic* was turning out to be a constant fight against time and nature.

The expedition I had waited so long for was a joint French-American undertaking. Jean-Louis Michel and I had spent the first six weeks on board the French ship, *Le Suroit*. We had used Jean-Louis' brand-new SAR system, a sonar tracking instrument that looked like a red torpedo. But we had not found anything. We had covered a lot of ground, but the ocean currents had been very strong. They had often pushed us off course, wasting precious time. Already we were behind schedule.

Sonar is used to find underwater objects by bouncing electronic sound waves off them. Towing Jean-Louis' SAR sonar "torpedo" underwater just above the ocean floor was a bit like towing a kite on a four kilometre string. And it had to be towed carefully back and forth so we wouldn't miss anything. An 265 metre-long ship is only a tiny speck in the vast ocean depths, with its underwater canyons and crevices. Unless we covered every metre of our search area, we might

Jean-Louis Michel and I plot our strategy on board the *Knorr*.

miss our target. We called it "mowing the lawn." Being careful and thorough day after day with no results got to be very tiring, and boring.

For the first while, the weather had been good. Then storms blew in, and we were bounced around like a cork in a churning whirlpool. This was not only rough and unpleasant; it also meant wasted time as we were forced to stop searching.

Jean-Louis and his crack French team had done their best, but, sadly, after six weeks we still hadn't found any sign of the *Titanic*. It was now up to the American half of the expedition, along

with Jean-Louis and two of his team, to try to find our target.

When we moved from *Le Suroit* to the *Knorr*, we also moved from using sonar technology to using video cameras. The *Knorr* was geared to tow one of my pet pieces of equipment, *Argo*. *Argo* is basically a steel sled with video cameras that film the ocean floor. Its moving images are sent up the tow cable to video screens on the ship, so we could see instantly what *Argo* was seeing on the bottom.

As we settled into the new ship, tension began to mount. We all knew that time was fast running out. To have any chance at all now,

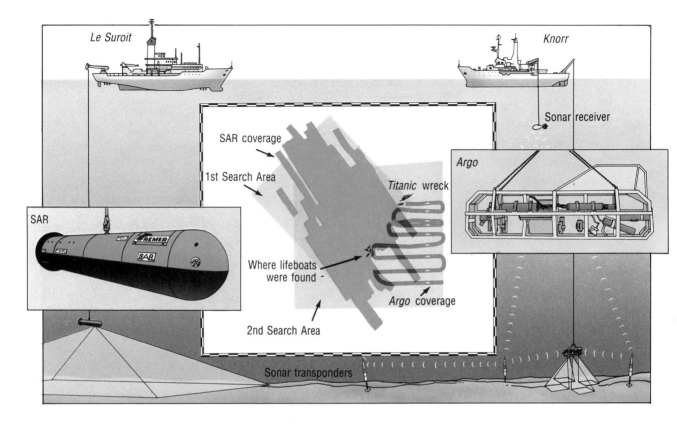

Le Suroit

Knorr

Sonar receiver

SAR coverage

1st Search Area

Titanic wreck

Argo

SAR

Where lifeboats
were found

Argo coverage

2nd Search Area

Sonar transponders

The French ship *Le Suroit* covered 80 percent of the 240-km target search area. The American ship *Knorr* worked north in wide arcs, hoping to locate debris from the *Titanic*.

we had to push really hard in our hunt for the *Titanic*.

And that's why I decided on a new search plan. I knew that when things fall in deep water, they tend to be scattered by ocean currents. The result is usually a long comet tail of debris that settles on the sea floor. I thought that this must have happened when the *Titanic* sank. A long trail of objects would have scattered out of her as she plunged to the bottom. And because the trail would cover a wider area than the ship itself, it would be easier to find. So to save time and make the search easier, I decided to look for the debris field, instead of the *Titanic*. I also hoped that cameras would succeed where sonar had

failed. Starting just south of where the lifeboats were found in 1912, we decided to work north and run *Argo* in east-west lines over the search area.

With our new plan in place, it was time to swing into action. Our search team poured into the control room to take their stations. *Argo* was ready to dive. The smell of hot buttered popcorn filled the room. We were relaxed, but concentrating on the job ahead. After the long slow trip out to the site, we were finally getting down to business.

But as *Argo* reached the ocean bottom at a depth of 3 807 m from the surface, its cameras revealed only faint tracks of deep-sea slugs etched in the mud. Otherwise, nothing. For the next several days all we saw was a gently rolling countryside made up of hills of mud.

A celebration breaks out in the control room after we realize that we have found the *Titanic*.

Towing *Argo* was a delicate balancing act. If the *Knorr* went too fast, *Argo* would lift too high off the bottom for its cameras to see anything. If the ship's speed was too slow, *Argo* might crash to the bottom. Keeping a tight balance between *Knorr* and *Argo* was very tough and very tiring work. And it went on hour after hour, day after day.

Then we had only five days left to go. The crunch had come. Suddenly the ocean seemed huge, and our doubts began to grow. Was the *Titanic* really in our carefully plotted search area? If so, surely something would have shown up on our monitor screens by now. Were we looking in the wrong place? Would we return empty-handed? I began to feel a rising panic.

In a last-ditch effort, we decided to check out a tiny portion of ocean bottom that Jean-Louis and his SAR sonar system had missed because of strong currents. We headed to that spot 16 km away.

But as we began to tow *Argo* back and forth across the new search area, our hopes really began to fade. There was nothing down there. By now the routine inside our control room had become mind-numbing: hour after hour of staring at video images of flat bottom mud. On top of that, we were exhausted. The strain of it all was getting to us, and the boredom was becoming unbearable. Then, with a bad turn in the weather and only four days left, we reached our lowest point. I began to face total defeat.

Just after midnight, on September 1, I went to my bunk for some rest, and the night shift led by Jean-Louis took their stations. About an hour into their watch, one of the team members asked the others, "What are we going to do to keep ourselves awake tonight?" All they'd seen so far was mud and more mud, an endless stretch of

(Above) One of the *Titanic's* boilers lying on the ocean floor.

(Left) This 1912 photograph of boilers being assembled helped us identify the large round object we saw on Argo's video screen.

nothing. Stu Harris, who was busy flying *Argo*, didn't answer. His eyes were glued to the *Argo* video monitor.

"There's something," he said, pointing to the screen. Suddenly every member of the sleepy watch was alive and alert. No one could believe it wasn't just another false alarm, or a joke. But, no, there on the screen were clear images of things man-made. Stu yelled, "Bingo!" The control room echoed with a loud "Yeah!" from the whole team, and then wild shrieks and war whoops. All sorts of wreckage began to stream by on the screen. Then something different appeared — something large and perfectly round. Jean-Louis checked in a book of pictures of the *Titanic*. He came across a picture of the ship's massive boilers, used to burn coal and drive the engines. He couldn't believe his eyes. He looked from book to video screen and back again. Yes, it was the same kind of boiler!

I scrambled out of my bunk when I got the news and ran to the control room. We replayed the tape of the boiler. I didn't know what to say. I turned to Jean-Louis. The look in his eyes said everything. The *Titanic* had been found. We'd been right all along. Then he said softly, "It was not luck. We earned it."

Our hunt was almost over. Somewhere very near us lay the R. M. S. *Titanic*.

Word had spread throughout the ship. People were pouring into the control room. The place was becoming a madhouse. Everyone was shaking hands and hugging and slapping each other on the back.

It was now almost two in the morning, very close to the exact hour of the *Titanic's* sinking. Someone pointed to the clock on the wall. All of a sudden the room became silent.

Here at the bottom of the ocean lay not only the graveyard of a great ship, but of more than 1 500 people who had gone down with her. And we were the very first people in seventy-three years to come to this spot to pay our respects. Images from the night of the disaster — a story I now knew by heart—flashed through my mind.

Out on the stern of the *Knorr*, people had started to gather for a few moments of silence in memory of those who had died on the *Titanic*. The sky was filled with stars; the sea was calm. We raised the Harland & Wolff flag, the emblem of the shipyard in Belfast, Ireland, that had built the great liner. Except for the shining moon overhead, it was just like the night when the *Titanic* had gone down. I could see her as she slipped nose first into the glassy water. Around me were the ghostly shapes of lifeboats and the piercing shouts and screams of passengers and crew freezing to death in the water.

Our little memorial service lasted about ten minutes. Then I just said, "Thank you all. Now let's get back to work."

In the short time remaining, I planned to get as many pictures of the wreck as possible. I wanted to show the world what condition the *Titanic* was in after seventy-three years on the bottom. A million questions flew through my mind. Would the ship be in one piece or broken up? Were the funnels still standing upright? Would the wooden deck be preserved in the deep salt water? And, a darker thought—would we find any remains of the people who had died that night? Photographs would give us the answers.

We started to make our first run with *Argo* over the major piece of wreckage we'd just found. But there were dangers lurking below. If *Argo* got caught in tangled wreckage, it would take a miracle to free it. It could mean the end of our mission.

As *Argo* neared the bottom, no one moved in the control room. Not a word was spoken. Now *Argo* was passing over the main hull of the *Titanic*. It was time to take a close look.

"Take it down farther. Go down to five metres."

"Roger."

On the video screen, I could see the dim outline of a hull. "It's the side of the ship. She's upright!"

Suddenly, out of the gloom the Boat Deck of the ship came into view. "Keep your eyes peeled for funnels."

But there were only gaping holes where funnels had once stood. Then as we crossed over the middle of the ship, we could see the flattened outline of the bridge. Was this where Captain Smith had stood bravely to the end?

Before we knew it, *Argo* had safely passed over the wreck and back into the empty murk.

(Above) We begin the task of lowering Argo down to the *Titanic*.

We had made it safely after all. All at once the crowded control room exploded. People were whooping, hugging, and dancing around while Jean-Louis and I quietly stood there thinking about what we had just seen. We now knew that the *Titanic* had landed on the bottom upright, and that a major piece of her appeared to be intact.

I wanted to make more passes over the wreck with *Argo*, but first it was time to clear the control room. I needed my team as rested as possible for the next sixty-four hours, which was all the time we had left. "Hey, we've got too many people up. You'll be exhausted when your watch comes up. Let's get some of you back in bed. This is a twenty-four operation."

During the rest of that afternoon and evening, we managed only two more *Argo* passes over the wreck because of bad weather. But we did discover to our surprise and sadness that the ship was broken in two — her stern was missing. Where the back of the ship should have been, our video images faded into a confusing mass of twisted wreckage.

By now the storm had reached its peak. We could no longer use *Argo*. For ten hours the wind howled across our rolling deck as the *Knorr* pitched and heaved in the rough sea. Well, I thought finally, if we can't use *Argo* and the video system, then we'll work with ANGUS.

ANGUS was quite like Argo, except that it was an older camera sled that took still photographs instead of video as it was towed over the sea floor. Our nickname for ANGUS was the "dope on a rope." Now we would bring our old friend to the rescue. After all, I had used ANGUS in rougher seas than this.

But our first runs over the wreck with ANGUS only produced blurry images. The cameras were working properly, but we had come over the wreck too high to get good pictures. We were now down to our final hours, and I felt victory slipping away. At that moment I just wanted to go home. My leg was sore from a fall on the deck, and I hadn't slept in days. We had found the *Titanic*. Wasn't that good enough? Who said we had to bring home pretty pictures?

But somehow I found the strength to continue. I was not going to leave the *Titanic* without trying one last time. We had four and a half hours left before we had to start back. The *Knorr* had to be back in port for another expedition.

I was so tired that I had to lie down or I would fall down. So I lay down in the control room and gave the commands for the last-ditch attempt. What we were about to do in these rough seas was even crazier than the risky ANGUS passes we had just made. We had to get our cameras within close range of the *Titanic's* decks. On the surface the seas were heaving up and down at least three to four metres. That motion would travel down our 3 750 m cable and make ANGUS hard to control. But what the heck, it was now or never.

"Down to four metres," I croaked.

"Four metres? Are you crazy?" said the pilot.

"Four metres," I repeated.

For the next three hours hardly a word was spoken as we made pass after hair-raising pass over the *Titanic*. One slip and ANGUS would be lost forever in the wreckage below. Outside, the wind rattled the walls of our control room as the storm blew itself out. Then, at about six in the morning, a simple message boomed over the *Knorr's* intercom from the captain: "You have to start up now."

Right on time, ANGUS was pulled back on deck. A few hours later, news came from our photo lab that we had good, clear photographs of the *Titanic*. We'd made it! By a whisker.

Now, finally, I went to my bunk to get some sleep. When I awoke, it was nighttime, and the good ship *Knorr* was steaming quietly and steadily to our home port.

On the clear, warm morning of September 9, 1985, as we steamed down Nantucket Sound, Massachusetts, the *Knorr* was mobbed by helicopters, small planes, and pleasure craft running circles around us and blowing their horns. News of our discovery of the *Titanic* had made headlines around the world.

Then a small boat with a welcoming party including my wife and two sons, Todd and Douglas, approached our ship. Having my family there was really important to me. They had paid a big price over the years during my long months away from home, but they'd never once complained.

As we came into port, I couldn't believe my eyes. The dock was a mass of people filling every centimetre of space. There was a platform bristling with television cameras and reporters. Banners were flying, a band was playing, schoolchildren hung on to balloons, and a cannon boomed out a salute.

What a victory welcome!

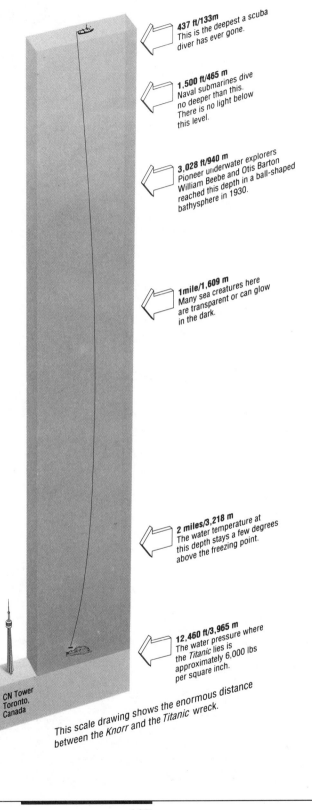

437 ft/133 m
This is the deepest a scuba diver has ever gone.

1,500 ft/465 m
Naval submarines dive no deeper than this. There is no light below this level.

3,028 ft/940 m
Pioneer underwater explorers William Beebe and Otis Barton reached this depth in a ball-shaped bathysphere in 1930.

1mile/1,609 m
Many sea creatures here are transparent or can glow in the dark.

2 miles/3,218 m
The water temperature at this depth stays a few degrees above the freezing point.

12,460 ft/3,965 m
The water pressure where the *Titanic* lies is approximately 6,000 lbs per square inch.

Great Pyramid of Cheops El Gizeh, Egypt

Eiffel Tower Paris, France

Empire State Building New York, U.S.A.

Sears Tower Chicago, U.S.A.

Ostankino Tower Moscow, U.S.S.R.

CN Tower Toronto, Canada

This scale drawing shows the enormous distance between the *Knorr* and the *Titanic* wreck.

The Shark

He seemed to know the harbour,
So leisurely he swam;
His fin,
Like a piece of sheet-iron,
Three-cornered,
And with knife-edge,
Stirred not a bubble
As it moved
With its base-line on the water.

His body was tubular
And tapered
And smoke-blue,
And as he passed the wharf
He turned,
And snapped at a flat fish
That was dead and floating.
And I saw the flash of a white throat,
And a double row of white teeth,
And eyes of metallic grey,
Hard and narrow and slit.

Then out of the harbour,
With that three-cornered fin,
Shearing without a bubble the water
Lithely,
Leisurely,
He swam —
That strange fish,
Tubular, tapered, smoke-blue,
Part vulture, part wolf,
Part neither — for his blood was cold.

By E. J. Pratt

Little Fish

The tiny fish enjoy themselves
in the sea.
Quick little splinters of life,
their little lives are fun to them
in the sea.

By D. H. Lawrence

Dark Water, Deep Water

You Can Pick Me Up
at Peggy's Cove/BRIAN DOYLE
What better way to work off his anger toward his runaway father than learning inshore fishing with a pair of oddball experts, and ripping off the hordes of tourists? Ryan's summer at Canada's most famous fishing village teaches him more than he ever bargained for.

Island of the Blue Dolphins/
SCOTT O'DELL
Karana is only twelve when she is accidently left behind on a Pacific island by her departing tribe. Based on a true tale, her lonely survival is a struggle. Can she make it until the ship returns?

The Summer the Whales Sang/
GLORIA MONTERO
"Ever since I can remember, I've wanted to be thirteen." But Vivi Aguirre's thirteenth summer is not turning out as planned. She spends it at a whaling station in Labrador, where she is forced to come to terms with herself and with her Basque background.

Adrift: Seventy-Six Days
Lost at Sea/STEVEN CALLAHAN
When Steven Callahan's small boat sinks near the Canary Islands, he finds himself adrift in the Atlantic in an inflatable raft. In this true tale of courage and determination Steve must use all his survival instincts to stay afloat and alive.

Danger on the River/J. ROBERT JANES
The river had always been there. Once a busy waterway, now it was a place for five teenagers to swim. But something was poisoning the river and threatening the environment. It was a mystery the five were determined to solve.

WORDS AND MUSIC

Papa would look so pleased when I was able to play my sonata, without any mistakes, even with the keyboard hidden!

Wonderkid/206

Last night I heard a ruckus down the road/No time to lose and so away I go.

Turn Me Round/212

"*That's* Craig the Cat? How do you know? He looks like an ordinary guy."

May I Have Your Autograph/216

The shouts got more urgent, and then we saw the bull.
Melody for a Bull/227

Dear Bruce Springsteen

BY KEVIN MAJOR

For a guy to write to his hero takes real guts.
But that's just what Terry Blanchard does.
Read on for a sample of his letters to Bruce Springsteen.

APRIL 5

Dear Bruce Springsteen,

This letter might never get to you. If it does, it might take years before you get around to reading it because you must get tonnes of mail. I'm going to write it anyway.

You see, I just want to say how much I like your music and to tell you a bit about myself. I don't want to take up much of your time. You probably got millions of things on your mind, but I figure if you ever had a few spare minutes you wouldn't mind listening. That's the kind of person I figure you are.

My name is Terry Blanchard. The story goes that my father named me after a buddy of his from high school who was killed in a motorcycle accident. I heard someone say once that the old man was going to go riding with him that day but changed his mind at the last minute. It's just what I've heard. He never really talked about it.

Hey, know what I just figured out? That you're old enough to be my father. In fact, my old man and you must be about the same age. Weird, right? You're not that much alike though.

I'm getting off track. I'm fourteen. I'm in the ninth grade at school. I got a sister who's ten. The place where I live is not very big, 15 000 people maybe. Big enough to have a McDonald's and a few other things, if that means anything. There are lot worse places to live, I guess. It used to be better, when the mill wasn't getting rid of people.

Bored yet? Guess I shouldn't be taking up your time.

Anyway, I just want to say that I really get off on your music and that my biggest dream is to see you in concert someday. Man, from the clips I've seen on TV, the concerts must be wicked.

Yours truly,
Terry

JUNE 8

Dear Bruce Springsteen,

I had to write you right away.

Man, the MUSE concert — it knocked me out. It's two hours later and I'm in bed, and I still haven't got over it. I knew you were something else in concert. I mean, I read all about them and I saw the videos, but this was something else. It really blew me away.

We played that part of the tape over about a half-dozen times. I'm not kidding.

"The River," the way you sang it was like it was really something special to you. Like it was you and all those people and you were telling them a story about the way things really are.

It made me think of my mother and the old man. Maybe they felt like that. Who knows?

I was wishing for a while that I was there in the house alone, because after three or four times my friend Sean wasn't getting off on that song much anymore. He wanted to move the tape ahead to the faster ones. I tried to ignore him.

Then "Thunder Road" — that was great, too. I don't understand all what you're trying to say in that song, but I love the way it builds up and builds up and then drives everything home. I love the sax part at the end. The big guy really gives it all he's got.

And then "A Quarter to Three." Wicked, man. Too much. You really get into it. It must be fantastic to let rip like that before all those people. The adrenaline was pumping mad just watching it.

Now I got to see the real thing. I got to get to one of your concerts. I don't know when, and I don't know how I'll get there, but someday I will. No two ways about it.

Hey, and you know what I really got off on, too? The short bit backstage when you were being introduced to some little kid and the way you said hello to him. Like, whataya sayin', man? How ya doin' there? Like you'd say that to anyone, no matter who you met, no matter if they were famous or not.

Man, real fine,
Terry

JULY 13

Dear Bruce Springsteen,

I spent almost the whole afternoon in front of Sean's TV set watching a tape of Live Aid. Today is the anniversary of the concert.

I got to tell you right off, though, that I'm still kind of disappointed you weren't there. You would have blown them away. I know you give a lot of money to charity, so I thought it was really something you would have wanted to do. I guess you were busy with other things.

The band I liked the best was The Who. I wish they were still together. And U2 — they were excellent.

The whole thing got me thinking again about how bad off some people are. It was great to see rock musicians helping out the way they did. Me and Sean were saying that it really must have been something to be a part of a concert like that.

Then tonight we called up Kirkland, our guitar teacher, and went over to his place with the guitars to get his help on a few songs. And we got to talking about how great it would be if we were good enough that we could put on a concert, like to raise money for a charity or something. We got to talking some more, and after a while I came up with this idea.

I don't know if it would work, but it really got me going. Why not just do a lip-sync concert? Set up a stereo system and have people do take-offs on different groups and singers, like it was a real concert. It's really big in some places. I've seen it on TV. Maybe have a few people singing for real, too. I think it would go over. We wouldn't charge much, maybe just a couple of bucks. I think people would pay that much when they knew it was for a good cause. Kirkland said he thought there'd be lots of people at school who'd want to take part. He said he'd sing for real himself.

We talked about who we could give the money to. There's lots of charities who could use it. Kirkland mentioned three or four. Then I thought about the Smiths who moved in down the street and how desperate they are. I told Sean and Kirkland if the concert did go ahead, then that would be a really good place for the money to go. They didn't need much convincing.

We're going to think about the whole thing over the summer and get back to him when school opens again. He said he'd be willing to give us a hand organizing it.

Man, I can really picture it now. I already know who I'd do. Give you one guess.

You're right,
Terry

From *Dear Bruce Springsteen: A Novel* by Kevin Major

A Newfoundland Perspective

Kevin Major remembers his own adolescence as being "difficult and rather confusing. I was much more timid than most of the characters I write about. Someone has said — and I've often wondered how true it is — that I'm writing about characters I would like to have been."

"Adolescence," Major writes, "is often a worrisome period of pressures — pressure to do well in school, to gain acceptance from friends, to cope with problems without the fund of experience that adults take for granted."

Born in 1949 in Stephenville, Newfoundland, Major has watched his island community undergo tremendous changes. The young especially — caught between traditional outport values and the influence of mainland popular cul-

ture — have had to deal with intense pressure and family conflicts.

Most critics agree that the strong sense of place in Major's first three novels — *Hold Fast, Far From Shore,* and *Thirty-Six Exposures* — all of which are set in Newfoundland, adds depth to his work. But the universality of the issues which his characters face makes his novels appealing to young people who have never set foot in Newfoundland.

Wonderkid!

BY F.N. MONJO

Minstrels in the Middle Ages and rock stars in the 1980s have at least one thing in common — they all go "on tour." But few musicians have begun touring at such an early age as the famous composer Mozart.

Johann Chrysostom Wolfgang Amadeus Mozart: all of these names were given to the Austrian boy at birth. Very soon he was also called *Wunderkind* — wonderchild! A true child prodigy, he was already "on the road" by the age of six, performing for kings, queens, and ordinary people all over Europe.

In this letter the boy wonder (now thirteen) writes to his sister Nannerl, giving her some inside information about musical tours over 200 years ago.

Mantua, Italy
January 18, 1770

Dear Nannerl,

It's been more than a month since I wrote a whole letter to you, of your very own. But I have been so busy, and so much has happened, that you must forgive me.

We were in Roveredo on December 24. And on Christmas Day (Mama's birthday!) I played the organ in the church, there. So many people came to hear me that a couple of strong fellows had to push some of the people aside so that I could get into the choir. Two days after that we were in the old Italian town of Verona, staying at an inn called The Sign of the Two Towers. Do you know what that is, in Italian? It's *Due Torre*.

Verona is a lovely town, on a rushing river called the Adige. Papa says this is where Romeo and Juliet lived.

Everyone in the streets of Verona was wearing masks when we were there, because Carnival had begun. I wish you could have seen the floats that were pulled through the streets by horses decorated with ribbons and flowers. And the costumes! Everyone dancing in the streets, or lining the balconies and crowding the windows, throwing flowers and streamers and bonbons and confetti and gilded chocolates and silver and copper coins into the crowd. The Italians go *mad* at Carnival time!

They have horse races by day, and plays and balls and fireworks at night.

I can't tell you how many melodies I put down safely into my memory bag, in Verona. One for a Harlequin clown that I think should be bright and silvery when played on the flute. Several for fireworks. And something just right for a lovely young girl, just beginning to fall in love…

The best thing about Carnival time is this: you don't have to be polite. You can talk to anyone you want. You don't have to be introduced to anyone, or call them by name, because everybody's incognito, wearing a mask, anyhow! *"Servitore umilissimo, Signora Maschera,"* you say. Know what *that* means? It means "Your most humble servant, Masked Lady." Doesn't that sound like fun? Just think what *you* might do in a crowd of maskers, Nannerl. Someday, I've promised myself, I'm going to write something in an opera, for people at a masked ball.

Good old business-like Papa Leopold has taken care to have letters of introduction with him, addressed to all the important people in Italy. So we find friends ready to help us wherever we go. That's why Signor Locatelli took us out in his carriage to see the huge old Roman amphitheatre, while we were in Verona.

And we gave another organ concert in the church, and everybody came crowding to see "the little organist." And guess what? While I was there, in Verona, Papa said I had to sit for my portrait. I wore my diamond ring on the little finger of my right hand. And the artist painted me in my wig and my new velvet suit with the gold braid trim. I was shown just turning away from the harpsichord, as if I were the *dearest* little angel. As if butter wouldn't melt in my mouth. You would laugh, Nannerl, to see the ridiculously innocent expression your brother has on his innocent little

mug! Papa *adores* the picture, but I know you and Mama will laugh when you see it — because that's what *I* wanted to do!

And then from Verona we came straight down to Mantua, where we are now.

Don't believe anything they tell you about "sunny Italy," Nannerl. It's *cold* here in winter. Cold! Cold! Cold! If Papa hadn't bought us two foot-bags lined with fur, our feet would have frozen in the carriage — in spite of the hay we put down on the floor of the coach. My face is chapped a reddish-brown from the cold — plus the fact that it gets scorched from the heat of the inn fire, whenever I come in from outside. (I'm only joking. Don't let Mama take me seriously and start worrying.)

Two days ago, on January 16, I gave a public concert here in Mantua, at the Accademia Filarmonica (the Philharmonic Academy to you). The Italians think I'm a lot younger than thirteen — but Papa doesn't mind that a bit! I'm so small I must look as if I'm only nine or ten, I suppose. But you and Mama know I'll be *fourteen* in a few days — on January 27.

Anyway, the concert was a big success, and Papa was happy because he was able to take in some gold pieces at the door, to offset the huge amount we've been spending. ("Money doesn't grow on trees, Wolferl," says Papa Leopold.)

You and Mama would laugh if you could hear what they *call* me. In Germany and Austria, when I was little, they used to call me the *Wunderkind* — the "wonderchild." You remember? Well, the Italians can't say Wolfgang. Or Johann. Or Chrysostom. Or *Wunderkind*, either, for that matter. So they call me Amadeo. That's right. They call me "that most accomplished youth, *Signor Amadeo*."

And here's what that "most accomplished youth" did at his concert:

1. Conducted a symphony of his own composition.
2. Improvised a harpsichord sonata, with variations — composed right then and there.
3. Composed and sang an aria to words given to him on the spot — never before seen by him.
4. Composed a fugue and variations on a theme given to him (and seen by him for the first time) in the concert hall.
5. Performed on the violin, in a string trio, in which he had to improvise his part.

So you see, Papa is still up to his old tricks! It's not enough for me to be simply a good musician. Or a good composer. I must still do tricks and improvisations to surprise the donkey's-ears in the audience.

Of course, it's not as bad as it was eight years ago—when I was about six and you were eleven—when Papa and Mama showed us off, the first time, in Vienna, to Emperor Francis and Empress Maria Theresa. Will you ever forget it, Nannerl? Such nonsense! They discovered I had perfect pitch, and some foolish lady would tinkle her spoon against her champagne glass and say, "What note is this, my dear little Wolfgang? My adorable little *Wunderkind?*" And I would have to answer, "That is F sharp, your ladyship." And then a fat gentleman would ring the little chime on his pocket watch, and ask me to tell him what note *that* was. And I would have to reply, "That is E flat, Prince Unterschlossberg. E flat, without a doubt!"

And the ladies would kiss, and kiss, and *kiss* me, and the gentlemen would say "Astounding! *Wunderbar!* Unheard-of! *Unglaublich!*"

Even the emperor wasn't content to let me play my sonatas on the harpsichord, and be done with it. For, when I was finished, he would make us cover the keyboard with a cloth—do you remember? And Papa would look so pleased when I was able to play my sonata, without any mistakes, even with the keyboard hidden! And then Empress Maria Theresa would take me up onto her fat lap and kiss me some more, and tell Papa I was a wonder. "A *Wunderkind,* Herr Mozart! A *Wunderkind* such as the world has never seen before!"

It was all very tiresome. Most of them didn't want to hear me play. Not really. They preferred to see me do my tricks, like a little monkey.

Now Papa says I'm too old for any more tricks of that kind. "You're much too old to play the *Wunderkind* in Italy, Wolferl," he says. But he *still* lets them give me melodies to improvise, and things like that, at my concerts.

Maybe someday, Nannerl, my music will be enough. Do you suppose that day will ever come?

While here, in Mantua, we've been to the opera. The prima donna was old, and not very good-looking, but she didn't have a bad voice. The opera was by Papa's friend, Herr Hasse. And the tenor had a beautiful voice. I forget his name.

Papa says the post is ready to leave, so I'll have to stop.

Your brother,
Wolfgang, in Austria but
Amadeo in Italy!

New Day Dawning

New Morning

BY BOB DYLAN

Can't you hear that rooster crowin' ?
Rabbit runnin' down across the road
Underneath the bridge where the water flowed through.
So happy just to see you smile, underneath the sky of blue
On this new morning, new morning,
On this new morning, with you.

Can't you hear that motor turnin'?
Automobile comin' into style,
Comin' down the road for a country mile or two.
So happy just to see you smile, underneath this sky of blue
On this new morning, new morning,
On this new morning, with you.

The night passed away so quickly;
It always does when you're with me.
Can't you feel that sun a-shinin'?
Groundhog runnin' by the country stream,
This must be the day that all of my dreams come true.
So happy just to be alive underneath this sky of blue
On this new morning, new morning,
On this new morning, with you.

So happy just to be alive, underneath this sky of blue
On this new morning, new morning,
On this new morning with you.

New morning,
New morning.

Song

BY ROBERT BROWNING

The year's at the spring
And day's at the morn;
Morning's at seven;
The hill-side's dew-pearled;
The lark's on the wing;
The snail's on the thorn:
God's in his heaven—
All's right with the world!

Prairie Portraits

Turn Me Round

BY K. D. LANG

Last night I heard a ruckus down the road
No time to lose and so away I go
I saw the lights, heard trucks and audio
Pulled up my wheels to check the show

Chorus:
Turn me round
They're dancing round, round, round
Turn me round
They're dancing round, round, round
Turn me round
They're dancing round, round, round
Turn me, turn me, turn me, turn me, turn, turn
They're dancing round

I couldn't belive it so I circled back and then
Pulled up my engine and I walked right in
A-la-main left and rip it on up, circle back and whoa
It was a square dance like a rockin' rodeo

Chorus

(square dance call)

I danced and partied 'til my feet went through the floor
I swung my partner 'til I couldn't spin no more
Then a-la-main left and circle back and circle right and then
We rocked and rolled around and did it again

Chorus
"The next dance will be a circle square"

The Red River Valley II

TRADITIONAL

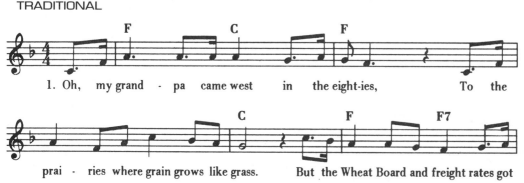

1. Oh, my grand - pa came west in the eight-ies, To the prai - ries where grain grows like grass. But the Wheat Board and freight rates got grand-pa So grand - pa went east sec - ond class.

1.
Oh, my grandpa came west in the eighties,
To the prairies where grain grows like grass.
But the Wheat Board and freight rates got grandpa
So grandpa went east second class.

REFRAIN
Oh, it's forty below in the winter
And it's twenty below in the fall,
And it rises to zero in the springtime,
And we don't have no summer at all.

2.
It was raining and hailing this morning
On the corner of Portage and Main;
Now it's noon and the basements are flooded
And the dust storms are starting again.

3.
Come and pay for my fare if you love me
And I'll hasten to bid you adieu,
And farewell to your Red River Valley
And its natives all shivering and blue.

Down Home

She's Called Nova Scotia

BY RITA MACNEIL

1. She grows on you slowly the first time you meet.
   There's just so much beauty the heart can believe.
   And you want to stay longer and she's ever so pleased.
   You're one of the many who don't want to leave.

   Chorus
   So walk through her green fields; go down to the sea.
   The fortune in your eyes is more like a dream.
   She's called Nova Scotia, and she so makes you feel
   You've discovered a treasure no other has seen.

2. It's hard to remember the places you've been,
   for once in her presence she's all that you see.
   And she cradles you softly, like a warm gentle breeze,
   and wins your heart over with a feeling of peace.

3. She welcomes the strangers from faraway shores,
   while deep down inside her some walk through her soul.
   And at night in her slumber, the winds softly call,
   and awaken her spirit that lives in us all.

   You've discovered a treasure no other has seen.

Down Here Tonight

BY BRUCE COCKBURN

sweet wind blowing off the bay
sweeping the heat of the day away
making the leaves of the palm trees sway
down here tonight everything's okay

net's coming in and the anchor's down
hour of darkness comes around
stars dust the sky and the lights go on
soon tonight will be filled with song

pans gonna play and the fire burn bright
talking drums say everything's all right
beating of the sea sends a message to the far starlight
"we're going okay down here tonight"

the end of the road's still far away
but the travelling's better by the light of day
this hour of darkness is the time to dance
lay down your burdens—give the beat a chance

pans gonna play and the fire burn bright
talking drums say everything's all right
beating of the sea sends a message to the far starlight
"we're doing okay down here tonight"

WRITTEN IN TOBAGO

May I Have Your Autograph?

BY MARJORIE SHARMAT

I am sitting in an overstuffed chair in the lobby of The Dominion Imperial International Hotel. So help me, that's really the name. I am surrounded by overgrown ferns, ugly but expensive floral carpeting, chandeliers that make me think of *The Phantom of the Opera*, stuck-up hotel employees in silly-looking uniforms who give me dirty looks — and nobody my age. Except my friend Wendy, who dragged me here.

Wendy is here to meet a guy, but he doesn't know it. In fact, he's never heard of Wendy. But that doesn't stop her from being in love with him. Well, maybe not in love. I think love is for people you've at least met. Wendy has never met Craig the Cat. That's the name of the guy. At least that's his stage name. He's a rock star who's been famous for over six months. Even *my* parents have heard of him.

Wendy is here to get Craig the Cat's autograph on his latest album. On the album jacket, Craig is wearing a black cat costume and he's sitting on a garbage pail with a bottle of spilled milk beside him. He is holding his guitar in his long, furry arms.

Wendy constantly talks about Craig the Cat. But it was like discussing something that was going on in another time frame, on another continent. I didn't mind. It was nicely, safely unreal. Until Craig the Cat came to town today. He's giving a string of benefit performances across the country for some kind of animal group that's devoted to saving "the cats."

"That includes everything from alley cats to exotic tigers," Wendy told me.

"How do you know?"

"I know."

We used our allowance money to buy tickets. That landed us exactly five rows from the back of the auditorium.

"This is so frustrating," Wendy said as we stretched our necks. "I must get closer."

"How close?" I joked.

"I want his autograph," she answered. "I'm not joking."

"Lots of luck."

Wendy doesn't believe in luck. After the concert she dragged me here, to this hotel lobby where we are now sitting. We just sit.

"Are we waiting for him to come into the lobby?" I ask.

"No. He probably got spirited into the hotel through a back or side entrance." Wendy looks at her watch. "He's showered and is relaxing now. He's feeling rested, triumphant, and receptive."

"Receptive to what?"

"To meeting us. To autographing *my* album."

"How are you going to accomplish that? You don't actually know that he's staying at this hotel, and even if he is, you don't know his room number."

Wendy stands up. "Don't be so negative, Rosalind. Come," she says.

I follow her to one of those telephones that connects the caller to hotel rooms. She dials a number. She waits. Then she says, "Craig the Cat, please." She looks at me. "I found him! Listen!" She tilts the receiver so that I, too, can hear what's being said. It's a strain, but I can hear.

A woman is on the other end. "How did you find out where Craig the Cat is staying?" she asks. "The leak. I need to know where the leak is."

"There isn't any. I'm the only one with the information. Please be nice. I want his autograph."

"Who doesn't."

"Help me get it, please. What are my chances?"

"Poor to nonexistent."

"Oh."

"I'm his manager and, my dear, I'm his mother. I protect Craig from two vantage points. I keep a low profile. Now, how many other fans know where he's staying?"

"None that I know of."

"You mean you didn't peddle the information to the highest bidder?"

"I wouldn't do that."

"Maybe not, dear, but I'm tired of his fans. They tug at Craig's whiskers. They pull his tail. Leave him alone! I'm hanging up."

Click.

Wendy sighs. "We'll just have to wait until he goes into that place over there to eat."

"Haven't you ever heard of room service?"

"Craig doesn't like room service. He doesn't like dining rooms, either. He's a coffee shop person."

"How do you know?"

"I know."

"How did you know his room number?"

"I knew."

"And you knew his mother is his manager?"

"I knew."

We are sitting in the overstuffed chairs again. Wendy is watching and waiting. I see no human-size cat in the lobby. I feel like going to sleep.

Almost an hour goes by. Suddenly, Wendy pokes me. "It's him! It's him!"

I look up. A guy who seems to be about twenty or twenty-five is passing by with a woman who looks old enough to be his mother. He is lean. She is not. They are dressed normally.

I whisper to Wendy. "*That's* Craig the Cat? How do you know? He looks like an ordinary guy."

Wendy doesn't answer. She stands up and starts to follow the guy and the woman. They are heading for the hotel coffee shop. I follow all of them. I see the guy and the woman sit down. They are looking at menus.

Wendy rushes up to them, clutching her album. "May I have your autograph?" she asks the guy.

The woman glares at Wendy. "He doesn't give autographs," she says. "He's just a civilian. Can't you see he's just a civilian?"

"*You're Craig the Cat!*" Wendy says to the guy.

She says it too loudly.

"How do you know I'm Craig the Cat?" the guy asks. Also too loudly.

People in the coffee shop turn and stare. They repeat, "Craig the Cat!"

Suddenly somebody with a camera materializes and aims the camera at Craig. Wendy bends down and puts her face in front of Craig's. It happens so fast, I can't believe it. The photographer says, "Get out of the way, kid."

Craig's mother glares at the photographer. "Shoo!" she says, waving her hand. "Shoo immediately!"

The photographer leaves. So does Wendy. She runs back to me. I am hiding behind a fern.

Wendy has lost her cool. "Let's get out of here before we're kicked out or arrested," she says.

We rush toward a door.

"Wait!" Someone is yelling at us.

When I hear the word *wait*, it's a signal for me to move even faster. But Wendy stops. "It's *him*!" she says, without turning around.

I turn. It *is* Craig the Cat. He's alone. He rushes up to Wendy. "How did you know me?" he asks. "I didn't tell the media where I was staying. And I certainly didn't give out my room number. I wasn't wearing my cat costume. And I was with my mother. So *how*?"

Wendy looks at me. She's trying to decide if she should answer. Something in her wants to and something in her doesn't want to. She turns back to Craig. "I'm an expert on you," she says. "I know you like fancy, old hotels, and this is the oldest and the fanciest in town. I know your lucky number is twelve, so I figured you'd stay on the twelfth floor in room 1212. I know you always wear red socks when you're not performing. So tonight I watched ankles in the lobby. And I knew you'd be with your manager — your mother."

"What about the photographer?"

"I know you don't want to be photographed without your cat costume. In an interview of October eighth of this year, you said it would wreck your feline image. So when I saw the photographer trying to take your picture, I put my face in front of yours."

"You did that for me?"

"I'd do it for any special friend."

"But you don't know me."

"Yes, I do. When I read about someone, I get to know him. I don't believe everything I read, of course. I pick out certain parts. I look for the reality behind the unreality. I went through seventy-one pages about Craig the Cat, in eleven different magazines, and I ended up thinking of you as my friend."

Craig the Cat is staring at Wendy as if *he's* the fan. He's in awe of *her*! It's nothing very earthshaking. It's not like there's a crowd roaring or it's a summit meeting of world leaders or a momentous change in the universe. It's just a small, nice moment in the lobby of The Dominion Imperial International Hotel, and it will never go away for Wendy.

We're back in the hotel coffee shop. Four of us are sitting around a table, eating. Craig's mother is beaming benevolently like a contented mother cat presiding over her brood, which now includes Wendy and me in addition to Craig. After we finish eating, Wendy hands her record album to Craig. "Now may I have your autograph?" she asks.

Craig pulls out a pen and writes on the album jacket. I hope that Wendy will show me what he writes. Maybe she won't. Whatever she does will be okay, though. Maybe this will be the first private entry in her collection of reality and unreality about her new friend, Craig the Cat.

She's entitled.

As for me, I'm now sitting in a chair in a hotel coffee shop as a new and honoured member of this Clan of the Cat. It has been a strange and kind of wonderful day, thanks to my friend, Wendy the Expert. I'm glad I'm here. If you take away some of the ferns and a few fat chairs and most of the carpeting, The Dominion Imperial International Hotel definitely has possibilities.

I WAS A BEATLEMANIAC

BY RON SCHAUMBURG

I was in the drug store the day I first heard the Beatles. As I walked through the aisles clutching my bags of Valentine's hearts, I heard the scratchy sound of the hi-fi department's two-speed record player. Despite the distortion of high volume, the music was unlike any I'd heard before.

"What's that song?" I asked the salesclerk. "It's kinda neat."

"It's by a new group called the Beatles," she said. "'I Want to Hold Your Hand.'"

You're not holding mine, I thought, and left.

During recess the next day, a group of us stood under the dark, cold clouds of winter. Some of the fellows were off playing kickball, but since I was usually the last one chosen, I didn't feel needed or welcome there. My teacher once tried to coach me privately in the fine art of football tossing, but little of it rubbed off. I usually hung around the jungle gym, taking as little part as possible in competitive sports. Just to make conversation I said to the others hanging by their heels, "Hey, have you guys heard that new song by…uh…by…" I stopped cold. I couldn't remember the title, or the name of the group, or

34,000 BEATLE FANS PAY $100,000 to hear themselves scream!

one note of the melody, so no one had any idea what I was talking about. It was to be the last time I'd ever forget the Beatles' name.

FAB FOUR MEMORABILIA

The wave of Beatlemania was about to break. It had swamped England in 1963, leaving screaming teenagers and amused, bemused parents in its wake. Even the Royal Family took a casual interest in the shaggy quartet. It's still hard to believe that in January 1964, North America didn't know who the Beatles were, but two weeks later we were talking of nothing else.

Shortly before the Beatles arrived in North America, the local dime stores were suddenly flooded with Beatle wigs, buttons, shirts, dolls, rings, lunchboxes, notebooks, and tennis shoes. Baskin-Robbins even introduced "Beatle Nut" ice cream. A newspaper columnist pointed out that the last time beetles came to the country we ignored them, and look what happened to the elm trees.

I remember how the Beatles' appearances on *The Ed Sullivan Show* on February 9 and 16, 1964, set the schoolyard buzzing with

---

IN CONTEXT
BACKGROUNDER

The British Invasion

Rock-and-roll erupted in 1955 when the energetic and exciting music of Elvis Presley, Bill Haley and the Comets, Chuck Berry, Little Richard, Jerry Lee Lewis and others challenged North Americans to rethink their ho-hum existence. But it nearly died in 1959 when profit-hungry record companies began to produce dozens of boring, tidy sound-alikes. North America took the rock out of rock-and-roll.

For five dreary years the air waves were noisy with sugar-coated imitators from the U.S. and Great Britain. Then, a decade after the movement had begun, it got a second wind. The North America of the fifties may have been

unprepared for the rock-and-roll revolution, but by 1964 it was ready and willing to be shaken up. Young people craved something exuberant and alive — something to believe in.

That something arrived in the shape of a new breed of musician. After years spent in basements and garages practising the music of their rock-and-roll idols — and making music of their own — one British band after another invaded North America. The Rolling Stones, Gerry and the Pacemakers, Herman and His Hermits, and the Dave Clark Five brought a continent of eager fans screaming to their feet. So Canadian teenagers were *ready* when the Beatles made their first earth-shaking North American appearance in Vancouver on August 22, 1964.

anticipation. Like 73 000 000 others, my friends and I sat in front of our television sets, watching as the Beatles sang through such songs as "She Loves You," "All My Loving," "I Saw Her Standing There," and "Twist and Shout." A friend of mine, Kathy Atkinson, says her father made her watch because it would be something she'd "always want to remember." "I hated it," she recalls. "At that time I hated anything my father *made* me do."

I watched, partly because of the general interest in the Beatles, but mainly because Ed Sullivan, like *Bonanza* and *My Favorite Martian*, was part of my regular Sunday night routine. My homework was usually done by the time Sunday night rolled around, so there was time for fun. Besides, the chief topic of conversation during any school day was the previous night's TV shows, and I didn't want to feel out of place or uninformed.

Television offered the sound of a radio, the movement of film, and the immediacy of a newspaper, and sent it all, free of charge, into our living rooms. During Sullivan's show we could see the Beatles singing, shaking those wild haircuts. Hysterical girls screamed out, "John!" "I love you, Paul!" "Auuggh!" "Look at me, George!" "RINGO!!" on live TV. I had never seen anything like it before. I thought they must have paid the audience, or at least rehearsed them.

It was thrilling. When the Beatles came on I left my seat to get closer to the screen, much as armchair quarterbacks do during the instant replay of a touchdown. I was as amazed by the Beatles as I was by the audience reaction to them. "Look at them!" I said to no one in particular, "They're going crazy!"

While we kids thrilled, so too did our parents. The Beatles, with their revolutionary haircuts (though they were obviously conservative

by later standards) and their charming manner-
isms, seemed "clean" to most teenagers' mothers.
The Beatles' clothes also set them apart. At the
time, my own wardrobe consisted of dorky print
shirts, baggy trousers, and scuffed black penny
loafers. I hated to tie shoes. My hair was as short
and fuzzy as lint from a clothes dryer. Sunday
dress-up found me in a white shirt with a too-tight
collar, a brown tweed suit coat, scratchy brown
pants, and the same scuffed black penny loafers.
I alternated between bowties and skinny black
neckties, both of which clipped on at the neck.

BUBBLE GUM CARDS AND SHAGGY MOPS

I found that most parents of my friends
accepted, if not openly endorsed, the Beatles,
in sharp preference to "those greasy rock-and-
rollers" or "that noisy garbage" that poured from
radios. Some adults even enjoyed their music.
A seventy-eight-year-old man said to me, "Yeah,
I like the Beatles. Watch them on television.
They's pretty good, ain't they?"

Here come THE BEATLES!

The girls at school started going collectively
crazy; they exchanged the treasured nickels of
their allowances for the infinite variety of Beatle artifacts. Bubble gum trading cards began to
circulate, and even the boys who couldn't stand
the group started to let their hair grow. My father
finally gave up trying to make my hair stand on

end and retired our jar of Butch Wax. I know of more than one fellow who pocketed his haircut money instead of going to the barber shop. Some of the kids tried to imitate the Beatle accent, although few had even heard of Liverpool before. Others wanted the Cuban boots and collarless jackets the group wore. I never actually saw the clothes in stores or knew anyone who owned them.

I somehow felt that guys weren't really supposed to like the Beatles, but their music so transcended anything else on the radio that I couldn't help falling under their spell.

THE MAKING OF THE LEGEND

Meanwhile the Beatles, unconcerned with the hoopla around them, were recording the best music of the decade. With such songs as "She Loves You," "I Saw Her Standing There," "All My Loving," "I'll Get You," "Can't Buy Me Love," "And I Love Her," and "This Boy," Lennon and McCartney began to be compared with Schubert and Beethoven. All the record companies that had rights to the early recordings began re-releasing them to cash in on the group's swelling popularity. The early songs were repackaged half a dozen ways. Record company people began to realize that the Beatles meant business. Young fans began to realize that they didn't examine records closely enough to discover they were the same ones that had appeared a month before with a different cover.

John Lennon made me jealous in March by publishing a short collection of his nonsense verse and drawings called *John Lennon In His Own Write*. I had visions of greatness myself and had wanted to publish my own stories. In fact, Ricky, Kevin, and I had even set up a small publishing firm with the unwieldy name of *Ron Schaumburg Kevin White Rick Patrick Books*

Cards and What-Not Printers and Publishers. We had collaborated on a tacky handmade calendar the year before, and tried to sell it around the neighbourhood. One man gave us fifty cents out of pity, and my mother finally informed us that "insurance companies give out nicer ones for free."

As I sat in my room, preparing for the class spelling bee or clipping news articles for current events, my mind often wandered to thoughts of what it would be like to be a Beatle, to be mobbed by adoring girls wherever I went. It all seemed very distant. What a fantastic life they must

BEATLES MADE PRISONERS ....by their own popularity

lead, I thought; they're rich, popular, they travel all over the world — how could they possibly be unhappy? When *A Hard Day's Night* came out that summer, though, I found how wrong this image was. The film is based on first-hand observations of the Beatles trapped in the hotel during their French tour. As I watched, I sensed the boredom, the tediousness of rehearsals, the frightening escapes from fans. It gave me a chance to experience the Beatles on a more personal level. Part of the lasting charm and strong effect of the movie was this sense of reality, the feeling of being present.

Most of this was wasted on the audience I saw the movie with. More than once I had to yell "Shut up!" In 1964 that was a quick way to become unpopular. I left after the matinee was over, blinking in the Saturday afternoon

sunshine, feeling very, very happy. The movie made me feel great, and I ran home singing the songs to myself.

The Beatles' first major tour of North America came close on the heels of the release of *A Hard Day's Night*. The group arrived in our town at two o'clock on the morning of the concert, looking pale and tired. They were whisked away through the rain to the hotel. The bedsheets they slept on that night were bought by two enterprising businessmen and cut into 160 000 tiny squares to be sold for a dollar each. What is not generally known, however, is that over 100 000 of those souvenirs sit, unsold, in a garage in California. I assume nobody ever tried to bottle Beatle bathwater, but I expect it would have met with a similar lack of success. Not everything the Beatles touched could be turned into gold.

Though far from a sellout, the group drew one of the largest crowds on the tour. Kathy Atkinson went, this time on her own initiative, since she had succumbed to Beatlemania after all. Her father bought her the souvenir pennant and program, but he said if she screamed *once* he would take her home. "So we sat," Kathy recalls, "the only two non-screamers in the place."

My sister and her best friend Nancy got to go to the concert that night because they were being escorted by Nancy's father. They didn't want little brothers to tag along, so I wasn't invited. To top it off, it was a Thursday, and I had to take my piano lesson. I was trapped with Bach, Beethoven, and Brahms — the wrong type of long-hair music. Susie was awfully smug about skipping her lesson and going to the concert, but I tried not to let her triumph register on my face. As she dressed in her junior-high-school jacket and went out the front door into the late-summer air, I felt frustrated and annoyed. Just wait till I'm older, I said to myself; then I'll do whatever I want to do, piano lessons or not!

Melody for a Bull

BY JOHN V. HICKS

Fergy Ferguson has a way with animals. Put him beside a cow and in no time at all he'll be talking to it. Not only that, the cow will likely flop its ears forward and stand there listening to what he has to say. I've seen it happen, and Beth Woodley will back me up. Horses, dogs, you name it — they at once accept Fergy as an equal. Beth and I once found him leaning on a fence rail talking confidentially to a pig, and when we burst out laughing he didn't seem to have the faintest idea what the joke was.

At school on Tuesday, we didn't think to tell Fergy about Dr. Johnston's Doberman. Now, *Doberman* is a mean word in dogs. The breed is often trained to hunt fugitives, and not many fugitives will try to argue with one. If you're running from the law and a Doberman comes scampering toward you with its dental work on display, you either stand still and await arrest or risk a shredded forearm.

Dr. Johnston had picked up a sleek black-and-tan that had learned the basics and then been retired from service for some reason. He needed a good watchdog for his premises, and Doby was already something of a threat to strangers.

Our athletic club committee consisted of Beth, Fergy, and me. We called on the doctor that evening to try and line him up for a talk on charley horses at our next meeting. When he opened the door to us he didn't realize, as he told us later, that the Doberman wasn't down in its basement quarters.

"Come on in," he said as he greeted us. "Make yourselves right at home."

Fergy, who refuses to wear anything he doesn't positively have to, strolled on into the front room alone while Beth and I were taking off scarves and outdoor jackets. When the rest of us trooped in from the vestibule I heard the doctor catch his breath.

Fergy had flopped into an easy chair. The Doberman was sitting upright on the floor in front of him, motionless, staring at him intently.

"Doby," said the doctor quietly, "you shouldn't be up here, you know. Come on, we'll let you downstairs."

"Nice to have met you, old fellow," Fergy said, calmly stroking one ear — the Doberman's ear.

About the only thing physically wrong with Fergy is that his fear glands have never developed. The doctor led Doby away.

Fergy also plays the flute. He owns a valuable instrument, all silver, and he cares for it as though it were alive. In fact that's the way it sounds when he plays it — like something breaking into song just before sunrise. Fergy's grandfather, who used to tour the West with the Cassenti Players of Vancouver, left it to him in his will. Since Fergy's granddad had the distinguished name of Henry Mozart Braun, the flute had acquired the nickname of Mozart's Magic Flute. Fergy, thrilled with the bequest, insisted that it was indeed a magic flute — that it, and not he, was responsible for any beautiful sounds that floated out of it. That's the way Fergy is — you can hardly get him to take credit for one blessed thing.

Mrs. Clifton, our school band leader, was quick to recognize Fergy's natural ability. She put him into the "A" band, the top-bracket group, in his first year at the school. She was also quick to emphasize that what exceptional talent needs most is a lot of good hard work. Magic flute or not, she told Fergy with a wry grin, you have to do some of it yourself. The more talent you have, the more reason to dig right in and cultivate it, she insisted.

Fergy applied himself diligently to Mrs. Clifton's lessons. Through his open window, any time before breakfast, you could hear him tootling away merrily, up and down scales, in and out of his technical exercises, showing the early birds in the garden how it was done.

The weekend band workshop was Mrs. Clifton's idea — though some of us thought *Mr.* Clifton had a lot to do with putting it into her mind. He teaches piano and conducts the Glee Club. He is also a gourmet cook, on the side, and we all love him.

The Cliftons had a friend who raised prize cattle near Swift Current and who had just built a big new barn. The idea of combining a barn warming with a session of music-making caught right on. So the "A" band converged on the ranch one Friday afternoon in late September and started practising right away. Soon the farm air crackled with music. The pastures stood dotted with cattle, all with their heads turned attentively toward the lyric commotion in the farmyard area. Bass drum is my specialty, and Beth plays a neat French horn.

The first sign of musical life on Saturday morning came, naturally enough, from Fergy's flute, bringing soft croonings from the roosts and crowings from the roosters. Fergy maintained it was he who had wakened the roosters. One by one, musicians crawled out of sleeping bags, pump handles began to squeak, delicate airs of frying bacon drifted from the camp cook's shed — that is, Mr. Clifton's. He had installed himself in the position; three cheers for him. There's nothing like a square meal, he said, to keep up an interest in the performing arts. By the time the sun had well cleared the horizon, the "B" and "C" bands had arrived and the whole place was one big sound track.

Mrs. Clifton put Fergy in charge of the "C" band — the kids who had just found out which end of a trumpet you blow into — for the first hour. They needed some preliminary drilling on lip and wind, and Fergy apparently had the patience to get them started.

"That's music?" asked Beth, covering her ears in mock pain. "Do they have to go looking for the notes after they've started to blow?"

"Don't knock it," I said. "They'll get their bearings after a while. Wait till their lips get the rubber worked out of them."

"Listen," said Beth. "I'm not the only one — somebody else is complaining too."

We heard shouts, but didn't think too much of it. A couple of farm hands calling back and forth somewhere, perhaps. But the shouts got more urgent, and then we saw the bull.

He was a big red Hereford with a mean set to his head. He came lurching around a corner of a haystack, pulling up a few metres behind Fergy. Fergy had his flute in one hand and was busy making like a conductor with the other. The "C" band kids in their bright T-shirts, intent on their music, didn't notice the creature at first. When they did, they all stopped playing. The bull began to paw the ground. Fergy, surprised at the sudden silence, swung around and found himself facing 700 kg of hostile beef with a wicked look in its eye.

What Fergy did, as he said later on, seemed to be just the natural thing to do. He put his flute to his lips.

Some of the young players had dropped their instruments and were ready to make a dash for cover. The nearest cover, as it happened, was a machine shed fifty metres distant. The whole group became a surging mass of colour. The bull snorted and lowered his head.

"Keep perfectly still!" Fergy barked at the kids as he started into a soft melodic passage, with a trill or two on the way. The bull stopped pawing the ground and cocked his ears forward. Fergy walked toward him, the liquid notes of his flute brightening the morning air. He halted not two metres from the big pink snout.

It was like some grotesque variation of a snake charmer's act. Fergy kept right on playing. The bull slowly raised his head and showed signs of puzzlement. Or was it enchantment? A minute or so later, what did Fergy do but turn slowly on his heel and begin to walk away in the direction of the stock pens, still running up and down the octaves — with the bull, if you please, following him.

It was a weird sight, a sort of slow-motion toreador scene in reverse. None of the spectators budged. In the meantime one of the officials, who had been watching the affair, opened a gate to admit them. They both walked slowly into the pen. Fergy stopped playing, slipped back out, and the show was over.

When the morning had settled back into place again, Mrs. Clifton came strolling over toward Fergy, who had by now rejoined the "A" band. The band leader had been a spectator from a distance too, it appeared.

"Bit risky, wasn't it, that two-piece Pied Piper parade?" she asked, her mouth becoming a stern line.

Fergy shrugged. "Not really," he said, tapping his magic flute. "With this thing…"

Mrs. Clifton ignored the explanation.

"If you ever take a chance like that again, young fellow," she said with a wink, "I'll wrap it around your neck." She snapped her fingers for attention and gave us the downbeat.

The band was only a few bars into a romantic bit of Schubert when a sort of strangled, melancholy roar from the bemused bull floated across to us — right in tune with the flute.

GOOD BOOKS

Words and Music

Star Shine/CONSTANCE C. GREEN
When Jenny and Mary's mother leaves town to work with a small theatre group for the summer, the two sisters manage to convince their father they can cope. Then Jenny lands a small part in a movie — just one unforgettable event in a summer on their own.

Dragonsong/ANNE MCCAFFREY
On the planet Pern, Menolly has been trained in music by the Harper — a knowledge her own community resents. In this first book of an exciting trilogy, Menolly finds a new way of life, and discovers the hiding place of the fire lizards who can keep her world safe.

Scenes for Young Actors/
LORRAINE COHEN, EDITOR
Whether you're in need of an exciting scene to perform, or just want to read a selection of drama suitable for teens, this book will entertain and inform. It includes scenes from *Macbeth*, *Little Women* and *The Diary of Anne Frank*, with full descriptions of plot and character.

Lizard Music/D. MANUS PINKWATER
Things really start to get weird for Victor when a late night TV show featuring a lizard quintet is followed by some strange messages and an introduction to the Chicken Man. The latter turns up in a multitude of disguises and introduces Victor to the wonders of the Pod People.

GETTING THE MESSAGE

It had never crossed my mind that Miss Ibbotson planned to read our journals.

A Writer's Education/234

And you don't know what she wanted/until after you've hung up.

Cultural Frustration/240

"To get a little fish for hungry humans is just too much for you. Well, I'm going to tell 'em you can talk."

Let Me Hear You Whisper/242

Getting a guest is just part of the interview process, and Kulwant never relaxes until his guest is actually at the studio.

On Camera!/265

A Writer's

EDUCATION

*Jean Little, the Canadian writer, describes
in her autobiography* Little by Little
*how she first discovered the power of
language and her own power over words.*

BY JEAN LITTLE

In the fall I went into Miss Ibbotson's class. We had to learn about decimals and percents. I disliked that year in school till the day Miss Ibbotson started us writing journals.

When she passed out the notebooks, they did not look special. They had blue paper covers and lined pages with a thin red margin. I could not see those faint lines when I was writing.

"For the last half hour, every day this month," Miss Ibbotson told us, "you will keep a diary. You will write in them what happened in your life that day and how you felt."

She talked on for a few minutes, but I was not listening. I could hardly wait to begin.

That first afternoon, I did write down what had actually happened in my life that day. I may even have stuck to the truth till page three or four. But long before the first week was up, I had begun fancying things up a little.

My real life was simply too dull to be worth recording.

I began stealing ideas from a book we had at home called *Boyhood Stories of Famous Men*. In the book one boy saved the day by carving a lion out of butter to be used as a decoration for the King's table. Another made his own paints by crushing berries and boiling roots, and little Wolfgang Mozart and his big sister went to perform on the harpsichord before the child Marie Antoinette. The book went on to explain how each boy later became famous.

I liked the story about the young Mozart best. What drew me to it was his older sister. She was shown in the illustration, standing behind Wolfgang and the pretty little princess. I knew exactly how she must be feeling. She, too, was a gifted musician, but her little brother was the hero of the story. It never said what happened to her.

In my journal, I had myself carving wonderful animals, playing the piano brilliantly before I was five and making my own paints.

One day's entry read like this:

Last night, a famous artist came to have supper at our house. Mother took him down to the cellar. The great painter stopped dead in his tracks and pointed to our cellar walls.

"Madam," he cried, "whoever painted these magnificent murals on your walls?"

Mother stared at the wondrous paintings.

"I have no idea," she said in a bewildered voice. She turned to her children.

"Children," she said, "have you any idea who painted these magnificent murals?"

The other children shook their heads.

"As a matter of fact," I said, "I painted them."

"But you had no paints!" Mother cried.

"I know," I said modestly, "but I so longed to paint that I boiled roots and squeezed berries and made my own paints."

The great artist patted my head.

"Madam," he said, with tears in his eyes, "someday this little girl of yours will be world famous as an artist."

Each afternoon when the bell rang and Miss Ibbotson told us to put the books away, I emerged from my fantasy life reluctantly. All day I looked forward to three-fifteen.

Then one afternoon, instead of telling us to put our books away, Miss Ibbotson told us to hand them in.

I was horrified. It had never crossed my mind that Miss Ibbotson planned to read our journals. I thought diaries were private.

The teacher was going to read all those stories. What if she called my mother and asked her for the name of the famous artist?

For days after, whenever the phone rang, I braced myself. But Miss Ibbotson did not call.

Then she gave our diaries back. Before she let us have them, she stood and glared at us.

"I have never, in my whole life, read such rubbish," she growled. Then, in a high-pitched, mimicking voice, she pretended to read from one.

"Today is Monday. I got up at seven-thirty. I got dressed. I had breakfast. I went to school. We had arithmetic. We had spelling. We had recess..."

She pretended to turn a page. She squeaked on.

"Today is Tuesday. I got up at seven-thirty. I got dressed. I had breakfast. I went to school. We had arithmetic. We had spelling..."

We sat and stared at her. Wasn't that what she had wanted? She had told us to tell about our lives, hadn't she? Well, what she had just read out was how our lives went.

"I have never been more bored," declared our teacher. Then she looked at me. I shrank down in my seat.

"The only diary that I enjoyed reading was Jean Little's," Miss Ibbotson said slowly and distinctly. "Hers was at least entertaining. I shall never assign journal writing to a class again. Sylvia, pass out the books."

I sat there dazed. She had liked it. Not only that, she had liked it best. Yet mine had been a bunch of lies almost from start to finish.

As my journal smacked down on the lid of my desk and I caught the baleful look on Sylvia's face, I knew the teacher had not helped me in my search for friends. But I didn't care. I wanted to hug my blue book. I had entertained Miss Ibbotson. That was far more important than being good at decimals and percents.

Real writers kept diaries. I would become a writer.

As I walked home, I thought about books I might write. Perhaps I should write one called "Girlhood Stories of Famous Women." No. I wanted instead to tell about the big sisters who stood at the back of the picture and had to put up with famous little brothers. I knew how they felt.

From *Little by Little: A Writer's Education* by Jean Little

Jean Little

Even without a guide dog to lead the way and a talking computer to help her compose, chances are good that Jean Little would still have found a way to be independent.

Born with only 10% normal vision, Little had the kind of childhood that teaches enough strength and self-reliance to last a lifetime. In the face of rejection by her insensitive schoolmates, Little retreated to her own secret places in the sanctuary of books. Her vision meant she could read only with difficulty, but books became her world.

Much later, when she discovered that there were no books that portrayed handicapped children realistically, Little began work on a book of her own. *Mine for Keeps*, the story of a young handicapped girl, won the Little, Brown Canadian Children's Book Award and launched her career as a world-renowned author of literature for young adults.

Thirteen books and numerous awards later, Little's career nearly came to an end. The earlier removal of her left eye had barely slowed her down, but when Little developed glaucoma in her right eye as well, she thought writing had become impossible.

"That was a very bad time," she says of the eight years it took her to write another book. "I did stop writing for a while — I just didn't know how to do it." But then she began to devise ingenious ways of using a typewriter and tape recorder to get her stories onto the paper that she could barely see. Frustrated and exhausted, Little finally abandoned the typewriter, dictating *Mama's Going to Buy You a Mockingbird* onto 97 tape cassettes.

A special contact lens preserved Little's

remaining sight, but with only 5% vision left, she welcomed the arrival of Zephyr, a golden Labrador guide dog, and SAM, a Synthetic Audio ("talking") Microcomputer. While Zephyr helped Little to go out into the world, SAM helped her to write about it by reading back to her whatever she had typed. "It's made me more independent than I ever was — even when I could see much better," she says. "I'm just like any writer."

Give Us This Day

By Raymond Souster

On the TV screen in front of me
a six-year-old boy from India

whose matchstick arms cry hunger,
whose swollen belly shouts out hunger,
whose sunken eyes scream out hunger,

is so intent on swallowing
the first fingerfuls of food
from the bowl just ladled out to him,

the he hasn't the time to stop
to brush off the flies that swarm around his face,
that light on his nose, his expressionless eyes—

as I break off another piece of Swiss chocolate,
let it slowly melt in my mouth.

Cultural Frustration

By Barry Elmer

You spend a week of every summer
helping grandma with her garden
and to visit.
    Grandma doesn't speak English
    and you can't speak Ukrainian.
The visit is spent
with little talk between us
a spare moment
and you look at her
and wonder about the thoughts
she can't express.
You try to understand her gestures
when mother-interpreter is not around.
Our leaving is kisses and hugs.
    The summer has passed
    someone phones unexpectedly
but you don't understand the voice
that asks for someone
who doesn't seem to live here
and you say you're sorry
because you don't understand her
and you don't know what she wanted
until after you've hung up.

The Dying Story

By Jannis Allan-Hare

An old man sits by the river.
Through hazy vapour from the smokehouses
he visions the bustling village.
He sees brown hands carve a sacred story in cedar.
The fin of a fish, the lifted wing of a bird,
fierce claws of the grizzly, sharp teeth of the dog,
and solemn, staring eyes.
Dyed with colour of their own making,
the woodcarvers raise their totem to the skies.

I see the leaning poles on the hill,
black silhouettes in the summer heat,
their faded colour split with age.
The fallen symbols lie broken.
Deep in the new grass the dying story lies.

I see an old man sitting, silent—
the mist of the Skeena in his eyes.

LET ME HEAR YOU whisper

BY PAUL ZINDEL

List of Characters

HELEN, an elderly cleaning lady who lives alone in a one-room apartment and spends most of her spare time feeding stray cats and dogs. She has just been hired to scrub floors in a laboratory that performs rather strange experiments with dolphins.

MISS MORAY, a briskly efficient custodial supervisor who has to break Helen in to her new duties at the laboratory.

DR. CROCUS, the dedicated man of science who devises and presides over the weird experiments.

MR. FRIDGE, assistant to Dr. Crocus.

DAN, a talky janitor, also under Miss Moray's control.

A DOLPHIN, the subject of an experiment being performed by Dr. Crocus.

TIME: *The action begins with the night shift on a Monday and ends the following Friday.*

"It is of interest to note that while some dolphins are reported to have learned English --up to 50 words used in correct context--no human has been reported to have learned dolphinese."
(Carl Sager, Christian Science Monitor Nov. 15/65)

ACT 1   Scene 1

(*DR. CROCUS and MR. FRIDGE are leaving the laboratory where they have completed their latest experimental tinkering with a dolphin, and they head down a corridor to the elevator. The elevator door opens and MISS MORAY emerges with HELEN.*)

MISS MORAY: Dr. Crocus. Mr.Fridge. I'm so glad we've run into you. I want you to meet Helen.

HELEN: Hello.

(*DR. CROCUS and MR. FRIDGE nod and get on elevator.*)

MISS MORAY: Helen is the newest member of our Custodial Engineering Team.

(*MISS MORAY and HELEN start down the hall.*)

MISS MORAY: Dr. Crocus is the guiding heart here at the American Biological Association Development for the Advancement of Brain Analysis. For short, we call it "Abadaba."

HELEN: I guess you have to.

(*They stop at a metal locker at the end of the hall.*)

MISS MORAY: This will be your locker and your key. Your equipment is in this closet.

HELEN: I have to bring in my own hangers, I suppose.

MISS MORAY: Didn't you find Personnel pleasant?

HELEN: They asked a lot of crazy questions.

MISS MORAY: Oh, I'm sorry. (*pause*) For instance?

HELEN: They wanted to know what went on in my head when I'm watching television in my living room and the audience laughs. They asked if I ever thought the audience was laughing at *me*.

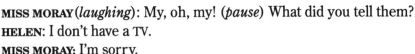

MISS MORAY (*laughing*): My, oh, my! (*pause*) What did you tell them?

HELEN: I don't have a TV.

MISS MORAY: I'm sorry.

HELEN: I'm not.

MISS MORAY: Yes. Now, it's really quite simple. That's our special soap solution. Fifteen millilitres to a pail of hot water, if I may suggest.
(*HELEN is busy running water into a pail which fits into a metal stand on wheels.*)

MISS MORAY: I'll start you in the laboratory. We like it done first. The specimen room next, and finally the hallway. By that time we'll be well toward morning, and if there are a few minutes left, you can polish the brass strip. (*She points to brass strip which runs around the corridor, halfway between ceiling and floor.*) Ready? Fine. (*They start down the hall,* MISS MORAY *thumbing through papers on a clipboard.*)

MISS MORAY: You were with one company for fourteen years, weren't you? Fourteen years with the Metal Climax Building. That's next to the Radio City Music Hall, isn't it, dear?

HELEN: Uh-huh.

MISS MORAY: They sent a marvellous letter of recommendation. My! Fourteen years on the seventeenth floor. You must be very proud. Why did you leave?

HELEN: They put in a rug.
(*MISS MORAY leads HELEN into the laboratory, where DAN is cleaning up.*)

MISS MORAY: Dan, Helen will be taking Marguerita's place. Dan is the night porter for the fifth through ninth floors.

DAN: Hiya!

HELEN: Hello. (*She looks around.*)

MISS MORAY: There's a crock on nine you missed, and the technicians on that floor have complained about the odour.
(*HELEN notices what appears to be a large tank of water with a curtain partly concealing it.*)

HELEN: What's that?

MISS MORAY: What? Oh, that's a dolphin, dear. But don't worry about anything except the floor. Dr. Crocus prefers us not to touch either the equipment or the animals.

HELEN: Do you keep him cramped up in that all the time?

MISS MORAY: We have a natatorium* for it to exercise in, at Dr. Crocus's discretion.

---

* natatorium: an indoor swimming pool for marine animals

HELEN: He really looks cramped.

(*MISS MORAY closes the curtain which hides the tank.*)

MISS MORAY: Well, you must be anxious to begin. I'll make myself available at the reception desk in the hall for a few nights in case any questions arise. Coffee break at two and six a.m. Lunch at four a.m. All clear?

HELEN: I don't need a coffee break.

MISS MORAY: Helen, we all need Perk-You-Ups. All of us.

HELEN: I don't want one.

MISS MORAY: They're compulsory. (*pause*) Oh, Helen, I know you're going to fit right in with our little family. You're such a *nice* person. (*She exits.*)

(*HELEN immediately gets to work, moving her equipment into place and getting down on her hands and knees to scrub the floor. DAN exits, HELEN gets in a few more rubs, glances at the silhouette of the dolphin's tank behind the curtain, and then continues. After a pause, a record begins to play.*)

RECORD: Let me call you sweetheart,

I'm in love with you.

Let me hear you whisper

That you love me, too.

(*HELEN's curiosity makes her open the curtain and look at the dolphin. He looks right back at her. She returns to her work, singing "Let Me Call You Sweetheart" to herself, missing a word here and there; but her eyes return to the dolphin. She becomes uncomfortable under his stare and tries to ease her discomfort by playing peek-a-boo with him. There is no response and she resumes scrubbing and humming. The dolphin then lets out a bubble or two and moves in the tank to bring his blowhole to the surface.*)

DOLPHIN: Youuuuuuuuuuu.

(*HELEN hears the sound, assumes she is mistaken, and goes on with her work.*)

DOLPHIN: Youuuuuuuuuu.

(*HELEN has heard the sound more clearly this time. She is puzzled, contemplates a moment, and then decides to get up off the floor. She closes the curtain on the dolphin's tank and leaves the laboratory. She walks the length of the hall to MISS MORAY, who is sitting at a reception desk near the elevator.*)

MISS MORAY: What is it, Helen?

HELEN: The fish is making some kinda funny noise.

MISS MORAY: Mammal, Helen. It's a mammal.

HELEN: The mammal's making some kinda funny noise.

MISS MORAY: Mammals are supposed to make funny noises.

HELEN: Yes, Miss Moray.

(HELEN goes to the lab. She continues scrubbing.)

DOLPHIN: Youuuuuuuuuuuu.

(She apprehensively approaches the curtain and opens it. Just then DAN barges in. He goes to get his reaching pole, and HELEN hurriedly returns to scrubbing the floor.)

DAN: Bulb out on seven.

HELEN: What do they have that thing for?

DAN: What thing?

HELEN: That.

DAN: Yeah, he's something, ain't he? *(pause)* They're tryin' to get it to talk.

HELEN: Talk?

DAN: Uh-huh, but he don't say nothing. They had one last year that used to laugh. It'd go "heh heh heh heh heh heh heh." Then they got another one that used to say, "Yeah, it's four o'clock." Everybody took pictures of that one. All the magazines and newspapers.

HELEN: It just kept saying, "Yeah, it's four o'clock"?

DAN: Until it died of pneumonia. They talk outta their blowholes, when they can talk, that is. Did you see the blowhole?

HELEN: No.

DAN: Come on and take a look.

HELEN: I don't want to look at any blowhole.

DAN: Miss Moray's at the desk. She won't see anything.

(HELEN and DAN go to the tank. Their backs are to the lab door and they don't see MISS MORAY open the door and watch them.)

DAN: This one don't say anything at all. They been playing that record every seven minutes for months, and it can't even learn a single word. Don't even say, "Polly want a cracker."

MISS MORAY: Helen?

(HELEN and DAN turn around.)

MISS MORAY: Helen, would you mind stepping outside a moment?

HELEN: Yes, Miss Moray.

DAN: I was just showing her something.

MISS MORAY: Hadn't we better get on with our duties?

DAN: All right, Miss Moray.

(MISS MORAY guides HELEN out into the hall, and puts her arm around her as though taking her into her confidence.)

MISS MORAY: Helen, I called you out here because…well, frankly, I need your help.

HELEN: He was just showing me…

MISS MORAY: Dan is an idle chatter-breeder. How many times we've told him, "Dan, this is a scientific atmosphere you're employed in and we would appreciate a minimum of subjective communication." So — if you can help, Helen — and I'm sure you can, enormously — we'd be so grateful.

HELEN: Yes, Miss Moray.

(*MISS MORAY leads HELEN back to the lab.*)

MISS MORAY: Now, we'll just move directly into the specimen room. The working conditions will be ideal for you in here.

(*HELEN looks ready to gag as she looks around the specimen room. It is packed with specimen jars of all sizes. Various animals and parts of animals are visible in their formaldehyde baths.*)

MISS MORAY: Now, you will be responsible not only for the floor area but the jars as well. A feather duster — here — is marvellous.

(*MISS MORAY smiles and exits. The sound of music and voice from beyond the walls floats over.*)

RECORD: Let me call you sweetheart…

(*HELEN gasps as her eyes fall upon one particular jar in which is floating a preserved human brain. The lights go down, ending Act I, Scene I.*)

Curtain

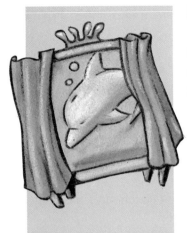

Scene II

(It is the next evening. HELEN pushes her equipment into the lab. She opens the curtain so she can watch the dolphin as she works. She and the dolphin stare at each other.)

HELEN: Youuuuuuuuuuuu. *(She pauses, watches for a response.)* Youuuuuuuuuuuu. *(Still no response. She turns her attention to her scrubbing for a moment.)* Polly want a cracker? Polly want a cracker? *(She wrings out a rag and resumes work.)* Yeah, it's four o'clock. Yeah, it's four o'clock. Polly want a cracker at four o'clock.

(She laughs at her own joke, then goes to the dolphin's tank and notices how sad he looks. She reaches her hand in and just touches the top of his head. He squirms and likes it.)

HELEN: Heh heh heh heh heh heh heh heh heh.

(MISS MORAY gets off the elevator and hears the peculiar sounds coming from the laboratory. She puts her ear against the door.)

HELEN: Heh heh heh heh heh...

MISS MORAY *(entering)*: Look how nicely the floor's coming along! You must have a special rinsing technique.

HELEN: Just a little vinegar in the rinse water.

MISS MORAY: You brought the vinegar yourself, just so the floors...they are sparkling, Helen. Sparkling! *(She pauses — looks at the dolphin, then at HELEN.)* It's marvelous, Helen, how well you've adjusted.

HELEN: Thank you, Miss Moray.

MISS MORAY: Helen, the animals here are used for experimentation, and...well, take Marguerita. She had fallen in love with the mice. All three hundred of them. She seemed shocked when she found out Dr. Crocus was...using...them at the rate of twenty or so a day in connection with electrode implanting.* She noticed them missing after a while and when I told her they'd been decapitated, she seemed terribly upset.

HELEN: What do they want with the fish — mammal?

MISS MORAY: Well, dolphins may have an intelligence equal to our own. And if we can teach them our language — or learn theirs — we'll be able to communicate.

HELEN: I can't understand you.

MISS MORAY *(louder)*: Communicate! Wouldn't it be wonderful?

HELEN: Oh, yeah...They chopped the heads off 300 mice? That's horrible.

---

* electrode implanting: attaching electrical wires to the body to record its electrical activity

MISS MORAY: You're so sensitive, Helen. Every laboratory in the country is doing this type of work. It's quite accepted.

HELEN: Every laboratory cutting off mouse heads!

MISS MORAY: Virtually…

HELEN: How many laboratories are there?

MISS MORAY: I don't know. I suppose at least 5 000.

HELEN: Five thousand times 300…that's a lot of mouse heads. Can't you just have one lab chop off a couple and then spread the word?

MISS MORAY: Now, Helen — this is exactly what I mean. You will do best not to become fond of the subject animals. When you're here a little longer you'll learn…well…there are some things you just have to accept on faith.

(*MISS MORAY exits, leaving the lab door open for HELEN to move her equipment out.*)

DOLPHIN: Whisper…(*HELEN pauses a moment.*) Whisper to me. (*She exits as the lights go down, ending the scene.*)

Curtain

Scene III

(It is the next evening. HELEN goes from her locker to the laboratory.)

DOLPHIN: Hear…

HELEN: What?

DOLPHIN: Hear me…

(DAN barges in with his hamper, almost frightening HELEN to death. He goes to dolphin's tank.)

DAN: Hiya, fella! How are ya? That reminds me. Gotta get some formaldehyde jars set up by Friday. If you want anything just whistle.

(He exits. HELEN goes to the tank and reaches her hand out to pet the dolphin.)

HELEN: Hear. *(pause)* Hear.

DOLPHIN: Hear.

HELEN: Hear me.

DOLPHIN: Hear me.

HELEN: That's a good boy.

DOLPHIN: Hear me…

HELEN: Oh, what a pretty fellow. Such a pretty fellow.

(MISS MORAY enters.)

MISS MORAY: What are you doing, Helen?

HELEN: I…uh…

MISS MORAY: Never mind. Go on with your work.

(MISS MORAY surveys everything, then sits on a stool. DAN rushes in with large jars on a wheeled table.)

DAN: 'Scuse me, but I figure I'll get the formaldehyde set up tonight.

MISS MORAY: Very good, Dan.

HELEN *(noticing the dolphin is stirring)*: What's the formaldehyde for?

MISS MORAY: The experiment series on…the dolphin will…terminate on Friday. That's why it has concerned me that you've apparently grown…fond…of the mammal.

HELEN: They're gonna kill it?

DAN: Gonna sharpen the handsaws now. Won't have any trouble getting through the skull on this one, no sir. *(He exits.)*

HELEN: What for? Because it didn't say anything? Is that what they're killing it for?

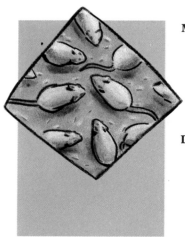

MISS MORAY: Helen, no matter how lovely our intentions, no matter how lonely we are and how much we want people or animals…to like us…we have no right to endanger the genius about us. Now, we've spoken about this before.

(*HELEN is dumbfounded as MISS MORAY exits. HELEN gathers her equipment and looks at the dolphin, which is staring desperately at her.*)

DOLPHIN: Help. (*pause*) Please help me. (*HELEN is so moved by the cries of the dolphin she looks ready to burst into tears as the lights go down, ending Act I.*)

Curtain

IN CONTEXT

BACKGROUNDER

Director's Notebook

The most difficult prop to make is also the most important: the dolphin. A cardboard or styrofoam cut-out might be the easiest to make. It can be painted or covered in cardboard. Be sure to make it large enough so an actor can hide behind it.

Don't forget to make a list of all the props and costumes you will need. It may be necessary to change some of the action if you can't make or get a particular prop or costume.

PROP	ACTOR	LOCATION
MOP & PAIL	HELEN	NEXT TO BOOKCASE
CLIPBOARD WITH CHART	MISS MORAY	RECEPTION DESK
LONG POLE	DAN	CARRY ON

ACT 2   Scene I

(The hall: It is the night that the dolphin is to be dissected. Elevator doors open and HELEN gets off, nods, and starts down the hall. MISS MORAY comes to HELEN at closet.)

MISS MORAY: I hope you're well this evening.

HELEN: When they gonna kill it?

MISS MORAY: Don't say kill, Helen. You make it sound like murder. Besides, you won't have to go into the laboratory at all this evening.

HELEN: How do they kill it?

MISS MORAY: Nicotine mustard, Helen. It's very humane. They inject it.

HELEN: Maybe he's a mute.

MISS MORAY: Do you have all your paraphernalia?

HELEN: Some human beings are mute, you know. Just because they can't talk we don't kill them.

MISS MORAY: It looks like you're ready to open a new box of steel wool.

HELEN: Maybe he can type with his nose. Did they try that?

MISS MORAY: Now, now, Helen—

HELEN: Miss Moray, I don't mind doing the lab.

MISS MORAY: Absolutely not! I'm placing it off limits for your own good. You're too emotionally involved.

HELEN: I can do the lab, honest. I'm not emotionally involved.

MISS MORAY (*motioning her to the specimen-room door*): Trust me, Helen. Trust me.

HELEN (*reluctantly disappearing through the doorway*): Yes, Miss Moray. (*MISS MORAY stations herself at the desk near the elevator and begins reading her charts. HELEN slips out of the specimen room and into the laboratory without being seen. The lights in the lab are out and moonlight from the window casts eerie shadows.*)

DOLPHIN: Help.

(*HELEN opens the curtain. The dolphin and she look at each other.*)

DOLPHIN: Help me.

HELEN: You don't need me. Just say something to them. Anything. They just need to hear you say something…You want me to tell 'em? I'll tell them. I'll just say I heard you say "Help." (*Pauses, then speaks with feigned cheerfulness*) I'll go tell them.

DOLPHIN: Noooooooooooooooo.

(*HELEN stops. Moves back toward tank.*)

HELEN: They're gonna kill you!

DOLPHIN: Plaaaaan.

HELEN: What?

DOLPHIN: Plaaaaaaaan.

HELEN: Plan? What plan?

(*DAN charges through the door and snaps on the light.*)

DAN: Uh-oh. Miss Moray said she don't want you in here.

(*HELEN goes to DR. CROCUS's desk and begins to look at various books on it.*)

HELEN: Do you know anything about a plan?

DAN: She's gonna be mad. What plan?

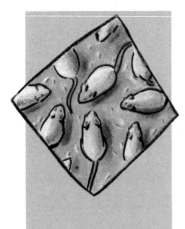

HELEN: Something to do with…(*She indicates the dolphin.*)

DAN: Hiya, fella!

HELEN: About the dolphin…

DAN: They got an experiment book they write in.

HELEN: Where?

DAN: I don't know.

HELEN: Find it and bring it to me in the animals' morgue. Please.

DAN: I'll try. I'll try, but I got other things to do, you know.

(*HELEN slips out the door and makes it safely back into the specimen room. DAN rummages through the desk and finally finds the folder. He is able to sneak it into the specimen room.*)

DAN: Here.

(*HELEN grabs the folder and starts going through it. DAN turns and is about to go back out into the hall when he sees that MISS MORAY has stopped reading. HELEN skims through more of the bulky folder. She stops at a page discussing uses of dolphins. MISS MORAY gets up from the desk and heads for the specimen-room door.*)

DAN: She's coming.

HELEN: Maybe you'd better hide. Get behind the table. Here, take the book.

(*DAN ducks down behind one of the specimen tables, and HELEN starts scrubbing away. MISS MORAY opens the door.*)

MISS MORAY: Perk-You-Up time, Helen. Tell Dan, please. He's in the laboratory.

(*HELEN moves to the lab door, opens it, and calls into the empty room.*)

HELEN: Perk-You-Up time.

MISS MORAY: Tell him we have ladyfingers.

HELEN: We have ladyfingers.

MISS MORAY: Such a strange thing to call a confectionery, isn't it? It's almost macabre.

HELEN: Miss Moray…

MISS MORAY: Yes, Helen?

HELEN: I was wondering why they wanna talk with…

MISS MORAY: Now, now, now!

HELEN: I mean, supposing dolphins *did* talk?

MISS MORAY: Well, like fishing, Helen. If we could communicate with dolphins, they might be willing to herd fish for us. The fishing industry would be revolutionized.

HELEN: Is that all?

MISS MORAY: All? Heavens, no. They'd be a blessing to the human race. A blessing. They would be worshipped in oceanography. Checking the

Gulf Stream…taking water temperatures, depths, salinity readings. To say nothing of the contributions they could make in marine biology, navigation, linguistics! Oh, Helen, it gives me the chills.

HELEN: It'd be good if they talked?

MISS MORAY: God's own blessing.

(*DAN opens the lab doors and yells over HELEN's head to MISS MORAY.*)

DAN: I got everything except the head vise. They can't saw through the skull bone without the head vise.

MISS MORAY: Did you look on five? They had it there last week for…what they did to the St. Bernard.

(*From the laboratory, music drifts out. They try to talk over it.*)

DAN: I looked on five.

MISS MORAY: You come with me. It must have been staring you in the face.

(*DAN and MISS MORAY get on the elevator.*)

MISS MORAY: We'll be right back, Helen.

(*The doors close and HELEN hurries into the laboratory. She stops just inside the doors, and it is obvious that she is angry.*)

DOLPHIN: Boooooooooook.

HELEN: I looked at your book. I looked at your book, all right!

DOLPHIN: Boooooooooook.

HELEN: And you want to know what I think? I don't think much of you, that's what I think.

DOLPHIN: Boooooooooook.

HELEN: Oh, shut up. Book book book book book. I'm not interested. You eat yourself silly — but to get a little fish for hungry humans is just too much for you. Well, I'm going to tell 'em you can talk.

(*The dolphin moves in the tank, lets out a few warning bubbles.*)

HELEN: You don't like that, eh? Well, I don't like lazy, selfish people — mammals or animals.

(*The dolphins looks increasingly desperate and begins to make loud* blatt *and* beep *sounds. He struggles in the tank.*)

HELEN: Cut it out — you're getting water all over the floor.

DOLPHIN: Boooooooooook!

(*HELEN looks at the folder on the desk. She picks it up, opens it, closes it, and sets it down again.*)

HELEN: I guess you don't like us. I guess you'd die rather than help us…

DOLPHIN: Hate.

HELEN: I guess you do hate us…

(*She returns to the folder.*)

HELEN (*reading*): Military implications...war...plant mines in enemy waters...deliver atomic warhead...war...nuclear torpedoes...attach bombs to submarines...terrorize enemy waters...war...They're already thinking about ways to use you for war. Is that why you can't talk to them? (*pause*) What did you talk to me for? (*pause*) You won't talk to them, but you...you talk to me because...you want something...there's something...I can do?

DOLPHIN: Hamm...

HELEN: What?

DOLPHIN: Hamm...

HELEN: Ham? I thought you ate fish.

DOLPHIN (*moving with annoyance*): Ham...purrrr.

HELEN: Ham...purrrr? I don't know what you're talking about.

DOLPHIN (*even more annoyed*): Ham...purrrr.

HELEN: Ham...purrrr. What's a purrrr?

(*Confused and scared, she returns to scrubbing the hall floor just as the doors of the elevator open, revealing MISS MORAY, DAN, and MR. FRIDGE. DAN pushes a dissection table loaded with shiny instruments toward the lab.*)

MISS MORAY: Is the good doctor in yet?

MR. FRIDGE: He's getting the nicotine mustard on nine. I'll see if he needs assistance.

MISS MORAY: I'll come with you. You'd better leave now, Helen. It's time. (*She smiles and the elevator doors close.*)

DAN (*pushing the dissection table through the lab doors*): I never left a dirty head vise. She's trying to say I left it like that.

HELEN: Would you listen a minute? Ham...purrrr. Do you know what a ham...purrrr is?

DAN: The only hamper I ever heard of is out in the hall. (*HELEN darts to the door, opens it, and sees the hamper at the end of the hall.*)

HELEN: The hamper!

DAN: Kazinski left the high-altitude chamber dirty once, and I got blamed for that, too. (*He exits.*)

HELEN (*rushing to the dolphin*): You want me to do something with the hamper. What? To get it? To put...you want me to put you in it? But what'll I do with you? Where can I take you?

DOLPHIN: Sea...

HELEN: See? See what?

DOLPHIN: Sea…

HELEN: I don't know what you're talking about. They'll be back in a minute. I don't know what to do!

DOLPHIN: Sea…sea…

HELEN: See?…The sea! That's what you're talking about! The river…to the sea!

(*She darts into the hall and heads for the hamper. Quickly she pushes it into the lab, and just as she gets through the doors unseen, MISS MORAY gets off the elevator.*)

MISS MORAY: Helen?

(*She starts down the hall. Enters the lab. The curtain is closed in front of the tank.*)

MISS MORAY: Helen? Are you here? Helen?

(*She sees nothing and is about to leave when she hears a movement behind the curtain. She looks down and sees HELEN's shoes. MISS MORAY moves to the curtain and pulls it open. There is HELEN with her arms around the front part of the dolphin, lifting it a good part of the way out of the water.*)

MISS MORAY: Helen, what do you think you're hugging?

(*HELEN drops the dolphin back into the tank.*)

MR. FRIDGE (*entering*): Is anything wrong, Miss Moray?

MISS MORAY: No…nothing wrong. Nothing at all. Just a little spilled water.

(*HELEN and MISS MORAY grab sponges from the lab sink and begin to wipe up the water around the tank. DR. CROCUS enters and begins to fill a hypodermic syringe while MR. FRIDGE expertly gets all equipment into place. DAN enters.*)

MR. FRIDGE: Would you like to get an encephalogram* during the death process, Dr. Crocus?

DR. CROCUS: Why not?

(*MR. FRIDGE begins to implant electrodes in the dolphin's head. The dolphin commences making high-pitched distress signals.*)

MISS MORAY: Come, Helen. I'll see you to the elevator.

(*MISS MORAY leads her out to the hall. HELEN gets on her coat and kerchief.*)

MISS MORAY: Frankly, Helen, I'm deeply disappointed. I'd hoped that by being lenient with you—and heaven knows I have been—you'd develop a heightened loyalty to our team.

HELEN (*bursting into tears and going to the elevator*): Leave me alone.

---

* encephalogram: an X-ray photograph of the brain

MISS MORAY (*softening as she catches up to her*): You really are a nice person, Helen. A very nice person. But to be simple and nice in a world where great minds are giant-stepping the micro-* and macrocosms,** well— one would expect you'd have the humility to yield in unquestioning awe. I truly am very fond of you, Helen, but you're fired. Call personnel after nine a.m.

(*As MISS MORAY disappears into the laboratory, the record starts to play.*)

RECORD: Let me call you sweetheart,

I'm in love with you.

Let me hear you whisper…

(*The record is roughly interrupted. Instead of getting on the elevator, HELEN whirls around and barges into the lab.*)

HELEN: Who do you think you are? (*pause*) Who do you think you *are*? (*pause*) I think you're a pack of killers, that's what I think.

MISS MORAY: Doctor, I assure you this is the first psychotic outbreak she's made. She did the entire brass strip…

HELEN: I'm very tired of being a nice person, Miss Moray. I'm going to report you to the SPCA,*** or somebody, because…I've decided I don't like you cutting the heads off mice and sawing through skulls of St. Bernards…and if being a nice person is just not saying anything and letting you pack of butchers run around doing whatever you want, then I don't want to be nice anymore. (*pause*) You gotta be very stupid people to need an animal to talk before you know just from looking at it that it's saying something…that it knows what pain feels like. I'd like to see you all with a few electrodes in your heads. Being nice isn't any good. (*looking at dolphin*) They just kill you off if you do that. And that's being a coward. You gotta talk back. You gotta speak up against what's wrong and bad, or you can't ever stop it. At least you've gotta try. (*She bursts into tears.*)

MISS MORAY: Nothing like this has ever happened with a member of the Custodial Engineering…Helen, dear…

HELEN: Get your hands off me. (*yelling at the dolphin*) You're a coward, that's what you are. I'm going.

DOLPHIN: Loooooooooveeeeeeeee.

(*Everyone turns to stare at the dolphin.*)

DOLPHIN: Love.

---

* microcosm: the world in miniature

** macrocosm: the universe

*** SPCA: Society for the Prevention of Cruelty to Animals

The dolphin *"is the only creature who loves man for his own sake."* (Plutarch)

DR. CROCUS: Get the recorder going.

(*HELEN pats the dolphin, exits. The laboratory becomes a bustle of activity.*)

DOLPHIN: Love…

DR. CROCUS: Is the tape going?

MR. FRIDGE: Yes, Doctor.

DOLPHIN: Love…

DR. CROCUS: I think that woman's got something to do with this. Get her back in here.

MISS MORAY: Oh, I fired her. She was hugging the mammal…and…

DOLPHIN: Love…

DR. CROCUS: Just get her. (*to MR. FRIDGE*) You're sure the machine's recording?

MISS MORAY: Doctor, I'm afraid you don't understand. That woman was hugging the mammal….

DR. CROCUS: Try to get another word out of it. One more word…

MISS MORAY: The last thing in the world I want is for our problem in Custodial Engineering to…

DR. CROCUS: (*furious*): Will you shut up and get that washwoman back in here?

MISS MORAY: Immediately, Doctor.

(*She hurries out of the lab. Helen is at the end of the hall waiting for the elevator.*)

MISS MORAY: Helen? Oh Helen? Don't you want to hear what the dolphin has to say? He's so cute! Dr. Crocus thinks that his talking might have something to do with you. Wouldn't that be exciting? (*pause*) Please, Helen. The doctor…

HELEN: Don't talk to me, do you mind?

MISS MORAY: It was only in the heat of argument that I…of course, you won't be discharged. All right? Please, Helen, you'll embarrass me….

(*The elevator doors open and HELEN gets on to face MISS MORAY. She looks at her a moment and then lifts her hand to press the button for the ground floor.*)

MISS MORAY: Don't you dare…Helen, the team needs you, don't you see? You've done so well — the brass strip, the floors. The floors have never looked so good. Ever. Helen, please. What will I do if you leave?

HELEN: Why don't you get a rug?

(*HELEN helps slam the elevator doors in MISS MORAY's face as the lights go down, ending the play.*) Curtain

ZOOT CAPRI:
A Magazine with Style

BY COLLEEN NIELSEN-HYDE

WHAT IS ZOOT CAPRI?

Is it a new soft drink? A type of swim wear? The name of a rock group? No, it's a magazine for young people that's as unusual as its name.

In fact, *Zoot Capri* is more than a magazine. It's a whole way of looking at life. It's full of colour, advice, sports, interviews, fashion, and humour. And it has a serious side, too, printing hard-hitting articles about current issues and ways of dealing with them. *Zoot* is about action, and is brimful of people, places, and things.

Zoot Capri means 'the ultimate," and that is what the magazine delivers to its readers. It is one element in a comprehensive prevention program aimed at Alberta youth. It's published by AADAC (Alberta Alcohol and Drug Abuse Commission). *Zoot* is the result of many talented people working to produce an exciting magazine for teenagers. It begins with ideas, and ends with what you see here...

WHAT'S IN IT FOR YOUNG PEOPLE

Each issue has feature articles that change each time the magazine is produced. But, like most magazines, regular columns recur from issue to issue.

One such regular feature is the *Zoot* interview. *Zoot* has spoken to rock groups and athletes. Recently, *Zoot* talked with Don Starkell and his sons Dana and Jeff, who set off on a two-year canoe trip from Winnipeg and travelled to the Amazon.

"Hot Kids" is another regular feature. Each issue of *Zoot* profiles several talented teens. Not just award-winning athletes, writers, artists, and musicians are chosen (although they're in there); *Zoot's* "Hot Kids" include armour makers, collectors, fashion designers, snowboarders, bagpipe players, and taxidermists. *Zoot* is interested in people who do something different, work hard at it, and succeed. Hot Kids are found through contacting schools and other youth organizations, and sometimes from letters.

Once a "hot kid" is chosen, *Zoot* conducts an interview by phone, writes a profile, and arranges a photo session. Below, meet Shari DeGrofft, and Brian Spronk, both *Zoot* Hot Kids!

HOW THE PIECES FIT TOGETHER

Each issue of *Zoot* begins with a brainstorming session of the editorial staff—the executive editor (who is an AADAC staff member), the editor, and his assistant. A theme is chosen, and appropriate articles discussed which tie in to the strategic direction outlined by AADAC. While several issues may be mapped out in advance, the specific content of each issue is flexible until the issue's production; in this way the content of the magazine is up-to-the-minute.

After the initial planning stages, it's the editor's job to assign articles to freelance writers, giving them guidelines…and, of course, a deadline!

"Living with a 40-Proof Parent" is an example of a *Zoot* feature article. It's about the problems of living with alcoholic parents and ways of coping. Over the page are the beginning paragraphs of the article as it was first submitted, with some editing and initial proofreading changes.

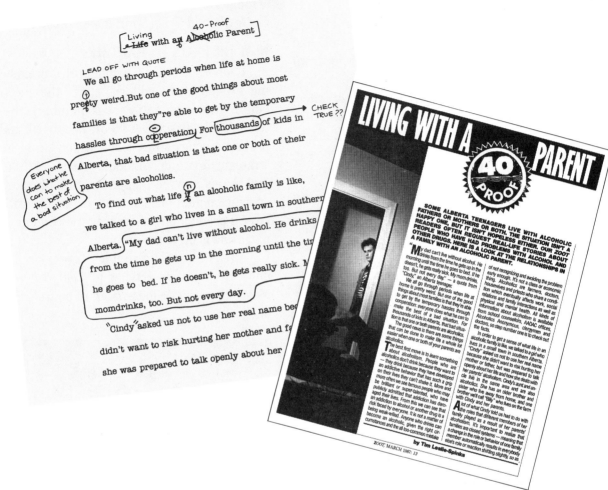

The editor keeps working on the copy until satisfied that it reads well and that the meaning is clear. Editing involves making changes, refining and streamlining the text. At *Zoot* the editor writes many feature articles as well as editing others.

Proofreading is an ongoing process. Mistakes are marked and corrected at every stage. With most magazines, however, a professional proofreader checks the text one final time before printing. It is said that no matter how many times something has been proofread, there will be one error every fifty pages. That means there's prob-ably at least one typo in every issue of *Zoot* (and perhaps even one in this article).

The assistant editor helps with the editing and proofreading process, and also does much of the background research, finding out names and numbers of people to contact for information. Working on a magazine means talking to sports and performers' agents, associations for career information, or theatre managers for free movie passes. Actually, it means talking to just about anyone! A typical day might be spent assembling watermelons or renting a St. Bernard for a *Zoot* cover shot, answering letters or doing an

interview, and, to end the day, reviewing a movie with a teen panel. Variety is the key to an assistant editor's job!

With every *Zoot* article, comic strip, or review, once editing changes (and in some cases rewrites) are finally complete, the *Zoot* executive editor gets involved, reading copy and giving approval or suggesting further changes. Every magazine reflects a certain viewpoint, and it's the executive editor who ensures that *Zoot* reflects AADAC's goals and strategic direction: for the magazine to be interesting and relevant, and to promote a positive, healthy way of looking at life.

Once the text of the magazine is approved, *Zoot's* art director begins sketching out design ideas for the layout.* Should this article be presented with photos or illustrations? How many and what size—full page, half page? The art director's goal is to make every page one that is inviting to the reader. On the next page is the *Zoot* interview with the Starkells, which shows the final layout of a variety of elements: introduction, interview, photographs and drawings.

---

* layout: design plan for magazines or books which shows the arrangement of both type and illustrations or photographs

Once the design is complete, the text is typeset.* The art director "marks the text up for type," specifying the type size to be used, the column widths, and other technical details. Illustrations are then changed to the proper shape and size in preparation for printing.

Now the text and illustrations can be combined. The magazine begins to look much like the final copy (except without colour), although several copies are made and checked before the final printing. The finished, colourful, glossy product you see is a far cry from both the first copy of the writer's words and the designer's initial pencil sketchings!

A MAGAZINE WITH A DIFFERENCE

Zoot is a magazine that is the product of both AADAC and the *Zoot Capri* staff. However, it's also the product of what its readers say they want it to be. Teens contribute in many ways to *Zoot Capri*, by doing movie, video, and film reviews but also by responding to questionnaires about the magazine and by writing in with comments, complaints, and suggestions.

So that's *Zoot Capri*. It's a magazine with a difference.

---

* typeset: type arranged in preparation for printing

ON CAMERA!

A Profile of A Teenage Sportscaster

BY ELIZABETH MACLEOD

Did you ever watch a TV show and think "I could do better than that"? Kulwant Saluja, 13, did, and now he has his own sports show.

"It's a lot of fun," says Kulwant, from Winnipeg, Manitoba. "I've met great people, learned about different sports, and sometimes I get press passes to pro hockey and football games, too."

It all began when Kulwant called a local TV station and asked for a chance to create his own sports show for them. Now *Sports Review*, Kulwant's show, is a weekly feature. Each program begins with a 30-second summary of that night's line-up, followed by the show's opening theme. Then Kulwant presents the scores and major sports events of the past week, covering everything from hockey, football and baseball to horse-racing, boxing and golfing. Often he brings in a guest to interview, either a player from a pro sports team or a sports broadcaster or writer.

"Getting a guest for the show is always tough," Kulwant says, "but it was even more difficult when I was first starting. A lot of people didn't believe I was for real!"

One interview that Kulwant's especially proud of is his interview with Scott Oake, a well-known TV sportscaster in Winnipeg.

"Scott was a terrific guest," explains Kulwant, "but the best part was that he invited me to be on his show the next day and he let me introduce a hockey segment. He was really funny, too. The first question he asked me was, 'Who's your favourite sportscaster?' Guess what I said!"

Kulwant spends hours preparing for each interview. He reads books, magazines and newspapers to come up with a list of ten questions to ask each guest.

"Actually, it's not too difficult talking with sports people because everyone likes to talk about his or her job. Just before the show, I give my guests my list of questions so they can be prepared. Sometimes they'll tell me they don't want to talk about certain subjects but usually there's no problem."

Kulwant writes a script to use when he's presenting scores and his analysis of the week's events, but he never writes a script for the interview portion of the show because he says you can never tell what a guest is going to say. But sometimes it's what they don't say that is more interesting.

"I interviewed Cal Murphy, the general manager of the Winnipeg Blue Bombers pro football team, the day before the Montreal Concordes team folded," remembers Kulwant. "Afterwards I found out that he knew that was about to happen but he didn't say a thing to me about it."

Getting a guest is just part of the interview process and Kulwant never relaxes until the guest is actually at the studio. "I'm not fun to be around while I'm waiting for my guest to arrive," admits Kulwant. "Once he or she gets to the studio then everything's okay." But one night Kulwant's guest got lost getting to the TV station and was late arriving. The worst night was when the guest didn't arrive at all.

"I got five minutes notice that he wasn't coming," Kulwant says. "My show was being shot live that night so I had to do it off the top of my head. No one noticed but I was really nervous."

Guests not arriving isn't the only mishap that can happen on a live show. "I was broadcasting a show just before Christmas one year," recalls Kulwant, "and the studio was decorated with a Christmas tree. Suddenly, while I was giving a hockey score, the tree fell over! I tried not to laugh but the whole crew was cracking up behind the cameras. People still talk about that night!"

The only training that Kulwant had before beginning his show was a three-hour course given by the TV station, so he really appreciates having a good crew to work with. They make sure everything looks professional and that all the equipment runs smoothly. To make his interviews a little less nerve-wracking Kulwant is making more use of the teleprompter.*

"I sure could've used the teleprompter for the interview part of my show the night I spoke to a horse-racing expert," recalls Kulwant. "That's one sport I don't follow regularly so I had to do a lot of research and I didn't know many of the terms. I also could have used some help when I interviewed Barry Horeczy, a sports writer from *The Winnipeg Sun*. I mispronounced his name throughout the entire show! I was really embarrassed but he just laughed."

Kulwant also gets to meet broadcasters and sports personalities when he receives press passes to games. "It's great sitting in the press box and meeting the sportscasters who are in from out of town. It does feel kind of weird to be isolated from the rest of the fans and the worst thing about it is that I have to be quiet — I can't cheer when Winnipeg is winning."

Kulwant is becoming quite a celebrity himself as his show gains in popularity, and he's appeared in newspaper articles and on TV and radio. "It's funny to walk down the street and have people recognize me. Sometimes they'll say, 'Aren't you…?' or 'Hey! It's him!' and sometimes I'll just hear people whispering as I walk by." Kulwant has also won awards for his work and was a judge in a major Winnipeg parade, too.

---

* teleprompter: a small screen that shows a TV commentator's script

GLEN SHIELDS PUBLIC SCHOOL
158 GLEN SHIELDS AVE.
CONCORD, ONTARIO L4K 1T8
TEL: (905) 738-0333

However, preparing for his show does take time away from all the other things Kulwant does, and he'd rather play sports than talk about them. Tennis is one of his favourites and he's won a number of provincial table tennis tournaments, too. He plays many instruments, including piano, violin, guitar, East Indian piano, and drums, and of course, he watches TV. "I'm always trying to pick up tips on how to do my job better — at least, that's what I tell my parents!"

What does Kulwant want to do when he finishes school? "Everyone asks me if I want to make sportscasting my career. I don't know yet. I think I'd like to study law too but right now I'm having fun with my show. It's a great experience and I like every minute of it."

THE FOREVER FLAVOUR FILE:
The Making of a TV Commercial

BY HAROLD EASTMAN

FOREVER FLAVOUR IS BORN

Continental Confectioneries' problems began six months ago.

As one of the biggest candy manufacturers in Canada, the company had the market for bubble gum all sewn up and was working on a *sugarless* gum.

Then, without warning, Continental's biggest competitor, Crandall Candies, introduced "The Big Chew," a sugarless gum designed to appeal to young teenagers. It was an instant hit.

Immediately, the Product Development Department at Continental began to work around the clock to finish *their* sugarless gum. After four months of frantic testing, they had a product that could compete with "The Big Chew."

They called it "Forever Flavour."

Now the challenge was to sell the new gum to the teen market. To do the job, the company turned to the advertising agency it had been using for all its other products: Lowell Lampman Leggett (known in the advertising business as LL&L).

So begins The Forever Flavour File.

The file consists largely of communication between four key individuals at LL&L:

SANDY BERKOWITZ - CREATIVE DIRECTOR. An ad agency's creative director supervises all of the agency's artists and writers.

RUTH ANN WONG - ART DIRECTOR. The art director determines what a commercial or print ad will look like.

TERRY BONNER - WRITER. Writers write the words ("copy") for print ads and the scripts for television commercials. Terry is Ruth Ann's partner. Together, they are the "creative team" on the project.

CATHY WOYCHESKO - ACCOUNT SUPERVISOR. The role of an account supervisor in an ad agency is to maintain regular contact between the agency and its clients, and to make sure the agency is meeting the client's needs. Cathy is the account supervisor in charge of the work LL&L does for Continental.

Things get rolling when Sandy sends a memo to her creative team.

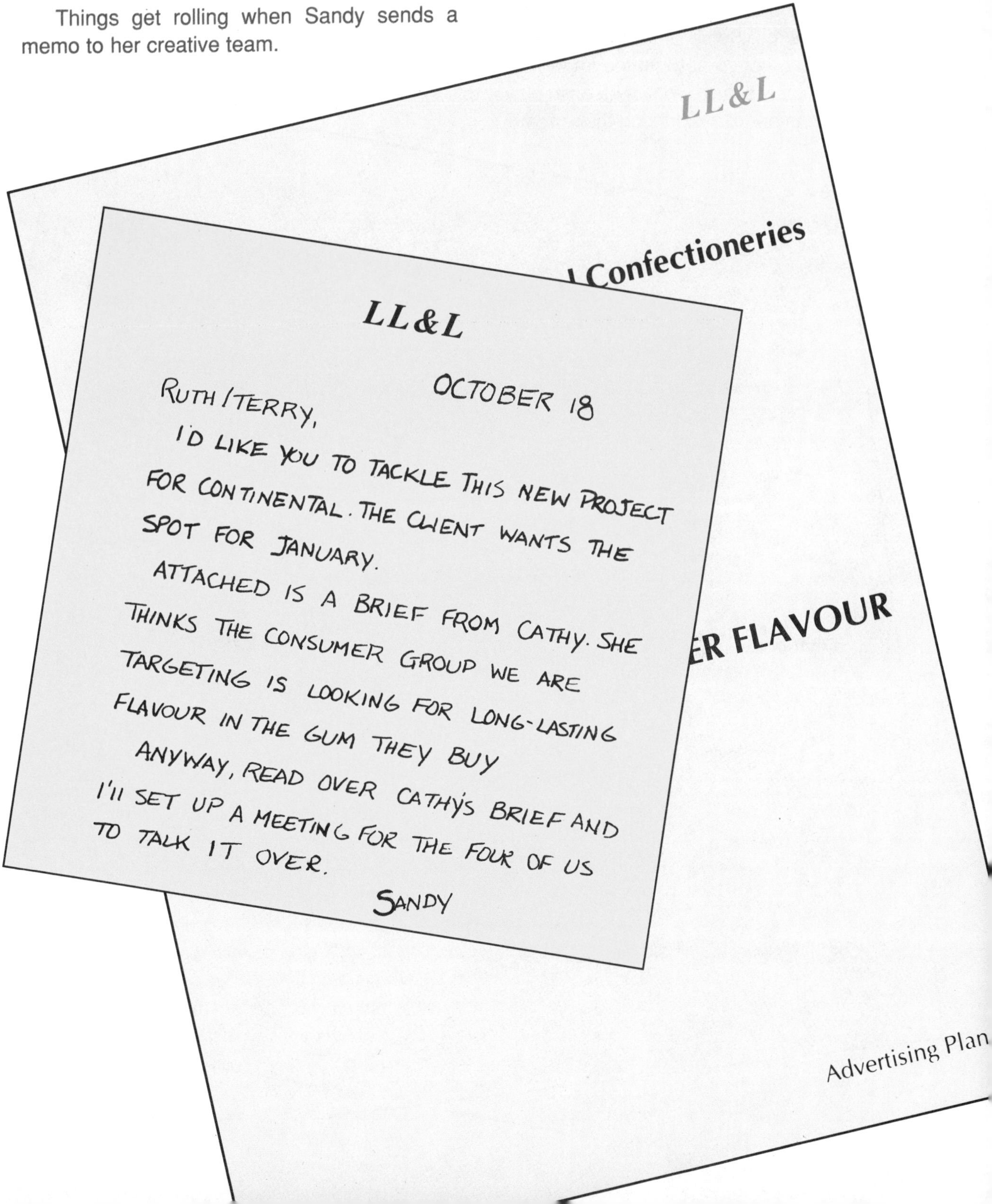

LL&L

Confectioneries

LL&L

OCTOBER 18

RUTH/TERRY,

I'D LIKE YOU TO TACKLE THIS NEW PROJECT FOR CONTINENTAL. THE CLIENT WANTS THE SPOT FOR JANUARY.

ATTACHED IS A BRIEF FROM CATHY. SHE THINKS THE CONSUMER GROUP WE ARE TARGETING IS LOOKING FOR LONG-LASTING FLAVOUR IN THE GUM THEY BUY

ANYWAY, READ OVER CATHY'S BRIEF AND I'll SET UP A MEETING FOR THE FOUR OF US TO TALK IT OVER.

SANDY

ER FLAVOUR

Advertising Plan

Ruth Ann and Terry brainstorm the Forever Flavour theme. Some of the proposed ads are great, some not-so-hot, but the important thing at this stage is to have a lot of ideas to play with. Sandy puts her comments on their memo.

LL&L

Confectioneries

FOREVER FLAVOUR

Advertising Pla

LL&L

November 4

Sandy,

Cathy wants a meeting ASAP to discuss how things are going on the creative for Forever Flavour. Here's a quick summary of the ideas Terry and I have had so far. What do you think? We can talk tomorrow.

GOOD! Music video. -- "Never ending music. Never ending taste."

Kid chewing a piece of gum. Next shot, the kid is old and grey, and still chewing the same piece of gum -- "Forever lasts a long, long time."

I LIKE IT!

Dracula presents gum. -- "Forever is a long, long time. I should know."

GET SERIOUS.

Wires running into Forever package, attached to detonator plunger like dynamite. -- "Power-packed flavour."

- OFF STRATEGY.
THE POINT ISN'T HOW STRONG THE FLAVOUR IS, BUT HOW LONG IT LASTS.

Direct comparison with Big Chew. Animation of two pieces of gum stretching out...

...over

270

MEETING THE CLIENT

Our team at LL&L holds a meeting to discuss Terry and Ruth's ideas for the Forever Flavour ad. The ideas they choose must be good enough to appeal to Continental Confectioneries. They will present their ideas at a meeting with Continental's president, John Menoudakis.

DATE: November 8
TO:
    Ruth Wong

    Terry Bonner

    Sandy Berkowitz
FROM:
    Cathy Woychesko
RE:
    Forever Flavor Project

LL&L

Just a quick memo to summarize the decisions we reached in our meeting yesterday.

On the "Growing Old" storyboard you presented, we agreed that shots of the product should appear earlier in the spot and that the phrase "longer lasting flavour" should be used in the copy.

It was also agreed that we would work up storyboards for the "Music Video" idea and "Comparison" as well. This will give us three finished boards to present to the client.

A reminder of the presentation meeting date: next Thursday, November 14. Continental's president, John Menoudakis, will be there. I suggest that I begin by reviewing the research. Sandy can follow with a summary of how we approached the problem, and then Ruth and Terry can present the three boards.

See you Thursday.

Cathy

THE STORYBOARD

"But what will it *look* like?" This is what a client wants to know when an agency presents the idea for a television commercial.

To help answer that question, the agency produces a storyboard.

SCENE#1 - OPENING SHOT OF ROCK BAND INTRODUCTORY MUSIC IS HEARD

SCENE #2 SHOT OF CAMERA MAN LOOKING THROUGH CAMERA. CAMERA PULLS BACK TO REVEAL...

SCENE #3 SEEN VOCAL- YOU' SOM

SCENE# 4- SINGER (COLOUR)
CLOSE-UP
VOCAL -" AND WHEN YOU
GET IT, YOU GOTTA
MAKE IT LAST."

SCENE#5 - CAMERA PULLS BACK
TO ENCOMPASS BAND
VOCAL -" YOU'RE LOOKIN' FOR A
TASTE TO COUNT ON,
THAT LONGER LASTING
FLAVOUR..."

GER (B+W)
ONITOR

OUT FOR
ECIAL "

A storyboard attempts to show, shot-by-shot, how the finished commercial will look. Each major change in what the viewer will see is portrayed by a new frame* on the storyboard, with a written description of the action or script underneath. In a way, it's like a comic-book version of the final product.

Storyboards are usually drawn by the art director, or by an artist on the agency's staff.

* frame: one of the series of fast-moving pictures that make up a film

The music video gets the go ahead! LL&L have sold their idea to Continental.

LL&L

RUTH & TERRY:
THOUGHT YOU'D LIKE
TO SEE THIS.
CATHY

**Continental
Confectioneries
Limited**

November 18

Ms. Catherine Woychesko
Lowell Lampman Leggett Advertising
1158 Front Street, Ste. 1409
Vancouver, B.C.

Dear Catherine,

After our meeting last Thursday, I felt I had to write to you to express my great satisfaction with the work your firm has done so far on our Forever Flavour project.

All three of the concepts presented were strong, and the choice was difficult. I feel certain, however, as I indicated in the meeting, that "Music Video" is most in tune with our young target market.

It is unusual, as I am sure you know, for a commercial concept to receive approval on its first presentation. I feel, however, that the "Music Video" concept is at the stage where we can move directly ahead to production.

Please pass on my thanks to Ruth and Terry, both of whom have done such outstanding work.

Sincerely,

John Menoudakis
President

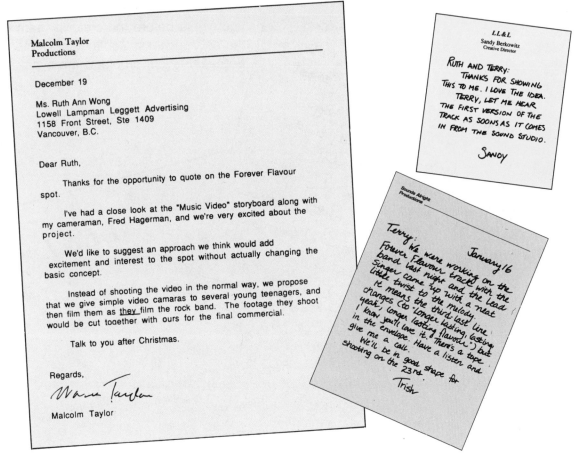

Malcolm Taylor
Productions

December 19

Ms. Ruth Ann Wong
Lowell Lampman Leggett Advertising
1158 Front Street, Ste 1409
Vancouver, B.C.

Dear Ruth,

Thanks for the opportunity to quote on the Forever Flavour spot.

I've had a close look at the "Music Video" storyboard along with my cameraman, Fred Hagerman, and we're very excited about the project.

We'd like to suggest an approach we think would add excitement and interest to the spot without actually changing the basic concept.

Instead of shooting the video in the normal way, we propose that we give simple video cameras to several young teenagers, and then film them as they film the rock band. The footage they shoot would be cut together with ours for the final commercial.

Talk to you after Christmas.

Regards,

Malcolm Taylor

LL&L
Sandy Berkowitz
Creative Director

RUTH AND TERRY:
THANKS FOR SHOWING THIS TO ME. I LOVE THE IDEA. TERRY, LET ME HEAR THE FIRST VERSION OF THE TRACK AS SOON AS IT COMES IN FROM THE SOUND STUDIO.

SANDY

Sounds Alright Productions

Terry: January 16
We were working on the Forever Flavour track with the band last night and the lead singer came up with the neat little twist to the melody. It means the third last line changes (to "longer lasting, lasting flavour") but yeah, longer lasting, lasting flavour.) I know you'll love it. There's a tape in the envelope. Have a lissen and give me a call. We'll be in good shape for shooting on the 23rd.

Trish

HIRING THE TALENT

The people who actually make a television commercial are almost never on an ad agency's staff. Instead, the agency hires a film production company to do the work.

Here's how it happens. The agency starts by selecting several companies with a film director[*] on staff whose style is suited to the commercial. Each of the companies is then asked to "quote"— indicate how much they would charge for that director's services, and for all the other services needed to complete the project. Then the agency makes its choice, usually based on cost.

Once the production company is chosen, it takes charge of the details, hiring the specialists needed to make the commercial, such as the set designer, camera operator, and actors.

The ad agency also hires a sound studio[**] to write the music for the commercial (if required) and to mix music and sound effects for the finished sound track.

---

[*] film director: the person who has overall responsibility for the creative side of rehearsing and shooting a film

[**] sound studio: like the film production company, the sound studio has all the people and equipment to do the music and sound for the commercial

There's some last minute suspense and late nights before the creative team is sure of the ad's success! Continental Confectioneries' Forever Flavour problems are over.

LL&L

Cathy:
It's 1:00 am and I'm pooped! but I wanted to leave you this note. You looked worried at the shoot today. DON'T BE. I know things seemed a little confused, but that's how Malcolm works.

Don't forget to bring the gum packs for the pack shots tomorrow morning (oops, this morning). See you at 8:00 - Ruth P.S. This is going to be a winner. I can feel it!

LL&L

Sandy,

By the time we came back from the editor, you were gone. Here's a dub of the rough cut.

I think you'll like it.

TERRY

LIKE IT? IT'S TERRIFIC. WHEN CAN WE SHOW A FINISHED VERSION TO CONTINENTAL? CATHY'S BEEN CALLING ME EVERY HALF-HOUR!

SANDY

DATE: February 7

TO: All Staff

FROM: Cathy Woychesko, Accounting Service

RE: Forever Flavour Project

LL&L

This is to inform everyone that once again LL&L has scored a major success!

Yesterday, we presented our new "Music Video" spot for Forever Flavour sugarless gum to Continental Confectioneries.

The client was delighted.

Congratulations are especially due to Ruth Ann Wong and Terry Bonner, and of course to our creative director, Sandy Berkowitz, for pulling off an outstanding job -- and putting up with me!

Let's get together in the board room at the end of business hours today. We'll show the spot and then do some celebrating.

Cathy Woychesko

GOOD BOOKS

Messages

Alan and Naomi/MYRON LEVOY
Ever since she was the horror-stricken witness of her father's death, Naomi will only talk to a puppet that Alan brings when he visits. Will substituting a real person for the puppet work?

The Tomorrow City/MONICA HUGHES
The master computer was designed to serve and protect the citizens of a great Canadian city. It co-ordinates essential services, but can it dictate and brainwash too? Only Caro and David can discover its real powers, and only they can challenge it.

The Minerva Program/CLAIRE MACKAY
Minerva was good with computers, and the school even gives her a job updating school records. When she is accused of falsifying some marks, she is banned from using the school computers. Minerva must expose the real culprit, and clear her name.

Hey World, Here I Am/JEAN LITTLE
This poetry collection shows both the funny and the serious side of adolescence through the eyes of 13-year-old Kate Bloomfield.

Alexander Graham Bell/A. ROY PETRIE
This extraordinary story of Alexander Graham Bell describes his invention of the telephone and his lesser-known accomplishments in aviation.

CHALLENGES

"I shall walk that ridgepole, Diana, or perish in the attempt."

An Affair of Honour/296

For weeks they had not left the dark, partially collapsed cellar that was their hiding place.

The Power of Light/304

"We'll make it home. A ship will find us — I'm sure of it."

Salt Water Sarah/314

Some Christmas this is going to be.
Like Father, Like Son/321

The New Kid

BY MORLEY CALLAGHAN

When Luke Baldwin was the new kid in town he was very lonely and didn't believe he would ever make any sincere friends. The trouble was that he was a city kid. When his father, a doctor, died he had come to live with his uncle at the sawmill three kilometres beyond the town. Uncle Henry, the manager of the mill, was a confident, important man, whom everybody respected, but he couldn't be expected to make friends for Luke. The only reliable friend Luke had in those days was the old collie dog, Dan, which was blind in one eye, and not much use to anybody around the mill.

The old dog helped Luke get better acquainted with the boys at school and particularly with Elmer Highbottom, the son of the rich merchant, who had Uncle Henry's approval. Luke himself was too reticent and too quiet; he spoke too politely; and so the other boys jeered at him and would not believe he was really one of them. But the dog was always with him when he showed up at the ball field behind Stevenson's orchard. The boys would talk with the dog and play with it and compare it with Elmer's dog, which also was supposed to be a clean-bred.

Elmer was a skinny red-haired kid, two years older than Luke, who had become the leader of the boys by the power of his abusive voice and his frantic bad temper. In the gang there were six others: Eddie Shore, the dark and muscular son of a grocer; Woody Alliston, the undertaker's son; Jimmie Stewart, the minister's boy; Dave Dalton, the left-handed first baseman, whose father owned the ice-cream parlour; Hank Hennessey, whose father worked in the shipyard; and Norm McLeod, whose father was the superintendent of the grain elevator. They all wanted to be big-league ball-players. If Luke missed a fly ball, Elmer, the potential big leaguer, would scream at him in derision, and Luke secretly hated him. Lying in the grass by the third-base line with Dan, Luke would whisper, "He's a one-armed ballplayer himself. He just swings that glove at the ball, Dan. If the ball sticks in the pocket he's all right, but he might as well be out there swinging a broom."

He was not afraid of Elmer, but he never said these things to him, for he wanted to go on hanging around with the bunch of boys. Elmer had decided that he would become a great left-handed pitcher. One way of being friendly with Elmer was to stand behind him when he was pitching and say, "Gee, did you see that curve? How did you throw it, Elmer?" Luke, who was lonely and wanted to have friends, also would stand behind Elmer, and one day he said enthusiastically, "Gee, what a hook you had on that one, Elmer! I wish you'd show me how to throw it." It made him a little sick at his stomach to say it, for the ball didn't have a curve at all. "Maybe I will sometime," Elmer said, and that day he took Luke home with him to show him his valuable clean-bred dog.

As soon as Luke saw this dog, Thor, which was chained up at a kennel at the back of the big Highbottom house, he doubted that the dog was a clean-bred. Its legs were too long; it didn't have the long-haired coat of a collie; the hair was more like that of an Alsatian; but it was a big, powerful, bad-tempered dog which was always kept on a leash.

"It's a thoroughbred," Elmer said, "and it can lick any dog in this town."

"If that dog's a thoroughbred, then our Dan isn't," Luke said.

"Then your Dan isn't. This is a fighting thoroughbred."

"Aw, go on," Luke said.

"Aw, go on yourself. Nuts to you."

"Nuts to you, Elmer. Why has it got that crazy look in its eyes?"

"Because he doesn't like strangers, see. And he doesn't like other dogs," Elmer said.

But then Mr. Highbottom, a plump, affable, sandy-haired man with rimless glasses and a round pink face, came out. He was a rich man and a good friend of Luke's Uncle Henry. When Elmer went into the house to get his new first-baseman's glove, Mr. Highbottom explained that Thor was kept as a watchdog; he had gotten the dog from some people in the city who had kept him locked up in an apartment; he had been badly treated. The first night he, Mr. Highbottom, had got the dog he had had to hit him on the head with a club to let him know who was master. He was half collie and half Alsatian. Luke said nothing to Elmer about knowing the dog was not a clean-bred, for he wanted to keep Elmer's friendship.

In the evenings they would all go up to the fairgrounds, especially if a team from one of the grain boats in the harbour was playing the town team. Luke was always ill at ease because he didn't even know the members of the town team; he could not stand behind the bench when the home team was batting, and chat and kid with these great players. So he would listen, or wander among the crowd with Dan following him, or he would drift out to left field, where the gang would sprawl in the grass. They would stay there till it was dark, then Elmer would whisper with Eddie Shore, the swarthy and muscular son of the grocer, and they and the others would go off by themselves on some night adventure on the main street of the town. Luke and Dan were left alone. On the way home, with the stars coming out and the night breeze rustling through the leaves of the great elms along the road, Luke would try to imagine that he was following the boys furtively into mysterious places where he had never been.

But on Saturday mornings it was really worthwhile to be with Elmer's friends, for then they would go down to the old dock by the rusty grain elevator. There they would swim, with the collie swimming with them, and afterward they would lie in the sun, talking and dreaming. When they had gotten dressed they would go along the pier to the place where the *Missouri* was tied up, and sit there, peering into the darkness of the hold.

A seaman in a torn black sweater, whose face was leathery and whose hair was iron gray, was sitting on the pier smoking his pipe. He smiled as he watched Elmer Highbottom strutting around. "Hey, kid, how old are you?" he called.

"Thirteen. Why?" Elmer asked.

"Oh, nothing," drawled the seaman. "It's just that I remember when I was thirteen around here."

"Are you from around here, mister?"

"Believe it or not," the sailor said, "I was a kid around here. It was a long time ago." Both Luke and Elmer, sitting cross-legged now at the seaman's feet, listened to him telling fabulous stories about his adventures. Maybe he was lying a little, but his voice was soft, his tone full of affection and his eyes were happy, and so Luke believed him. And after a profound silence Luke said suddenly, "I could do that too. I could stow away some night, I could go down the St. Lawrence. I could sail to Siam."

"When are you going to make the break, son?" the sailor asked with a smile.

"One of these nights. I'll pick a night."

"You," Elmer jeered. "Listen to him, mister. He's never been on a ship. He doesn't know one end of a ship from another. He's just a punk around here."

"I was a punk once," the sailor said, in such a way that Luke felt grateful. He couldn't figure out why he endured Elmer's jeering insults. Gradually all the boys had adopted Elmer's tone with him.

One day they were in Johnson's lumberyard on the south side of the tracks, playing around the great pile of sawdust which was heaped at the back of a two-storey brick building. A ladder hooked to the wall of the building ran up to the flat roof. "Come on, everybody up on the roof," Elmer yelled, and they followed him up the ladder. Sitting on the edge of the roof they all looked down at the pile of sawdust, which was about six metres below.

"I'll stump you to jump down," Elmer said, and without waiting for them to yell, "Stumpers go first," he jumped.

One by one the boys began to jump, and as each one fell Dan barked excitedly. But the second boy to jump had taken a little longer to make up his mind, and the third one hesitated even longer, the jump becoming longer and more frightening as he kept looking down; and Luke, who was the last one, had had too much time to think about it.

"Come on, Luke," they yelled…"What's the matter with you, Luke? What are you scared of?"

"I'm taking my time. What's the matter with taking my time?"

He wanted to jump, he knew he was going to jump, only he couldn't bring himself to do it at the moment. It was really an easy jump, so he laughed and tried to keep on kidding with them, but he had tightened up and every time he got ready to jump a queasy feeling came at the base of his spine.

"I think he's yellow," Elmer shouted. "He's got glue on his pants." Then they all began to jeer.

Luke wanted to close his eyes and jump, but was ashamed to let them see that he was closing his eyes. That all this was happening bewildered him. And then the collie began to bark impatiently. "Okay, Dan," Luke yelled. Waving his arms carelessly as if he had been only kidding with them, he suddenly pushed himself blindly off the roof and fell heavily on the sawdust, where the dog leaped at him joyfully.

"Well, there you are, bigmouth," he said to Elmer as he got up, dusting his clothes.

"Who's a bigmouth?"

"You've got the biggest, loudest mouth in this town, Elmer," Luke said quietly. "You're a blowhard. A great big blowhard."

"Listen, punk, you want something?"

"You don't worry me, bigmouth."

"You want I should smack you, stupid?"

"Go ahead, smack me, Elmer. I'll show you who's stupid."

"Come on!" Elmer yelled.

Then they were circling around each other and Luke now was happy. It was a crazy kind of happiness; it seemed as if Elmer had been pounding him for a long time and now at last he could openly smack him. As they feinted at each other Dan began to growl. Eddie Shore grabbed the dog by the collar. Impressed by the wild glare in Luke's eyes, Elmer feinted cautiously and then suddenly he ducked and charged, swinging his right, and Luke blindly stuck out his left hand like a rod. Elmer walked right into it. The fist got him on the nose, which spurted blood. Screaming like an old woman, he came clawing at Luke and got his arms around him and they rolled in the sawdust. He was heavier and stronger than Luke and had gotten on top of him.

"Let him up. Let him up and go on fighting," the others yelled. But Elmer, frantic now, his freckled face white, with the mouth gaping open and a trickle of blood from his nose running into the corner of his mouth, had grabbed Luke by the hair and kept banging his head on the ground.

The collie had growled; he lay back, growling, then suddenly jerked his head free and leaped at Elmer. He didn't look like a wild dog, but like a dog being workmanlike. He slashed at Elmer's leg, only at the cloth, but

the growl and the sound of the ripping cloth seemed to jerk Elmer out of his frenzy. He was scared. Jumping up, he shouted, "I'll kill that dog. I'll brain it. Where's a brick, gimme a brick!"

"Come here, Dan. Come here, quick," Luke cried. As the dog turned to him he grabbed him by the collar. "You're not hurt," he said to Elmer. "It's only your pants torn a little. Dan didn't bite you."

"I'll brain that dog," Elmer shouted. "I've got a right to kill it now."

"If you want to hit somebody, come on, hit me now I'm standing up. Here," he said to Eddie Shore. "You hold Dan's collar — and hold him this time."

"I'll get you when your vicious dog isn't with you," Elmer yelled. "I'll get you after my father has that dog destroyed."

"You can get me any time you want, Elmer. I'll fight you any time you're willing to have a fair fight."

"Aw, go on, beat it. Do you hear? Beat it."

As Luke dusted himself off, taking a long time, he waited for one of the other boys to make a friendly remark, or invite him to stay with them. But they had all grown profoundly meditative. So finally Luke said, "Come on, Dan," and he went off by himself.

Luke got home just in time for dinner. At the table his Uncle Henry said, "Is that a scratch on your face, Luke?"

"I was playing up in the lumberyard with Elmer, jumping in the sawdust, Uncle Henry."

"Oh, you and Elmer are becoming great friends, aren't you?" he said approvingly.

Uncle Henry, in his shirt sleeves, big-faced, thin-haired, his great shoulders hunched over the table, looked as if he had the strength of character to protect fearlessly everything that belonged to him. But Uncle Henry and Mr. Highbottom admired each other. Luke seemed to see Mr. Highbottom coming into the room and explaining that the collie had bitten Elmer. Luke could almost hear them talking as one practical man to another, and coming finally to a practical arrangement to destroy Dan. Suddenly Uncle Henry looked up, their eyes met, and Uncle Henry smiled. But no complaint came to Uncle Henry from Mr. Highbottom, and at school Elmer was as nonchalant with him as if nothing had happened.

On Friday afternoon Eddie Shore, Elmer's good friend, said to Luke, "Going to play ball tomorrow, Luke? Guess we'll see you there, eh?"

"Sure, I'll be up there," Luke said with a grateful grin.

That Saturday morning at about ten o'clock he walked up to the ball field with Dan. Only two other kids were there, Eddie and Woody Alliston, the undertaker's son. It was a cloudy day; it had rained a little early in the morning. While Dan lay under the hawthorn tree, Luke and Eddie and Woody played three-cornered catch. Then the sun came out.

"Here comes Elmer now," Eddie Shore said laconically.

"Soon they'll all be here," Luke said. Feeling a little embarrassed about Elmer, he did not turn to watch him coming across the field. But Eddie, who had the ball, held on to it, a big excited grin on his face. With Elmer was the big dog, Thor, on a chain. The powerful dog was dragging Elmer along. "Why has he got that crazy dog?" Luke asked, turning. Then his heartbeat came up high in his throat and he felt weak, for now he knew why Eddie Shore had grinned. "Come here, Dan," he called quickly. As the old dog came to him slowly, he whispered, "You stay right here with me, Dan. No matter what happens, you stay here with me."

The big dog with the wicked, crazy eyes had already growled at Dan. Thor was somewhat higher and years younger than Dan.

"I see you've got your dog with you, Luke," Elmer said with a smirk.

"Yeah, Dan's always with me, Elmer."

"That dog of yours is a mighty savage dog," Elmer said softly. "It goes around biting people, doesn't it?"

"Dan's not savage. Dan never bit anybody."

"Of course, I'm nobody. A dog that bites me isn't really a savage dog. That's not the way I heard it, eh, guys?" With a grin he turned to Eddie Shore and Woody Alliston, but they did not grin, for now that they were close to Thor and had heard him growl they were frightened.

"You better take that dog home, Elmer," Luke said placatingly. "I don't think your father would like it if it made trouble for anybody."

"I'm going to see if that dog of yours wants to growl and bite when there's another dog around," Elmer jeered. Slipping the chain off Thor's collar, he pointed to Dan. "Go get him, boy," he yelled. "Sic him."

"Grab him, Elmer. Oh, please," Luke cried.

Thor had growled, his lips trembling and drawing back from the long white teeth; he growled a little as Dan stiffened, then growled again, his mane rising. And Dan, too, growled, his head going down a little, waiting, and showing his teeth, which were blunted and old.

Suddenly Thor leaped at Dan's throat, trying to knock him over with the weight of the charge and sink his teeth in the throat and swing him over. But Dan pivoted, sliding away to the side, and Thor's snapping jaws missed the throat. Then Dan drew on the strength and wisdom of his breed. His strength was all instinct and heart, and it was against that instinct to snap or chew, or grip with his teeth and snarl and roll over, clawing and kicking and cutting until it was over. As Thor missed, Dan did not back away and wait again. Doing what he would have done five years ago, he wheeled, leaping past the big dog and slashing at the flank; then, wheeling again, returned for the slashing rip at the flank again.

These splendid, fearless movements were executed so perfectly that Luke sobbed, "Oh, Dan," but the slashes at Thor's flank had not gone deep.

The sun, which was now bright, was shining in Thor's wild empty eyes. Growling and scraping at the ground with his claws he charged again; it was like the pounce of a great cat. Again the snapping jaws missed Dan's throat, but the weight of the charge, catching him on the hip, spun him around off balance and bewildered him a little.

Luke was watching with both his hands up to his face. It was as if he was prepared to cover his eyes and scream but couldn't; he was frozen to the one spot. The two boys, Eddie Shore and Woody Alliston, were close together, crouching a little and crazy with excitement. Elmer's jaw was moving loosely and he kept blinking his eyes.

The thin clouds overhead broke up, a blue patch of sky appeared. The damp grass glistened. Thor had learned that Dan was vulnerable on the left flank; the blind eye saw nothing, the good eye couldn't shift quickly enough. Whirling quickly, Thor charged in again on that left flank, knocking Dan over, but the weight of his own charge caused Thor to sprawl over Dan. The teeth could only snap at the flank, and though both dogs had rolled in the grass, snarling and clawing, Dan was soon on his feet again.

But Dan knew now that his instinctive style was no good. When this heavy dog came whirling to the left of him he couldn't see him in time, and he was bleeding just behind the shoulder. It was like watching a bewildered old dog suddenly becoming aware of its age, and yet with courage trying to break itself of a style of fighting which was the only one its breed had known for a hundred years. Circling and backing, Dan drew near the trunk of the hawthorn tree. There he stood with the tree on his left, protecting that flank, so that Thor would have to charge toward the good eye. His head dropped and he waited.

"No, oh no, Elmer," Eddie Shore said weakly.

"Elmer. Have some sense, Elmer," Woody Alliston pleaded.

"Elmer," Luke shrieked suddenly, and he grabbed Elmer by the throat. "I'll kill you. I'll kill you. Call him off or I'll kill you," he shrieked.

But with a low exultant growl Thor had leaped in again to pin Dan against the tree, and as Dan swerved a little Thor got his teeth in the shoulder, snarling and shaking his head as he rolled Dan over, shaking and stretching his own neck away from Dan's teeth, and holding on tight till he could draw Dan underneath him on his back and then shift his jaws to Dan's throat and kill him.

The agonized growling and snarling was terrible and yet exultant, and Luke screamed, "Elmer, Elmer, oh, please call him off. He'll kill him, Elmer."

And the other two boys, Eddie Shore and Woody Alliston, awed and sick, yelled, "Do something, Elmer. Don't let him kill him, Elmer."

Fascinated by the power and viciousness of his dog, which he believed he couldn't control, Elmer cried, "I can't stop it."

And Luke sobbed, for it was as if Dan was more than a dog. The collie seemed to have come out of that good part of his life which he had shared with his own father. "Dan! Dan!" he screamed. He looked around wildly for help. On the other side of the tree was a thick broken branch. It flashed into his mind that he should use this branch as a club; this was in his mind as he rushed at the snarling dogs. But instead he kicked at Thor's flank; he kicked three times with the good heavy serviceable shoes Uncle Henry had bought for him.

Thor snarled, his head swinging around, his bright eyes now on Luke, the lip curled back from the fangs. Luke backed away toward the club. As

he picked up the branch and held it with both hands, he felt numb all over. There was nothing but the paralyzing beat of his own heart — nothing else in the world.

Seeing him there with the club, Thor tried to hold Dan down with his paws. Then he suddenly growled as he let go Dan's shoulder and whirled on Luke.

"Luke, come away from him," Elmer screamed.

"Run, Luke," Eddie Shore yelled. "Get someone at Stevenson's, Woody."

Woody Alliston started to run across the field to Stevenson's house as Luke, waiting, watched Thor's trembling lip. The big dog's growl was deep with satisfaction as he came two steps closer, the head going down.

In Luke's mind it was all like a dream. It was like a dream of Mr. Highbottom telling him he had once pounded Thor on the head with a club, and of a story he had once read about people pounding the heads of wild dogs with clubs. But it was important that he should not wait, that he should attack the dog and cow him.

Dan, free now, had tried to get up and then had fallen back and was watching him with his glowing eye.

With a deep warning growl Thor crouched, and Luke rushed at him and cracked him on the skull, swinging the club with both hands. The big dog, trying to leap at him, knocked him down, and when he staggered to his feet Thor was there, shaking his head stupidly, but still growling. Not waiting now, Luke rushed at him and whacked him on the head again and again. The crazy dog would not run; he was still trying to jump at him. Suddenly the dog lurched, his legs buckled, he rolled over on his side and was still.

While Elmer and Eddie Shore were looking at him as if they were afraid of him, Luke did a thing he hated himself for doing. He went over and sat down beside Dan and put his hand on Dan's head, and then he started to cry. He couldn't help it; it was just relief; he felt weak and he ground his fists in his eyes.

"Holy cow," Elmer said in relief, "you might have got killed."

"Gee whiz, Luke," Eddie said softly.

"Are you all right, Luke?"

"You better put the chain on that dog of yours, Elmer," Luke said when he could get his breath. "You'd better tie him up to the tree."

"Maybe he's dead. Oh, Luke, what if he's dead?"

"Not that dog. Not that crazy dog. It's Dan that's hurt."

When Elmer was linking the chain to his dog's collar, the animal's legs trembled convulsively. Opening his eyes he tried to get to his feet, but

Elmer had no trouble dragging him over to the tree and looping the chain around it.

Across the field at the gate to the Stevenson house, Mr. Stevenson was talking with Woody Alliston. They could see him point and shrug—there seemed to be no trouble over there by the tree—then he turned back to the house and Woody came on alone.

"Let's see your shoulder, Dan," Luke said gently to the collie lying quietly beside him. The collie knew he had been hurt, knew the muscle above the shoulder was torn and bleeding, yet he lay there quietly and patiently, regaining his strength while his flanks heaved.

"Okay, okay," Luke said softly. Taking out his handkerchief he dabbed at the blood already congealing on the fur. The other boys, kneeling down beside Luke, were silent. Sometimes they looked at Luke's white face. When he had mopped up the blood, he began to stroke Dan's head softly, and Dan, wiggling his tail a little, thumped the grass three times.

"Maybe he's not hurt so bad," Elmer said nervously, for Dan, swinging his head around, had begun to lick the wound patiently; the clean pink tongue and the saliva on the tongue were cleaning and soothing the slash, and Luke and the other boys seemed to be waiting for Dan to come to a conclusion about the seriousness of his wound.

"Can you get up, Dan?" Luke whispered. "Come on, try, boy."

Slowly the collie rose and hobbled on three legs in a little circle, the wounded right leg coming down delicately and just touching the ground as it completed the little circle. Coming over to Luke, who was kneeling and waiting anxiously, the old collie rubbed his nose against Luke's neck, then flopped down again.

"I guess he'll be all right, will he?" Elmer asked anxiously.

"Maybe that leg won't be so good again," Luke said mournfully. "Maybe it'll never be good again."

"Sure it will, if nothing is broken, Luke," Elmer insisted, as he got up and thrust his hands into his pockets and walked around aimlessly, his freckled face full of concern. Once he stopped and looked at his own dog, which was crouched by the tree, his eyes following Elmer. Thor was a subdued dog now. Growing more meditative and more unhappy, Elmer finally blurted out, "I guess you'll tell your uncle what happened, eh, Luke?"

"You knew Dan was my uncle's dog," Luke said grimly.

"If you tell your uncle—well, your uncle will tell my father, and then there will be awful trouble, Luke."

"Well, you knew there'd be trouble, Elmer."

"I only wanted to scare you and chase Dan," Elmer insisted. "I thought

Dan would run and howl. I didn't know Thor would turn on you. Gee, Luke, I was crazy. I didn't stop to think." With a sudden pathetic hopefulness he muttered, "I could have told my father that your dog slashed at me. Only I didn't Luke. I didn't say anything, though he asked me how I tore my pants."

"Okay, you didn't say anything, Elmer. So what?"

"Maybe if you don't say anything, eh, Luke?"

"Aw, I can look after myself too," Luke said grandly.

'Well—in that case I'd sure think you were a great guy, Luke," Elmer said.

"Sure, he's a great guy," Eddie Shore agreed firmly.

Eddie and Woody Alliston wanted to make friendly gestures to Luke, and they didn't quite know how to do it. They felt awkward and ashamed. They took turns petting Dan lovingly. They asked Luke if he wouldn't go swimming down at the dock after lunch. "I'll walk home with you, Luke," Eddie said. "I'd like to see if Dan gets home all right."

"I'm not letting him walk all that distance," Luke said, and he knelt down, gathered Dan in his arms and hoisted him up on his shoulder. On the way across the field Luke and Eddie took their time and worried about Dan.

"Let me carry him now," Eddie said.

"No, we'll see if he can walk a little," Luke said.

It was extraordinary how effectively the old dog could travel on three legs. He hopped along briskly. Sometimes he would stop and let the wounded leg come down firmly, as if testing it, then come hopping along until Luke picked him up again.

"We should take it easy," Luke said. "We should rest a little now and then." When they got to the road leading to the mill they sat down in the grass and took turns stroking Dan's head.

Going along that road, and resting every 300 m, Luke and Eddie were beginning a new relationship with each other. They both knew it, and so they were a little shy and very respectful to each other. While they were talking about Dan they were really trying to draw closer together. Eddie was offering a sincere admiring friendship, and Luke knew it and accepted it gravely.

"Well, I'll look for you this afternoon," Eddie said.

"At the dock. Sure, Eddie."

"Yeah. At the dock. Well, I'll be seeing you, Luke."

Halfway up the path Luke suddenly dropped on his knees and put his arms around Dan. It was as if the dog had really been struggling not only against the big wild Thor but against the barrier between Luke and the other boys. "You're some dog, Dan," he whispered, rubbing his face against the dog's nose, trying to show his gratitude.

But when he got back to the mill and saw Uncle Henry going toward the house, mounting the veranda steps, opening the screen door, his step decisive, his face so full of sensible determination, Luke longed to be able to tell him what had happened, not only because the dog was Uncle Henry's property — and property ought to be protected — but because he suddenly believed that Uncle Henry would have done just what he himself had done, and would be proud of him. "Why, the sensible thing would have been to pick up a club and smack that crazy dog on the head," he could almost hear Uncle Henry say. "Why, that's just what I did, Uncle Henry," Luke imagined himself explaining as he followed Uncle Henry into the house. But of course he would never be able to see this glow of approval in his uncle's eyes.

The Lost and Found Stories of Morley Callaghan

Morley Callaghan was still publishing at the age of eighty-four. He has been writing for sixty years, and is one of the most respected — and prolific — Canadian writers.

How does he keep track of the literally hundreds of short stories, essays, plays, and novels written over the years? The story "The New Kid" comes from a collection of stories by Callaghan entitled *The Lost and Found Stories*, and the story behind the story shows that keeping track can be difficult.

Morley Callaghan's son, Barry, who is also a writer, says that one day he and his father were standing in their dining room when Morley commented that he had probably left two or three stories out of his book *Morley Callaghan's Stories.*

"Where do you think they are?" asked Barry.

"Over there, I think. With the bills."

Morley was pointing at a small pile of unopened telephone and gas bills. Sure enough, there was not only three but four stories buried in the clutter. But that was not all. Barry and his father Morley started to look first in an old linen closet, then throughout the house, finding box after box of story after story.

That's how *The Lost and Found Stories* got their name.

Heritage

By Lola Sneyd

Walking behind the plow
they urged the yoked oxen on
past the wild roses of summer

the dry winds of August
whispered the griefs and joys
of their long journey to now

at the end of the furrows
shading their eyes, they gazed
on long lines of pioneer clearings

with reverence they reached down
and scooped a handful of freedom
sifting it through dry, cracked hands

homesick and work-scarred
they carried a dream, and
denying themselves,
stocked their farms with children

They nourished the roots

You are their dreams
Memorials to freedom and land

The Earth and the People

An Inuit Song

The earth was here before the people.
The very first people
came out of the ground.
Everything came from the ground,
even caribou.
Children once grew
out of the ground
just as flowers do.
Women out wandering
found them sprawling on the grass
and took them home and nursed them.
That way people multiplied.

This land of ours
has become habitable
because we came here
and learned how to hunt.

Even so, up here where we live
life is one continuous fight
for food and for clothing
and a struggle against bad hunting
and snow storms and sickness.

But we know our land is not the whole world.

295

An Affair of Honour

BY L.M. MONTGOMERY

A week after the tea at the manse Diana Barry gave a party.

"Small and select," Anne assured Marilla. "Just the girls in our class."

They had a very good time and nothing untoward happened until after tea, when they found themselves in the Barry garden, a little tired of all their games and ripe for any enticing form of mischief which might present itself. This presently took the form of "daring."

Daring was the fashionable amusement among the Avonlea small fry just then. It had begun among the boys, but soon spread to the girls, and all the silly things that were done in Avonlea that summer because the doers thereof were "dared" to do them would fill a book by themselves.

First of all Carrie Sloane dared Ruby Gillis to climb to a certain point in the huge old willow tree before the front door; which Ruby Gillis, albeit in mortal dread of the fat green caterpillars with which said tree was infested and with the fear of her mother before her eyes if she should tear her new muslin dress, nimbly did, to the discomfiture of the aforesaid Carrie Sloane.

Then Josie Pye dared Jane Andrews to hop on her left leg around the garden without stopping once or putting her right foot to the ground, which Jane Andrews gamely tried to do, but gave out at the third corner and had to confess herself defeated.

Josie's triumph being rather more pronounced than good taste permitted, Anne Shirley dared her to walk along the top of the board fence which bounded the garden to the east. Now, to "walk" board fences requires more skill and steadiness of head and heel than one might suppose who has never tried it. But Josie Pye, if deficient in some qualities that make for popularity, had at least a natural and inborn gift, duly cultivated, for walking board fences. Josie walked the Barry fence with an airy unconcern which seemed to imply that a little thing like that wasn't worth a "dare." Reluctant admiration greeted her exploit, for most of the other girls could appreciate it, having suffered many things themselves in their efforts to walk fences. Josie descended from her perch, flushed with victory, and darted a defiant glance at Anne.

Anne tossed her red braids.

"I don't think it's such a very wonderful thing to walk a little, low, board fence," she said. "I knew a girl in Marysville who could walk the ridgepole of a roof."

"I don't believe it," said Josie flatly. "I don't believe anybody could walk a ridgepole. *You* couldn't, anyhow."

"Couldn't I?" cried Anne rashly.

"Then I dare you to do it," said Josie defiantly. "I dare you to climb up there and walk the ridgepole of Mr. Barry's kitchen roof."

Anne turned pale, but there was clearly only one thing to be done. She walked toward the house, where a ladder was leaning against the kitchen roof. All the girls said, "Oh!", partly in excitement, partly in dismay.

"Don't you do it, Anne," entreated Diana. "You'll fall off and be killed. Never mind Josie Pye. It isn't fair to dare anybody to do anything so dangerous."

"I must do it. My honour is at stake," said Anne solemnly. "I shall walk that ridgepole, Diana, or perish in the attempt. If I am killed you are to have my pearl bead ring."

Anne climbed the ladder amid breathless silence, gained the ridgepole, balanced herself uprightly on that precarious footing, and started to walk along it, dizzily conscious that she was uncomfortably high up in the world and that walking ridgepoles was not a thing in which your imagination helped you out much. Nevertheless, she managed to take several steps before the catastrophe came. Then she swayed, lost her balance, stumbled, staggered and fell, sliding down over the sun-baked roof and crashing off it through the tangle of Virginia creeper beneath — all before the dismayed circle below could give a simultaneous, terrified shriek.

If Anne had tumbled off the roof on the side up which she ascended, Diana would probably have fallen heir to the pearl bead ring then and there. Fortunately she fell on the other side, where the roof extended down over the porch so nearly to the ground that a fall therefrom was a much less serious thing. Nevertheless when Diana and the other girls had rushed frantically around the house — except Ruby Gillis, who remained as if rooted to the ground and went into hysterics — they found Anne lying all white and limp among the wreck and ruin of the Virginia creeper.

"Anne, are you killed?" shrieked Diana, throwing herself on her knees beside her friend. "Oh, Anne, dear Anne, speak just one word to me and tell me if you're killed."

To the immense relief of all the girls, and especially of Josie Pye, who, in spite of lack of imagination, had been seized with horrible visions of a future branded as the girl who was the cause of Anne Shirley's early and tragic death, Anne sat dizzily up and answered uncertainly:

"No, Diana, I am not killed, but I think I am rendered unconscious."

"Where?" sobbed Carrie Sloane. "Oh, where, Anne?"

Before Anne could answer Mrs. Barry appeared on the scene. At sight of her Anne tried to scramble to her feet, but sank back again with a sharp little cry of pain.

"What's the matter? Where have you hurt yourself?" demanded Mrs. Barry.

"My ankle," gasped Anne. "Oh, Diana, please find your father and ask him to take me home. I know I can never walk there. And I'm sure I couldn't hop so far on one foot when Jane couldn't even hop around the garden."

Marilla, Anne's adoptive mother, was out in the orchard picking a panful of summer apples when she saw Mr. Barry coming over the log bridge and up the slope, with Mrs. Barry beside him and a whole procession of little girls trailing after him. In his arms he carried Anne whose head lay limply against his shoulder.

At that moment Marilla had a revelation. In the sudden stab of fear that pierced to her very heart she realized what Anne had come to mean to her. She would have admitted that she liked Anne — nay, that she was very fond of Anne. But now she knew as she hurried wildly down the slope that Anne was dearer to her than anything on earth.

"Mr. Barry, what has happened to her?" she gasped, more white and shaken than the self-contained, sensible Marilla had been for many years.

Anne herself answered, lifting her head.

"Don't be very frightened, Marilla. I was walking the ridgepole and I fell off. I expect I have sprained my ankle. But, Marilla, I might have broken my neck. Let us look on the bright side of things."

"I might have known you'd go and do something of the sort when I let you go to that party," said Marilla, sharp and shrewish in her very relief. "Bring her in here, Mr. Barry, and lay her on the sofa. Mercy me, the child has gone and fainted!"

It was quite true. Overcome by the pain of her injury, Anne had one more of her wishes granted to her. She had fainted dead away.

Matthew, Marilla's brother, hastily summoned from the harvest field, was straightway dispatched for the doctor, who in due time came to discover that the injury was more serious than they had supposed. Anne's ankle was broken.

That night, when Marilla went up to the east gable, where a white-faced girl was lying, a plaintive voice greeted her from the bed.

"Aren't you very sorry for me, Marilla?"

"It was your own fault," said Marilla, twitching down the blind and lighting a lamp.

"And that is just why you should be sorry for me," said Anne, "because the thought that it *is* all my own fault is what makes it so hard. If I could blame it on anybody I would feel so much better. But what would you have done, Marilla, if you had been dared to walk a ridgepole?"

"I'd have stayed on good firm ground and let them dare away. Such absurdity!" said Marilla.

Anne sighed.

"But you have such strength of mind, Marilla. I haven't. I just felt that I couldn't bear Josie Pye's scorn. She would have crowed over me all my life. And I think I have been punished so much that you needn't be very cross with me, Marilla. It's not a bit nice to faint, after all. And the doctor hurt me dreadfully when he was setting my ankle. I won't be able to go around for six or seven weeks and I'll miss the new lady teacher. She won't be new any more by the time I'm able to go to school. And Gil — everybody will get ahead of me in class. Oh, I am an afflicted mortal. But I'll try to bear it all bravely if only you won't be cross with me, Marilla."

"There, there, I'm not cross," said Marilla. "You're an unlucky child,

there's no doubt about that; but, as you say, you'll have the suffering of it. Here now, try and eat some supper."

"Isn't it fortunate I've got such an imagination?" said Anne. "It will help me through splendidly, I expect. What do people who haven't any imagination do when they break their bones, do you suppose, Marilla?"

Anne had good reason to bless her imagination many a time and oft during the tedious seven weeks that followed. But she was not solely dependent on it. She had many visitors and not a day passed without one or more of the school girls dropping in to bring her flowers and books and tell her all the happenings in the juvenile world of Avonlea.

"Everybody has been so good and kind, Marilla," sighed Anne happily, on the day when she could first limp across the floor. "It isn't very pleasant to be laid up; but there *is* a bright side to it, Marilla. You find out how many

IN CONTEXT

AUTHOR PROFILE

How Anne Came to Life

"I had always kept a notebook in which I jotted down, as they occurred to me, ideas for plots, incidents, characters, and descriptions. In the spring of 1904 I was looking over this notebook in search of some idea for a short serial I wanted to write for a certain Sunday School paper. I found a faded entry, written many years before: "Elderly couple apply to orphan asylum for a boy. By mistake a girl is sent them." I thought this would do. I began to block out the chapters, devise and select incidents, and "brood up" my heroine. Anne Shirley began to expand in such a fashion that she soon seemed very real to me and took possession of me to an unusual extent. She appealed to me, and I thought it rather a shame to waste her on a little serial. Then the thought came,

"Write a book. You have the central idea. All you need do is to spread it out over enough chapters to amount to a book." The result was *Anne of Green Gables*.

The next thing was to find a publisher. Four of them returned it with a cold, printed note of rejection; one of them wrote that "our readers report that they find some merit in your story, but not enough to warrant its acceptance."

That finished me. I put *Anne* away in an old hat-box in the clothes room.

The manuscript lay in the hat-box until I came across it one winter day in 1907 while rummaging. I began turning over the leaves, reading a bit here and there. It didn't seem so very bad. "I'll try once more," I thought. The result was that a couple of months later an entry appeared in my journal to the effect that my book had been accepted. After some natural jubilation, I wrote:

'Well, I've written my book! The dream dreamed years ago at my old brown desk in school has come true at last, after years of toil and struggle.'"

friends you have. Why, even Superintendent Bell came to see me, and he's really a very fine man. Not a kindred spirit, of course; but still I like him and I'm awfully sorry I ever criticized his prayers. I believe now he really does mean them, only he has got into the habit of saying them as if he didn't. He could get over that if he'd take a little trouble. I gave him a good broad hint. I told him how hard I tried to make my own little private prayers interesting. He told me all about the time he broke his ankle when he was a boy. It does seem so strange to think of Superintendent Bell ever being a boy. Even my imagination has its limits for I can't imagine *that*. When I try to imagine him as a boy I see him with grey whiskers and spectacles, just as he looks in Sunday school, only small. Now, it's so easy to imagine Mrs. Allan as a little girl. Mrs. Allan has been to see me fourteen times. Isn't that something to be proud of, Marilla? When a minister's wife has so many claims on her time! She is such a cheerful person to have visit you, too. She never tells you it's your own fault and she hopes you'll be a better girl on account of it. Mrs. Lynde always told me that when she came to see me; and she said it in a kind of way that made me feel she might hope I'd be a better girl, but didn't really believe I would. Even Josie Pye came to see me. I received her as politely as I could, because I think she was sorry she dared me to walk a ridgepole. If I had been killed she would have to carry a dark burden of remorse all her life. Diana has been a faithful friend. She's been over every day to cheer my lonely pillow. But oh, I shall be so glad when I can go to school for I've heard such exciting things about the new teacher. The girls all think she is perfectly sweet. Diana says she has the loveliest fair curly hair and such fascinating eyes. She dresses beautifully, and her sleeve puffs are bigger than anybody else's in Avonlea. Every other Friday afternoon she has recitations and everybody has to say a piece or take part in a dialogue. Oh, it's just glorious to think of it. Josie Pye says she hates it, but that is just because Josie has so little imagination. Diana and Ruby Gillis and Jane Andrews are preparing a dialogue, called 'A Morning Visit' for next Friday. And the Friday afternoons they don't have recitations Miss Stacy takes them all to the woods for a 'field' day and they study ferns and flowers and birds. And they have physical culture exercises every morning and evening. Mrs. Lynde says she never heard of such goings-on and it all comes of having a lady teacher. But I think it must be splendid and I believe I shall find that Miss Stacy is a kindred spirit."

"There's one thing plain to be seen, Anne," said Marilla, "and that is that your fall off the Barry roof hasn't injured your tongue at all."

From *Anne of Green Gables* by L.M. Montgomery

CASEY AT THE BAT

The outlook wasn't brilliant for the Mudville nine that day;
The score stood four to two with but one inning more to play.
And then when Cooney died at first and Barrows did the same,
A sickly silence fell upon the patrons of the game.

A straggling few got up to go in deep despair. The rest
Clung to the hope which springs eternal in the human breast;
They thought if only Casey could but get a whack at that—
We'd put up even money now with Casey at the bat.

But Flynn preceded Casey, as did also Jimmy Blake,
And the former was a lulu and the latter was a cake;
So upon that stricken multitude grim melancholy sat,
For there seemed but little chance of Casey's getting to the bat.

But Flynn let drive a single, to the wonderment of all,
And Blake, the much despised, tore the cover off the ball;
And when the dust had lifted, and they saw what had occurred,
There was Jimmy safe at second and Flynn a-hugging third.

Then from five thousand throats and more there rose a lusty yell;
It rumbled through the valley, it rattled in the dell;
It knocked upon the mountain and recoiled upon the flat,
For Casey, mighty Casey, was advancing to the bat.

There was ease in Casey's manner as he stepped into his place;
There was pride in Casey's bearing and a smile on Casey's face.
And when, responding to the cheers, he lightly doffed his hat,
No stranger in the crowd could doubt 'twas Casey at the bat.

Ten thousand eyes were on him as he rubbed his hands with dirt;
Five thousand tongues applauded when he wiped them on his shirt.
Then while the writhing pitcher ground the ball into his hip,
Defiance gleamed in Casey's eye, a sneer curled Casey's lip.

And now the leather-covered sphere came hurtling through the air,
And Casey stood a-watching it in haughty grandeur there.
Close by the sturdy batsman the ball unheeded sped—
"That ain't my style," said Casey. "Strike one," the umpire said.

From the benches, black with people, there went up a muffled roar,
Like the beating of the storm waves on a stern and distant shore.
"Kill him! Kill the umpire!" shouted someone on the stand;
And it's likely they'd have killed him had not Casey raised his hand.

With a smile of Christian charity great Casey's visage shone;
He stilled the rising tumult; he bade the game go on;
He signalled to the pitcher, and once more the spheroid flew;
But Casey still ignored it, and the umpire said, "Strike two."

'Fraud!" cried the maddened thousands, and echo answered, "Fraud!"
But one scornful look from Casey and the audience was awed.
They saw his face grow stern and cold, they saw his muscles strain,
And they knew that Casey wouldn't let that ball go by again.

The sneer is gone from Casey's lip, his teeth are clenched in hate;
He pounds with cruel violence his bat upon the plate.
And now the pitcher holds the ball, and now he lets it go,
And now the air is shattered by the force of Casey's blow.

Oh, somewhere in this favoured land the sun is shining bright;
The band is playing somewhere, and somewhere hearts are light,
And somewhere men are laughing, and somewhere children shout;
But there is no joy in Mudville—mighty Casey has struck out.

By Ernest Lawrence Thayer

The Power of Light

BY ISAAC BASHEVIS SINGER

During World War II, after the Nazis had bombed and bombed the Warsaw ghetto, a boy and a girl were hiding in one of the ruins — David, fourteen years old, and Rebecca, thirteen.

It was winter and bitter cold outside. For weeks Rebecca had not left the dark, partially collapsed cellar that was their hiding place, but every few days David would go out to search for food. All the stores had been destroyed in the bombing, and David sometimes found stale bread, cans of food, or whatever else had been buried. Making his way through the ruins was dangerous. Sometimes bricks and mortar would fall down, and he could easily lose his way. But if he and Rebecca did not want to die from hunger, he had to take the risk.

That day was one of the coldest. Rebecca sat on the ground wrapped in all the garments she possessed; still, she could not get warm. David had left many hours before, and Rebecca listened in the darkness for the sound of his return, knowing that if he did not come back nothing remained to her but death.

Suddenly she heard heavy breathing and the sound of a bundle being dropped. David had made his way home. Rebecca could not help but cry "David!"

"Rebecca!"

In the darkness they embraced and kissed. Then David said, "Rebecca, I found a treasure."

"What kind of treasure?"

"Cheese, potatoes, dried mushrooms, and a package of candy — and I have another surprise for you."

"What surprise?"

"Later."

Both were too hungry for a long talk. Ravenously they ate the frozen potatoes, the mushrooms, and part of the cheese. They each had one piece of candy. Then Rebecca asked, "What is it now, day or night?"

"I think night has fallen," David replied. He had a wristwatch and kept track of day and night and also of the days of the week and the month. After a while Rebecca asked again, "What is the surprise?"

"Rebecca, today is the first day of Hanukkah, and I found a candle and some matches."

"Hanukkah tonight?"

"Yes."

"Oh, my God!"

"I am going to bless the Hanukkah candle," David said.

He lit a match and there was light. Rebecca and David stared at their hiding place — bricks, pipes, and the uneven ground. He lighted the candle. Rebecca blinked her eyes. For the first time in weeks she really saw David. His hair was matted and his face streaked with dirt, but his eyes shone with joy. In spite of the starvation and persecution David had grown taller, and he seemed older than his age and manly. Young as they both were, they had decided to marry if they could manage to escape from war-ridden Warsaw. As a token of their engagement, David had given Rebecca a shiny groschen he found in his pocket on the day when the building where both of them lived was bombed.

Now David pronounced the benediction over the Hanukkah candle, and Rebecca said, "Amen." They had both lost their families, and they had good reason to be angry with God for sending them so many afflictions, but the light of the candle brought peace into their souls. That glimmer of light, surrounded by so many shadows, seemed to say without words: Evil has not yet taken complete dominion. A spark of hope is still left.

For some time David and Rebecca had thought about escaping from Warsaw. But how? The ghetto was watched by the Nazis day and night. Each step was dangerous. Rebecca kept delaying their departure. It would be easier in the summer, she often said, but David knew that in their predicament they had little chance of lasting until then. Somewhere in

the forest there were young men and women called partisans who fought the Nazi invaders. David wanted to reach them. Now, by the light of the Hanukkah candle, Rebecca suddenly felt renewed courage. She said, "David, let's leave."

"When?"

"When you think it's the right time," she answered.

"The right time is now," David said. "I have a plan."

For a long time David explained the details of his plan to Rebecca. It was more than risky. The Nazis had enclosed the ghetto with barbed wire and posted guards armed with machine guns on the surrounding roofs. At night searchlights lit up all possible exits from the destroyed ghetto. But in his wanderings through the ruins, David had found an opening to a sewer which he thought might lead to the other side. David told Rebecca that their chances of remaining alive were slim. They could drown in the dirty water or freeze to death. Also, the sewers were full of hungry rats.

But Rebecca agreed to take the risk; to remain in the cellar for the winter would mean certain death.

When the Hanukkah light began to sputter and flicker before going out, David and Rebecca gathered their few belongings. She packed the remaining food in a kerchief, and David took his matches and a piece of lead pipe for a weapon.

In moments of great danger people become unusually courageous. David and Rebecca were soon on their way through the ruins. They came to passages so narrow they had to crawl on hands and knees. But the food they had eaten, and the joy the Hanukkah candle had awakened in them, gave them the courage to continue. After some time David found the entrance to the sewer. Luckily the sewage had frozen, and it seemed that the rats had left because of the extreme cold. From time to time David and Rebecca stopped to rest and to listen. After a while they crawled on, slowly and carefully. Suddenly they stopped in their tracks. From above they could hear the clanging of a trolley car. They had reached the other side of the ghetto. All they needed now was to find a way to get out of the sewer and to leave the city as quickly as possible.

Many miracles seemed to happen that Hanukkah night. Because the Nazis were afraid of enemy planes, they had ordered a complete blackout. Because of the bitter cold, there were fewer Gestapo guards. David and Rebecca managed to leave the sewer and steal out of the city without being caught. At dawn they reached a forest where they were able to rest and have a bite to eat.

Even though the partisans were not very far from Warsaw, it took David and Rebecca a week to reach them. They walked at night and hid during the days — sometimes in granaries and sometimes in barns. Some peasants stealthily helped the partisans and those who were running away from the Nazis. From time to time David and Rebecca got a piece of bread, a few potatoes, a radish, or whatever the peasants could spare. In one village they encountered a Jewish partisan who had come to get food for his group. He belonged to the Haganah, an organization that sent men from Israel to rescue Jewish refugees from the Nazis in occupied Poland. This young man brought David and Rebecca to the other partisans who roamed the forest. It was the last day of Hanukkah, and that evening the partisans lit eight candles. Some of them played dreidel on the stump of an oak tree while others kept watch.

From the day David and Rebecca met the partisans, their life became like a tale in a storybook. They joined more and more refugees who all had but one desire — to settle in the Land of Israel. They did not always travel

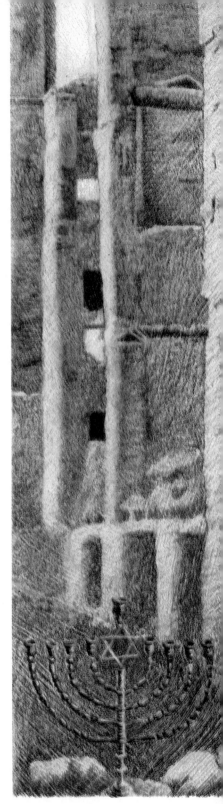

by train or bus. They walked. They slept in stables, in burned-out houses, and wherever they could hide from the enemy. To reach their destination, they had to cross Czechoslovakia, Hungary, and Yugoslavia. Somewhere at the seashore in Yugoslavia, in the middle of the night, a small boat manned by a Haganah crew waited for them, and all the refugees with their meager belongings were packed into it. This all happened silently and in great secrecy, because the Nazis occupied Yugoslavia.

But their dangers were far from over. Even though it was spring, the sea was stormy and the boat was too small for such a long trip. Nazi planes spied the boat and tried without success to sink it with bombs. They also feared the Nazi submarines which were lurking in the depths. There was nothing the refugees could do besides pray to God, and this time God seemed to hear their prayers, because they managed to land safely.

The Jews of Israel greeted them with a love that made them forget their suffering. They were the first refugees who had reached the Holy Land, and they were offered all the help and comfort that could be given. Rebecca and David found relatives in Israel who accepted them with open arms, and although they had become quite emaciated, they were basically healthy and recovered quickly. After some rest they were sent to a special school where foreigners were taught modern Hebrew. Both David and Rebecca were diligent students. After finishing high school, David was able to enter the academy of engineering in Haifa, and Rebecca, who excelled in languages and literature, studied in Tel-Aviv — but they always met on weekends. When Rebecca was eighteen, she and David were married. They found a small house with a garden in Ramat Gan, a suburb of Tel-Aviv.

I know all this because David and Rebecca told me their story on a Hanukkah evening in their house in Ramat Gan about eight years later. The Hanukkah candles were burning, and Rebecca was frying potato pancakes served with applesauce for all of us. David and I were playing dreidel with their little son, Menahem Eliezer, named after both of his grandfathers. David told me that this large wooden dreidel was the same one the partisans had played with on that Hanukkah evening in the forest in Poland. Rebecca said to me, "If it had not been for that little candle David brought to our hiding place, we wouldn't be sitting here today. That glimmer of light awakened in us a hope and strength we didn't know we possessed. We'll give the dreidel to Menahem Eliezer when he is old enough to understand what we went through and how miraculously we were saved."

Whatever Happened to Hope?

*Sometimes a guy will do almost
anything to belong to the
"in" crowd—even if it's the
wrong crowd to be in.*

BY KATHY WILMORE

List of Characters

Eric Murphy
Hope Hopkins
Jeff Collins
Buffy
Kyle
Sherry
Narrator

SCENE I

NARRATOR: Eric stands alone on stage. He talks directly to the audience.

ERIC: There are two kinds of people in this world. The kind who fit in, and the kind who don't. I don't. Sure, I hang out with our school's "in" crowd: Jeff Collins and his friends. But I don't really belong. You know what I mean? I got in with them, all right. But I lost Hope.

You see, Hope Hopkins and I might have become good friends. She was the kind of kid who never fitted in, either. Her family moved a lot, so she was always "the new kid."

Hope Hopkins…That all seems so long ago now. But it wasn't, not really. In fact, it was only last year…

SCENE II

NARRATOR: It's February, a year ago. Hope is at her locker. Jeff Collins and his "cool" friends come by shouting and laughing.

BUFFY: Well, if it isn't Hope the Dope. How are you doing, Hope?

JEFF: Hope, baby! What's the good word?

KYLE: Why ask *her*? She's just a dope. Right, Hopie?

HOPE (*angry*): Get lost.

SHERRY: Whoa! Tough talk. Better watch it, Hope. Kyle's bite is worse than his bark.

NARRATOR: Just then, Eric comes along.

BUFFY: Forget the Dope, you guys. Here comes Mr. Smurf!

ERIC: Huh? Oh, hi, Buffy.

KYLE: Miss Buffy to *you*, Murphy!

ERIC: What? Yeah, okay. Sure.

JEFF (*copying Eric*): "Yeah. Okay. Sure." What a wimp.

SHERRY: Yeah. Smurf and Dopey would make a great team!

NARRATOR: Jeff pushes Eric into Hope. He and his friends go off down the hall, laughing.

HOPE: Why do you let them treat you that way, Eric? You don't have to take it!

ERIC: Oh, hey, I don't mind. They're okay.

HOPE: Yeah? Well, I think you are ten times better than they are. (*She smiles*). I'd better get to class. See you later, okay?

ERIC (*thoughtful*): Yeah, sure.

NARRATOR: It is several days later, in the cafeteria.

JEFF *(joining his friends at a table)*: Hi, guys. What's new?

SHERRY: Not much. *(Louder, so Hope, at the next table, can hear)* But Hope the Dope has green, hairy stuff crawling out of her sandwich.

JEFF: What? Oh, barf!

KYLE: Yeah. There's some weird lumpy stuff in there, too.

BUFFY *(calling to Hope)*: Hey, Hopie! What's that thing that's dying in your sandwich? *(They all laugh.)*

HOPE *(smiling proudly)*: It was tuna and cheese, with bean sprouts. And it was delicious, thank you. *(She walks away.)*

NARRATOR: On his way into the cafeteria, Eric bumps into Hope.

HOPE *(smiling)*: Hi, Eric!

ERIC: Oh, hi, Hope.

KYLE *(very loud)*: Look at that! Mr. Smurf has finally made a friend.

HOPE *(angry again)*: Ignore him. Listen, Eric. I've been thinking. You and I—

ERIC *(flustered)*: I—I'm kind of in a hurry, Hope. Excuse me. *(He moves away. Hope shrugs and leaves.)*

NARRATOR: Eric gets his lunch, then heads to a table. As he passes Jeff's table…

SHERRY: Hey, Eric. Come over here. We need your help.

ERIC *(excited)*: Really? *(He goes to them.)*

JEFF: We've been thinking, Murphy. You're a pretty smart guy. We could use you.

KYLE: Yeah. Hope Hopkins gets on our nerves. She's rude, you know? Not the friendly type.

BUFFY: So we want to set her straight. Any ideas? You know her better than we do.

ERIC *(embarrassed)*: I—don't know, really. I—

JEFF: Hey, forget it! I thought you'd like to be friends. But if you don't, that's cool.

NARRATOR: Eric hesitates a moment, thinking. Then, slowly, he smiles.

BUFFY: Hey! Murphy looks like he's got an idea.

ERIC: Yeah, I do. *(Getting excited)* How's this? Tomorrow is Valentine's Day. Let's send Hope some valentines!

JEFF *(disgusted)*: Oh, man. What a jerk! Get out of here, you—

SHERRY *(grinning)*: No, wait a minute! Murphy's all right! A genius, in fact.

KYLE: What?!

SHERRY: It's a *great* idea. Valentines are for telling people what you *really* think of them, right? What do we think of Hopie?

JEFF (*slowly*): I get it! You mean like this: "Roses are red, violets are blue. Hope Hopkins' breath belongs in a zoo!"

SHERRY: Exactly!

KYLE: Looks like we underestimated old Murphy.

BUFFY: We sure did. Hey, Eric — join the club! Sit down.

ERIC (*pleased, but a little uncomfortable*): Oh, I…thanks. But wait a minute. I didn't really mean —

JEFF: Let's do it! We'll meet at my house after school. Why don't you come, too, Eric? We could use your help making a few valentines!

SCENE IV

NARRATOR: The next day is Valentine's Day. Hope finds a large envelope taped to her locker. At first, she's excited. But when she sees the cruel valentines inside, she is angry — and hurt. Just then, Eric comes down the hall. When he sees her, he starts to leave. But she sees him.

HOPE: Eric! You won't believe what they've done this time. I'm so sick of them!

ERIC: I — I know what you mean.

HOPE: How do you stand it, Eric? You've had to put up with them much longer than I have. They think they're so hot. But they're just childish.

ERIC (*thoughtful*): You know, Hope, you're right. They *are* childish, aren't they? I never thought of it that way before. I always thought they were funny.

HOPE: Funny?! (*She stops, and smiles at him.*) You know something, Eric? You're nuts. But I like you.

ERIC (*smiling back*): Thanks. I like you, too!

NARRATOR: Just then, Jeff, Kyle, Buffy, and Sherry come along.

JEFF: There he is! There's our man! Mr. Murphy, the main brain.

SHERRY: How goes it, Eric?

ERIC (*suddenly remembering*): Oh! Hi, guys.

KYLE: So, Eric. What does Ms. Dope think of our work?

HOPE: It's as dumb as you are.

BUFFY: Yeah? Well, you can thank our pal Eric for that.

HOPE (*startled*): What do you mean?

ERIC (*quietly*): Don't mind them, Hope. Let's go.

JEFF: No, sir. We couldn't have done it without good old Murphy here. (*He laughs.*) "Let's make Hope some valentines!" he says. And so we all —

HOPE (*furious): You,* Eric? You? This is *your* idea? How could you stand here and be so friendly with me when you did *this*?! You are worse than they are. Much worse. At least I know where *they* are coming from! (*She storms out.*)

NARRATOR: Eric stands a moment, stunned. The others are laughing.

JEFF: Eric Murphy! What a guy. You *did* it, Murphy! We're rid of *her!*

SCENE V

NARRATOR: Eric stands alone on stage. He talks directly to the audience.

ERIC: That was a year ago. I tried to make it up to Hope. But she wouldn't have anything to do with me. I don't really blame her! A few months later, the Hopkins family moved again. I haven't seen her since.

These days, a lot of kids in this school look up to me. After all, I hang out with Jeff Collins and the other cools. They all think of me as good ol' Murph, "the Main Brain." But I know I'm just plain old Eric Murphy — the *real* dope of this story.

You know, I just can't get her off my mind. It's Valentine's Day again. I can't help but wonder: Whatever happened to Hope?

SALT-WATER
Sarah

A hundred years ago, before the age of steamships, some of the greatest trading vessels that criss-crossed the world's oceans set sail from Halifax. Sturdy wooden ships, they were sailed by equally sturdy "Bluenose" sailors.

BY JOSEPH SCHULL

Mutiny was so rare a hazard in the lives of Bluenose mariners that they seldom thought about it. Discipline, hardhanded but generally fair, made the ship an organized community where each man knew his place and kept it. More and more, as voyages extended and the size of ships increased, sea life took on a settled character of its own. The hardships were indisputable and unavoidable, but in between the hardships comfort began to be thought of, sometimes even elegance, and always food. The importance of food, and the insistence of the Bluenose men that it be good, gave cooks a rare standing. In one respect their privileges were equalled only by those of the captain. They were permitted, on many ships, to take their wives to sea. The women were signed as galley * helpers and stewardesses, and it must have been a lonely life for them on the long voyages. The

---

* galley: the kitchen of a ship

free and easy comradeship of the forecastle* was not for them. The captain's wife, if she were aboard, was a lady of exalted station and they saw little of her. Nevertheless, many a cook shipped his wife and many a wife came willingly.

Sarah Farrington of Digby, Nova Scotia, was one of the women for whom seafaring was the normal way of life. Her husband was cook on the *James W. Elwell* which had been built in Saint John and sailed to England with timber in the summer of 1872. She was a sturdy, cheerful, energetic woman who spent most of her time in the galley with her husband, and on most days sang as she worked. The principal hazards of the rough Atlantic crossing, so far as she was concerned, were smashed crockery and spilled soup.

She held the same view of the trip round the Horn which lay ahead that September. *Elwell* had discharged its cargo of timber in England, and was now putting out from Cardiff with coal for Valparaiso. The voyage would be a long one, and it might be rough, but that was the concern of the men. Her business was to satisfy those enormous sea-going appetites which remained unchanged in any latitude.

The trip down through the North Atlantic and into the warmer southern waters was monotonously pleasant until they came off the mouth of the River Plate, on the eastern coast of South America. There the first gale struck them from the regions of the Horn. Sarah, struggling in the galley to keep hot food coming to the men,

---

* forecastle: the upper deck and sailors' quarters at the front of a ship

heard a crash on the deck and then shouts which told of an accident. A spar had fallen on the mate's foot and crushed it. He was carried to his cabin, and Sarah took over as nurse. The captain gave what assistance he could from his scanty store of medical supplies and knowledge, but neither his help nor the plentiful poultices* from the galley were enough. Gangrene developed, and after six days of suffering the mate died.

He was buried at sea, and the ship went on south in better weather. Staten Island, the eastern outrider of Cape Horn, was sighted, and then the Horn itself. The Cape was rounded in almost tranquil weather. Diego Ramirez on its western flank fell away astern, and the ship steered up along the western coast of South America for ten days. Then came the second accident, this time in the galley.

Sarah's husband was cutting meat with a large knife when a sudden roll of the ship flung him against the bulkhead.** The knife slipped and cut a long, ugly gash in his leg. By nightfall, in spite of everything Sarah and the captain could do, the gash was swelling and beginning to turn an angry purple.

Captain John Wren was a kindly, capable, matter-of-fact sailor from St. Andrews, New Brunswick. He relieved Sarah of most of her duties in the galley and left her to watch her husband. But he must have had a premonition of some sort, or at any rate he attached an odd importance to the casual happenings of the next two days. "The day before the cook died," he said in his report afterward, "I was leaning over the companionway* when a Cape pigeon flew on board and alighted close beside me. I stroked it down the back with my hand, and it never attempted to fly away. I went to the cabin and got some bread and pork, which it ate from my hand. It hopped about for a while and then flew away."

Whether or not the captain recognized the bird as an omen, death was near the *Elwell* again. The poison from his wound reached the cook's heart, and early next morning he died. In its weighted shroud of sailcloth, the body was laid out under the flag while the captain read the words of the burial service. Sarah and the crew stood around him. There were no tears on her face. Her cabin was the place for that; and it was no time for adding her own grief to the anxieties of the men. There had been two fatal accidents in two weeks, and it did not bode well for the voyage.

As the body was committed to the deep, the captain gave orders to bring the ship back onto her course. It had been riding easily before the wind to give a steady deck for the service. The

---

* poultices: a heated mass of bread, meal, herbs, or clay applied to the body for healing

** bulkhead: an upright partition dividing a ship into fireproof, watertight compartments

* companionway: a stairway leading down from the deck of a ship

yards** came round, the ship swayed a little with the changing thrust, and suddenly smoke began to spurt from the after ventilators. Deep down in the hold the cargo of coal was on fire.

The captain realized instantly that he was faced with a serious situation. It was so serious that he took the unusual step of holding a consultation with the crew. Explaining the situation, he also explained his decision. He was going to turn back south and run for the Straits of Magellan. It was the shortest course to a safe harbour, and they were most likely to meet passing vessels on the way.

The wind was against the ship for three days, and then a heavy westerly gale set in. *Elwell* had to heave to and ride with the wind. The pumps

were worked continually but the fire below was spreading, and the water drawn up by the pumps was already hot.

The gale began to moderate on the fourth day, and the captain made preparations for abandoning ship. The large ship's boat was stocked with water, provisions, and a compass, but after it was hoisted outboard the usual reluctance of a Bluenose master gained the upper hand. *Elwell* might still make the coast, which was only two hundred and fifty kilometres away. The angry glare in the holds seemed to have subsided a little under the continual stream of water from the pumps. "It was six days since the discovery of the fire," says Captain Wren, "and we were running considerable risk of the ship bursting into flames or blowing up at any moment, but I trusted it would smoulder for a day or so longer."

** yard: a long, slender beam fastened across a mast to support a sail

He made as much sail as he dared, and turned in toward the coast. Just before dark a ship was sighted, and it seemed to the men on *Elwell* that their signal of distress had been recognized. They waited anxiously till midnight, with lanterns in the rigging and along the deck, but there was no hail from across the water. Instead there came "a rushing sound like a chimney on fire, and a dull report." The hatch coverings blew off, and smoke poured from the holds.

In darkness, with a heavy sea running, the boat was lowered. All hands jumped for it through choking clouds of smoke. Sarah, who had travelled many seas without bothering to learn much about boats, missed her timing and fell four metres. She was badly shaken up, and she had sprained her ankle.

Suddenly, as the boat pushed away from the smoking ship, the vessel they had sighted at twilight loomed before them. *Elwell*'s men pulled for it, shouting with relief. But the stranger crossed their bows a kilometre away and disappeared in the darkness. An hour later, in the first light of dawn, *Elwell*'s decks burst open in a cloud of flame and smoke. Lumps of coal shot high in the air and rained about the twelve men and the woman in the open boat. They sat watching as the rigging of their ship blazed and burnt away. Then the masts fell and the hull burned slowly down to the water's edge.

Land was four days' sailing to the east. Placing everyone in the boat on strict rations of food and water, Captain Wren set his course for the Straits of Magellan. The north coast came in sight on the fourth day, but it was a bleak landfall. Snow-covered mountains glared above rocky shores, and the treacherous harbourage was lashed for two weeks after they reached it by rain, sleet, and hail. Sarah, who had lain in the boat white and sick during the journey to land and for a week afterward, somehow now began to mend. "The weather will clear," she told the younger sailors. "There'll be a better harbour farther along."

When the wind and rain let up a little, Captain Wren set the boat nosing along the coast again. There was no shelter and no sign of life. Each day the second mate, in charge of provisions, looked at his dwindling store and decreased the ration. When at last they ran into a rocky cleft of the shore, it was only to bury two of the men.

They put out again, bearing northward in the Straits. A gale roared in through that channel between mountainous rocks, flung the weakened occupants of the boat against the thwarts*, and filled it halfway to the gunwales** with water. Two more men died on the third night of this trip, and the rest gave up. "My only help," says the captain, "was the woman. She bailed while I steered with an oar, the rudder being disabled."

There was no anchorage to be found, and without the help of the men it was impossible to hoist the little sail. Twisting with the wind and currents, the boat drove blindly throught the rock-infested waters of the worst strait in the world. Seven men clung to the gunwales in paralysed silence, looking at the bodies of their mates. Just before morning three of them burst into wild screams and started to jump overboard. Sarah took the tiller while the captain grappled with them and pulled them back.

All next day, with two dead men tossing in the bilge, and three others lashed to the thwarts, they drove along. Toward evening they came under the lee of an island and found a shore where the dead could be buried. The

---

* thwarts: the seats in a rowboat
** gunwales: the upper edges of a boat's sides

men lashed to the thwarts were set free, and the others gathered round to share the last of the provisions. There were no screams or groans now. A dull apathy had settled on everyone except Sarah. She limped back and forth, grimacing at the pain from her wrenched ankle, searching for the mussels and limpets which clung to the rocks. "We'll make it home," she said. "A ship will find us — I'm sure of it."

The captain had little confidence in Sarah's words, and none whatever in his men. For two weeks he did not dare to leave the rocky shelter. One or two of the crew roused themselves to scrape the rocks for mussels, and Sarah produced some bits of shrub gathered along the shore which she called wild celery. A sunny day came and the captain managed to get a fire going by concentrating the rays of the sun through a marine glass onto some cotton wool from his vest. But fire was dangerous, and not tried again. There would be no hope for anyone if smoke attracted the attention of the scattered islanders who lived here and there like birds on the rocks.

Little by little the men became too weak to clamber over the rocks in search of food. By the end of the second week four had died. The rest were starving, and the horrible last symptoms began to appear. When Wren saw the live men of his crew looking with hungry eyes at the bodies of the dead, he knew they must try to move on.

With Sarah's help he bundled the three breathing skeletons over the side of the boat and put out into the strait again. That night the blackened flesh began to peel from the legs and feet of one of the remaining seamen. Sarah tried to bathe him with rainwater and had to give it up, because the flesh fell away at a touch. In the morning he died, and next day the carpenter followed him in the same horrible way. Now only the captain, Sarah, and one young sailor were left.

They put into another rocky shelter along the coast and again lived for a week or so on mussels. The diet racked them with nausea, and they had hardly strength to scrape the shellfish from the rocks. The young sailor lay through the days and nights in a despairing coma. "I now became despondent myself," says the captain in his account. " It was ten weeks since leaving the ship. We were in an uninhabited country, always exposed to the weather, with no warming fire and nothing to eat but shellfish. Could Nature endure longer?"

Sarah, apparently, never asked herself such a question. And she had a way of reinforcing nature. Seating herself on a rock beside the captain, nursing her swollen ankle with one hand, and brushing back the lank hair from her emaciated face with the other, she turned a hard eye on him and began to talk. One by one she ran down a list of all the favourite dishes she and her husband had prepared for him in the *Elwell*'s galley. She described, course by course in succulent detail, all the best meals she had seen or served. She invented new menus and dishes. Phantom joints of beef, mountains of golden brown potatoes, suckling pigs and roasted geese and vast dishes of mutton and greens floated under the captain's nostrils on the relentless tide of her imaginings. She drove him to impotent, ravening fury, but she kept him sane and gave him back his will.

They were sheltering in a curve of the shore from which a bold headland could be seen, about thirteen kilometres across the water. As the captain's sea-sense returned he concluded that a bay or channel, perhaps one frequented by

ships, might lie beyond the headland. Weak and sick, he hauled the boat into the water again. Sarah helped him, in fact did most of the work. She dragged the unconscious sailor to the boat and got him over the side. Her strength or her nerve seemed undiminished. "Really, she was becoming a heroine in my estimation," says the captain.

She helped again in getting the sail up, but it was the captain who had to set the course. He did it with aching care, because the weather was foggy, and an error would have sent the boat onto the rocks at the foot of the headland. Then they began to move, the captain tending the sail, Sarah bailing, and the young sailor unconscious in the bottom. About halfway across, the sea lifted in a long swell, and the captain through sheer weakness rolled from his seat and fell against the thwarts. He struggled up painfully and glanced back the way they had come. He rubbed his eyes. The dreams of delirium must be coming back, he thought, because he was seeing the smoke of a steamer.

The White Star liner *Tropic*, bound from the Pacific coast to Liverpool, had happened on that voyage to take an unusual course through the channels of the strait. *Tropic* bore down quickly on the little boat, and the feverish vagueness cleared from the captain's eyes. "Ship in sight!" he gasped, and lifted his voice in a croaking hail. An hour later, seventy-two days after they had left the blazing *Elwell*, the three who remained of its company were hoisted gently to the liner's decks.

As they carried her off to sick-bay, Sarah raised her head from the stretcher, looked back at the captain, and said, "I told you so."

From *The Salt-Water Men* by Joseph Schull

Like Father, Like Son

BY DON LEMNA

The winter that I was thirteen my life changed suddenly and dramatically. Although I didn't own a pair of skates and had no interest in hockey, one Saturday evening in November I somehow wound up in the downtown hockey arena watching the Medicine Hat Tigers play against the Lethbridge Native Sons. The memorable event, the thing that was to alter my life forever, happened late in the third period when one of the referees skated over to me and placed a broken hockey stick in my surprised hands.

The next morning I set about to repair my hockey stick. I got two pieces of wood lath and layered them over the break, attaching one piece to each side of the broken shaft with a long row of shingle nails. Then my friend Ernie, ever resourceful, lent me three large rolls of his father's heavy electrician's tape. I spent the next hour winding the tape across the splints, around and around, over and over and over, until the mend was about the thickness of my leg. But I wasn't through yet. In order to make sure that my precious hockey stick would never wear out, I hammered a hundred tacks into the surface of the blade on both sides, then covered this armour plating with six layers of tape. All seemed to be going well, but when I was finished with my repairs and improvements I discovered that my hockey stick weighed at least six kilograms.

Stick in hand, I went to the Allowance Avenue rink, where I found a scrub hockey game in progress. A large cluster of kids, some with skates and some, like me, without, were all busy chasing an unfortunate hockey puck around the rink. And when they caught up with it, they poked, swatted, and pushed at it until it was forced to flee from them again. Into this melee I flew, pushing my armour-plated hockey stick ahead of me and, by the end of that afternoon, my formidable stick and I had slashed a permanent place for ourselves in the hockey cluster.

I was tired, wet, and bruised when I finally had to leave the game to get some supper. Every bone in my body ached and I felt like a walking icicle. However, on the positive side, I noticed that the blood from the cut above my left eye had congealed very nicely and my vision was pretty well normal again. The winter sun was now on the other side of the hill, and light was failing. But as I walked up 11th Street I did not notice the encroaching darkness. My heart, still burning with the ecstasy of exciting play, lighted the way home. I had fallen head over heels in love with hockey.

In the days that followed, my whole being was entirely focussed on hockey. I played on the school rink at noon every day and, after school and at night after supper, I played furiously on Allowance Avenue rink. Oh, how I loved hockey! However, by now I had discovered that lack of skates is a serious impediment to speed on ice. Moreover, I had lost entirely my fondness for my armour-plated hockey stick. Because it was so heavy, it had a tendency to resist the sudden changes in direction that are necessary when stick-handling a puck. Of course I asked my father if he would provide me with a pair of skates and a hockey stick. However, he responded to my request exactly as expected—in the negative. Times were hard, and other things took priority over skates to my parents.

One day in December, when I was returning home, I saw Mr. Golden hanging a holly wreath in the frost-ridden window of his grocery store.

Christmas? Why hadn't I thought of it before? Christmas! My heart leapt and the crisp air around me seemed suddenly warm and full of promise. Christmas! It was that wonderful time when parents are expected to lavish gifts on their children and thus prove that they love them. That night at supper I dropped my first hint.

"Guess what I want for Christmas," I said. "I want a pair of skates and a hockey stick and a puck."

"Skates cost too much and you've already got a hockey stick," my father said.

"But it's too heavy," I protested.

"You're lucky to have it," he said. "When I was a kid, I never even had a hockey stick."

Granpa, who happened to be with us for supper that evening, took his soup spoon out of his mouth and tapped it against the rim of his bowl.

"Wasn't much money around in them days," he commented.

This confirmed my suspicions about Granpa. He was a skinflint too.

My older sister Betty looked up. "Could I just have a little canary for Christmas?" she asked.

"That's all I need," Father said with a sigh on hearing this. "Another mouth to feed."

"I want a chemistry set," Arnold my brother announced.

"What the heck would you do with a chemistry set?" Father said gruffly. "Blow us up?"

"There are all kinds of important things you kids need before that kind of stuff," Mother commented.

"Times ain't so tough now," Granpa mumbled. "Seems to me you might get them some of the things they want."

"They'll get what they get," Father said.

"I was just thinkin' out loud," Granpa said. "No need to get mad."

"I'm not mad," Father said angrily. "But I can't afford to buy them what they want and that's all there is to it."

Some Christmas this is going to be, I thought. It wasn't even here yet and already I was disappointed with it. However, although I was down, I was not out. I still had one more arrow left in my quiver.

The next day, when I came home from school, I sat down at the kitchen table and began to compose a letter. This was to be a very important letter, so I used my newly acquired technique of handwriting, instead of the childish printing I used to do. This letter was intended for my Aunt Eunice, who, because she was married to a Canadian Pacific Railway station agent, was very, very wealthy.

My letter was to the point. I merely asked her how she was and I informed her that I sincerely hoped someone would buy me a pair of skates for Christmas. Very plain, very simple, yet somehow heartrending. I did close the letter with a "Very, Very, Very Sincerely Yours", hoping that this masterly flourish, coming right at the end, would sway her to my way of thinking.

My whole being was entirely focussed on hockey in the weeks that followed. By the 24th of December, my mind was fully declutched and racing at fever pitch. But I had to put on the brakes and force it down into low gear, because that night I was to sing the third part of "We Three Kings" at the Christmas Concert in the basement of St. Pat's. I enjoyed singing and I had actually looked forward to hearing myself, but when the moment for my solo rolled around, I felt strangely depressed and nervous. I was not depressed and nervous about the singing, but about whether Aunt Eunice had received my letter and whether she had followed through on my request.

The song I was singing at the moment seemed to echo in my brain, especially the words "bitter perfume," "dying" and "gloom." And when I came to the end of it, I somehow knew that Aunt Eunice had failed me.

In the morning I rushed into the living room and, at the same instant that Betty spotted the bird cage, my eyes discovered a beautiful hockey stick leaning against the wall, near the tree. And while my brother lifted the cover off his new chemistry set, I simply stood there, transfixed by the sight of the stick.

Dad put his hand on my shoulder and smiled. "It's a very high quality hockey stick," he said. "It'll last you for years, maybe even for the rest of your life." At that moment, I knew that I had been blessed with the kindest, most generous Father in the world—even though he was too strict.

I began to ferret about at the base of the tree, but I could not find my skates.

"What are you looking for, Basil?" Mother asked me.

"My present from Auntie Eunice. I can't find it," I replied. There was a note of mild desperation in my voice.

"It's right there in front of your nose," Betty said contemptuously.

"Where?" All I saw in front of me was a pair of skis.

"The skis," Mother said. "They're your present from Auntie Eunice. She said you asked for them in a letter. Don't you remember?"

"Skis!" I cried. "I asked for skates! I don't want skis! I hate skiing! I can't ski! I've never skied! I don't want to ski!"

"They're top-quality skis," Father said calmly, turning one of them over in his hands. "Look at this," he said. "Made in Chicago. Made from genuine hickory wood. They'll last a lifetime."

I was very unhappy with the way things had worked, but at least I had my beautiful new hockey stick that was made in Canada. That was something, at least, and an hour later I headed down to the rink to try it out. In my pocket I had a new puck to go with my stick and, although I still felt a sting of disappointment over the skates, I knew I had nothing to complain about.

Little Larry Altinkinker was alone on the rink when I arrived and that was fine with me. I stickhandled my new puck past him again and again and again, and he was unable to do anything about it. I had the talent and, with my new hockey stick, I was unstoppable. Then he accidently stopped me. Rather, he stopped my hockey puck when I was on the way by and, with all his might, he shot it like a bullet into the snowbank at the edge of the rink. I might have killed him on the spot, but he had a big brother. So instead I gave him a tongue-lashing he'd not soon forget. Alas, while I was shouting at him, I lost track of exactly where it was my puck had disappeared to in the snow. We searched for it in the banks unsuccessfully for more than half an hour.

In the meantime, others had arrived at the rink and a fierce hockey game was now underway. Energized as I was, partly by anger and frustration and partly by my new hockey stick, I plunged into it like a Tasmanian Devil. Within seconds my anger had vanished and I was totally immersed in the game. This is what I was meant to do in life, I was sure of it.

Later, while I was catching my breath on a snowbank, Big Herman came by and picked up my stick.

"It's my new hockey stick," I said, with tears in my eyes.

"I'm just gonna borrow it for a second," he replied gruffly. What could I do? Nothing. And for the next ten minutes I watched in agony as my new stick played hockey without me.

When, finally, Big Herman threw my hockey stick on the snowbank beside me, I breathed a heavy sigh of relief. I had envisioned having some difficulty getting it back from him. There was a smile of gratitude on my face as I watched him disappear down Tenth Street, then I headed towards

the hockey cluster. But before I reached it, I made a heart-stopping, gut-wrenching discovery. The blade on my beautiful, brand-new hockey stick was cracked across the middle, from one end to the other. In fact, there was little, if anything, to hold it together, as I discovered when it fell apart.

The cry I let out brought everyone on the rink to a dead stop.

"It's broke!" I screamed. "It's busted!"

Tears were running down my face and fear was cartwheeling around in my heart as I plodded towards home. I knew I would have to tell Father about the stick immediately, because I knew it would be much worse for me if I concealed the disaster from him and he discovered it for himself. It had been that way with the broken window. When I came into the kitchen, he looked at me and smiled.

"How's the stick?" he asked.

"It's broken," I said.

Father stared dumbly at me for a split second, then erupted.

"Broken? Broken! How the heck can it be broken? It's brand-new!"

I explained rapidly what had happened, but it didn't help. It didn't lessen his anger at all. In fact, it only made him more furious.

"I'm sorry," I said dejectedly.

"At least you've still got your puck," Mother said, ever the optimist.

"I lost the puck," I said glumly.

"What!" Father roared. "*You what?*"

"John," Mother broke in, "don't be too hard on him. He's feeling bad enough as it is. And it's Christmas, after all."

"Christmas!" Father yelled. "I'll Christmas him on his backside!"

"You'll do nothing of the sort, unless you want a real battle on your hands," Mother said. "Now sit down and cool off!"

Instead of sitting down, Father drew himself up to his full height. Now carefully controlling his rage, he spoke very slowly in a low voice.

"I'll tell you one thing," he said emphatically. "You're not going to lay your mitts on those skis until you've learned to look after things."

That was fine with me. I didn't want them in the first place.

"Now that is ridiculous!" Mother responded angrily. "They're his skis. Eunice gave them to him and you've got no right to take them away."

"Please don't fight," Betty interjected. "You're scaring my canary."

In the end, Mother won the argument. Or so it seemed to me, because when the shouting finally subsided into angry silence, there was just the hint of a smile in the way she looked at me.

"All right, Basil," she said. "It's okay for you to go."

"Go where?" I asked.

"Go skiing," she said. "What do you think we've been arguing about?"

"But I don't want to go skiing," I protested.

She then levelled her eyes at me and they were like two black cannons ready to discharge their shot.

"Go and ski," she hissed.

Unfortunately, there is no shortage of hills in Medicine Hat. The flats in which we lived had hills on two sides of it. I chose the hill at the end of Sixth Street, because it had wooden steps up to the top, which, I reasoned, would make the ascent easier. I plodded disconsolately along toward Sixth Street, my skis over my shoulder and my heart pitted by the worm of despair. Something was wrong with this particular Christmas…I remembered Christmases past and the thrill that had once infused my being when the Christmas tree went up and the lights were turned on and then fixed. I remembered the thrill of a world coloured differently. But now it had all become a thing remembered and no longer felt.

I climbed the steps with leaden feet, followed by a pack of little kids who evidently had never seen a skier before. In fact, when I told them what I was going to do, most of them didn't believe me.

I climbed halfway up the hill, then went under the pipe railing. I then managed to point my skis downhill and actually began to move in that direction, travelling at top speed for a total distance of about three metres before I went careening head over heels. When I'd dug my face out of the snow, I heard laughter and hoots of derision from the sidelines. This made me downright angry and when I get angry, I tend to get stupid. I vowed then and there not to leave this accursed hill until I'd gone down it in an upright position.

After two hours of falling down the hill, it seemed to me I was beginning to acquire some skill at the business of skiing. And during the struggle I'd made a significant discovery. It was fun. Of a sort. I began to wonder absently if there might be a future for me in the ski business.

"Why don't you go down all the way from the top," someone suggested when, later on, I trudged up the steps for the hundredth time. I looked up at the top of the hill. It was a very long distance away and, moreover, the top half of the hill was much steeper than the gentler bottom slope I'd been coming down. On the other hand, there was a clear run right to the bottom and it occurred to me that skiing all the way down from the very top would be an impressively brave way to end the afternoon. And if I did happen to make it down without falling, my feat would live forever in the memories of these tiny witnesses. But was it safe? I was certain it was. It only looked dangerous. At that time, I was certain that it's impossible to really hurt yourself falling in the snow.

When I reached the top, I put on my skis, clenched the poles firmly in my mitted hands, and squared my shoulders to the cloud opposite me. I then proceeded to inch my way to the edge of the hill and looked down. It was a vertical precipice. *I'm going to get killed if I go down there*, I thought. On the other hand, it was going to be difficult for me to back out at this late date, for I now had a large audience thirsting for my blood.

While I was wondering how to extricate myself from the situation, I happened to move my skis slightly and my problem was solved. I was on my way down. Instantly I resolved to make the best of it and maybe, just maybe, fortune would smile upon me at last and I would actually make it all the way to the bottom. Would I? Faster and faster I went, faster and faster, down, down, down the hill, and suddenly it looked like I might actually do it. But then I noticed a large lump of snow directly ahead of me. Regrettably, being unable to turn while in motion, I could not avoid it.

The lump of snow was very hard and very substantial and the next thing I knew, I was cartwheeling through the air…

When I opened my eyes, I saw several skis poking up through the snow in front of me. Like the loaves and the fishes in the parable, my skis had multiplied before my eyes. But a moment later I realized there had not been a miracle on the Sixth Street hill, after all. My skis had not multiplied. When all the pieces were added up, there was still only one set. Yes, my brand new skis from Chicago, U.S.A., were smashed to smithereens and it was all Aunt Eunice's fault for not being able to read my handwriting.

A few moments later, I limped back up to the lump of snow and discovered it was not a lump of snow at all, but rather a concrete and steel abutment which protruded about half a metre above the surface of the hill. It was, in slightly different words, the top of a sewer access manhole, built into the hill for the purpose of killing people.

A half hour later, when my thumping heart and the rest of me entered the warm kitchen, I observed, as in a dream, that my mother was still happily engaged with the cooking and Betty was still talking to her canary. Arnold was nowhere in sight, but Father was there. He was sitting at the corner of the table, staring morosely out the window.

What would be the use of putting it off? I steeled myself for the slaughter and, in a trembling voice, I made my announcement.

"I skied all the way down the Sixth Street hill," I said.

"Oh?" Mother replied. "Good for you."

"I hit a big sewer cover," I said.

"Oh?" she responded. "You didn't hurt yourself?"

Now it had to come. I looked at my father and trembled…

"I broke my skis," I said.

"Oh no!" Mother exclaimed. "Not your new skis!"

I heard her well enough, but my eyes did not move from him. Yet he only kept on staring out of the window. His head did not turn, not even a fraction. Did he not hear what I'd said?

"Yeah," I said in a quaking voice, "I really busted them up. There's five pieces altogether."

Still the figure by the window did not move or speak.

"Dad?" I said.

"I heard you," he replied in a distant voice. "Too bad."

That was it? Just "too bad?"

"What's wrong with Dad?" I whispered.

"Don't bother him now," Mother whispered back. "He's still recovering from the shock of the explosion."

"What explosion?" I asked in a mystified voice.

"Arnold blew up the front porch with his chemistry set," Betty informed me in a whisper.

"Blew it up? Is he dead?" I asked.

"He's just got a little burn on his arm," she responded. "He was lucky this time."

"You should have been here," Betty said. "First there was this loud 'BOOM'—like thunder, only a little bit more muffled—and the whole front porch was on fire and Dad had to use a blanket to put it out and everything!"

"Fire?" I said. I looked around as Arnold entered.

Arnold had a bandage on his arm, which he displayed proudly.

"You shoulda seen it!" he exclaimed, moving his arms in a big circle in the air. "I just mixed all this stuff together and I lighted this match and then 'BOOM'!"

Later in the day, Betty reported from the window that Granpa's Model A had just stopped in front of the house. I paid little attention, because Granpa was always coming to visit us and get a free meal. But then there was a great yell from the window.

"He's got presents!"

It was not Granpa's custom to give presents to us at Christmas. But this year he *did* have presents. And what presents they were! Topping everything else, there was a brand new pair of CCM skates for me. FOR ME!

The others fared equally well, according to their own lights. Betty got a large bird cage with a canary in it—her second of the day—and she was delirious with happiness. As for Arnold, Grandfather gave him a large Deluxe Model (74 piece) "All Star" chemistry set.

I wondered absently what had happened to Granpa to change him overnight from a skinflint to a person of unbounded generosity. However, such miracles are not uncommon during the Christmas season.

Highlighted as it was by a very well-basted turkey, Christmas dinner was wonderful. While we ate and ate, the conversation went on intermittently, Christmas carols came softly out of the radio, and everyone was very happy again, even Father. Towards the end of the meal, I proudly told Granpa about my experience that afternoon on the Sixth Street hill and how thoroughly I'd broken my skis. For some reason, he seemed to think the whole thing was funny. I didn't, but I laughed to keep him company because I now loved him.

After he'd quit laughing, he glanced at Father. "Remember that hill, John?"

Father looked away and bit his lip. Either he didn't remember it or he didn't want to. Everyone instantly sensed something was up and we all listened intently as Grandfather went on, searching his long memory…

"Remember, John? It was the summer my father—your Grandfather—bought you that bicycle you always wanted and then you, like a fool, tried to ride it down that hill."

Grandfather chuckled to himself, then continued on…

"I still remember the look on your face when you brought it home, all twisted up like a pretzel. I tanned your hide, didn't I?"

"Yeah," Father said, frowning at the memory.

"What was it you ran into, anyway?" Grandfather asked.

"A manhole cover," Father replied with a slight smile in my direction.

Challenges

Nobody Said It Would Be Easy/MARILYN HALVORSON

Lance has no mother, so he's used to coping on his own. An airplane crash kills the pilot, but leaves Lance, his friend Red, and cousin Kat alive. The three teens must learn to co-operate, as they face the grim realities of surviving alone in the mountains.

The Cripples Club/WILLIAM BELL

Fifteen-year-old refugee George Ma is suffering from severe memory loss. Hassled by a tough school gang, George, a self-defence expert, must protect himself and his newfound friends. "Hook," confined to a wheelchair, Amy, a blind computer whiz, and Heather, who is deaf, join George—with unexpected results.

Hey Dad!/BRIAN DOYLE

Another family trip is more than Megan can stand. All across Canada in a car trapped in the back seat beside her little brother—she may as well "have been in prison"!

Mama's Going To Buy You A Mockingbird/JEAN LITTLE

Jeremy is faced with his father's battle with cancer, and the grief of his mother and little sister. In a sad and difficult time, Jeremy eventually triumphs.

Anne Frank: The Diary of a Young Girl/ANNE FRANK

Anne's diary remains a remarkable book. It is a true account of how a young girl hiding from the Nazis survives on hope and her belief in the good of humankind.

Waiting for the Rain/SHEILA GORDON

Two boys are growing up in the same country—South Africa. The black boy must struggle for an education while his white friend takes his schooling for granted. Can these two maintain a friendship in a country that condones such injustice?

Index of Titles

Index of Authors

Index of Selections by Genre

Index of In Context Features

ACKNOWLEDGEMENTS

The authors would like to express their gratitude to Nancy Randall and the students of D.A. Morrison Junior High School for "Settling In."

"With My Foot In My Mouth" by Dennis Lee from NICHOLAS KNOCK AND OTHER PEOPLE by Dennis Lee, published by Macmillan of Canada. Copyright © 1974, Dennis Lee. Reprinted by permission.

"The Trouble With Friends" by Frances Duncan from KAP SUNG FERRIS by Frances Duncan copyright © 1977. Reprinted by permission of Macmillan of Canada, A Divison of Canada Publishing Corporation.

"Priscilla and the Wimps" by Richard Peck from SIXTEEN: STORIES FOR YOUNG ADULTS edited by Donald R. Gallo. Copyright © 1984 by Richard Peck. Reprinted by permission of Delacorte Press, a division of Bantam, Doubleday, Dell Publishing Group, Inc.

"Papa's Parrot" by Cynthia Rylant from EVERY LIVING THING by Cynthia Rylant. Text copyright © 1985 by Cynthia Rylant. Reprinted with permission of Bradbury Press, an Affiliate of Macmillan Inc.

"When Someone I Love is Hurt" from HEY WORLD, HERE I AM by Jean Little. Text copyright © 1986 by Jean Little. Reprinted by permission of the publisher Kids Can Press Ltd., Toronto, Ontario, Canada.

"Together" by Paul Engle from EMBRACE: SELECTED LOVE POEMS by Paul Engle. Reprinted by permission of Random House Inc.

"Two girls of twelve" by Charles Reznikoff, copyright © 1959 by Charles Reznikoff. Reprinted by permission of New Directions Publishing Corporation.

"Twin Telepathy" by Jay Ingram adapted from TWINS: AN AMAZING INVESTIGATION by Jay Ingram. Text copyright © 1988 by Jay Ingram. Reprinted with permission of the publisher Greey de Pencier Books.

"The Wild Goose" by Ernest Buckler from CANADIAN STORIES OF ACTION AND ADVENTURE. Used by permission of the Canadian Publishers, McClelland and Stewart, Toronto.

"The Education of Grandma" by Elsie Morris. Copyright Elsie Morris. Used by permission of the author.

"MOGA Madness" by Lauren E. Wolk. Copyright © by Nelson Canada, a Division of International Thomson, Ltd.

"A Shattering Experience" by Donald Honig. Copyright © Donald Honig. Used by permission of the author.

"Fly Like an Eagle" by Elizabeth Van Steenwyck from FLY LIKE AND EAGLE AND OTHER STORIES by Elizabeth Van Steenwyck. Copyright © 1978 by Elizabeth Van Steenwyck. Reprinted by permission of Walker and Company.

"Wild Pitch" by Raymond Souster is reprinted from COLLECTED POEMS OF RAYMOND SOUSTER by permission of Oberon Press.

"Pole Vault" by Shiro Murano first appeared in POETRY, translated by Satoru Sato and Constance Urdang. Copyright © 1956 by The Modern Poetry Association. Reprinted by permission of the Editor of POETRY.

"The Women's 400 Metres" by Lillian Morrison from THE SIDEWALK RACER AND OTHER POEMS OF SPORTS AND MOTION by Lillian Morrison. Copyright © 1977 by Lillian Morrison. Reprinted by permission of the author.

"The Hockey Sweater" by Roch Carrier from THE HOCKEY SWEATER AND OTHER STORIES, translated by Sheila Fischman (Toronto: House of Anansi Press, 1979). Reprinted by permission.

"Imaging for Success" by Avery Gietz used by permission of the author. BAUMANN, GRAHAM, ORSER, PODBORSKI, KRYCZKA, BOUCHER, FUNG and HALL quotations are from PSYCHED: INNER VIEWS OF WINNING by Terry Orlick and John Partington. Reprinted with the permission of the Coaching Association of Canada.

"The Finish Line" by Walter Farley from THE BLACK STALLION AND THE GIRL by Walter Farley. Copyright © 1971 by Walter Farley. Reprinted by permission of Random House Inc.

"It Takes Talent" by Mel Glenn originally published as "Joel Feit" from CLASS DISMISSED by Mel Glenn. Copyright © 1982 by Mel Glenn. Reprinted by permission of Clarion Books/Ticknor & Fields, a Houghton Mifflin Company.

"Reggie" by Eloise Greenfield from HONEY I LOVE YOU AND OTHER LOVE POEMS by Eloise Greenfield published by Thomas Y. Crowell. Text copyright © 1978 by Eloise Greenfield. Reprinted by permission of Harper & Row, Publishers, Inc.

"Good Sportsmanship" by Richard Armour, copyright © 1958 by Richard Armour. Reprinted by permission of John Hawkins & Associates Inc.

"Amazing But True Sports Stories" : "Olympic Fun and Games" by Norman Giller from THE 1984 OLYMPICS HANDBOOK. Copyright © 1983 by Winchmore Publishing Services Limited. Reprinted by permission of Henry Holt

and Company, Inc. "Channeling One's Love" and "Called on Account of Grasshoppers" from AMAZING BUT TRUE SPORTS STORIES by Zander Hollander. Copyright © 1986 by Associated Features Inc. All rights reserved. Reprinted by permission of Scholastic Inc. "Spit It Out," "Good-by, Ref," and "Self-Destruction" from THE GIANT BOOK OF MORE STRANGE BUT TRUE SPORTS STORIES, illustrated by Joe Mathius. Copyright © 1983 by Random House, Inc. Reprinted by permission of the publisher.

"The Journey of Charles Wayo" by Charles Sanders. Reprinted by permission Johnson Publishing Company.

"Underground to Canada" by Barbara Smucker from UNDERGROUND TO CANADA by Barbara Smucker. Copyright © 1977. Reprinted by permission of Irwin Publishing Inc., Toronto, Canada.

"What Do I Remember of the Evacuation" by Joy Kogawa from A CHOICE OF DREAMS by Joy Kogawa. Used by permission of the Canadian Publishers, McClelland and Stewart, Toronto.

"The Delay" by Sheila Burnford from THE INCREDIBLE JOURNEY by Sheila Burnford. Used by permission of the publisher: Hodder and Stoughton.

"The Wandering Time" from BEYOND THE HIGH HILLS collected by Knud Rasmussen is reprinted by permission of the estate.

"Horses of the Sun" by Bernard Evslin, Dorothy Evslin and Ned Hoopes. Copyright © by Scholastic Inc. Reprinted by permission of Scholastic Inc.

"Sailing In On Five Years Of Memories" by Jack Cahill. Reprinted with permission of the Toronto Star Syndicate.

"Stopping By Woods on a Snowy Evening" by Robert Frost. Copyright © 1923 by Holt, Rinehart and Winston and renewed 1951 by Robert Frost. Reprinted from THE POETRY OF ROBERT FROST edited by Edward Connery Lathem, by permission of Henry Holt and Company, Inc.

"The Listeners" by Walter de la Mare reprinted by permission of The Literary Trustees of Walter de la Mare and The Society of Authors as their representative.

"Johanna" by Jane Yolen from THE SHAPE SHIFTERS by Jane Yolen. Copyright © 1978 by Jane Yolen. Reprinted by permission of Curtis Brown, Ltd.

"The Cremation of Sam McGee" by Robert Service. Reprinted by permission of Feinman & Krasilovsky, Attorneys. Illustration from THE CREMATION OF SAM McGEE.

"The Midnight Visitor" by Robert Arthur. Copyright © 1939 and renewed 1967 by Robert Arthur. Reprinted from MYSTERY AND MORE MYSTERY by Robert Arthur, by permisson of Random House, Inc.

"A Crime Fanatic" by H. R. F. Keating originally published as "The Crime Fanatic" in TALES FROM ELLERY QUEEN'S MAGAZINE: SHORT STORIES FOR YOUNG ADULTS. Reprinted by permission of Sterling Lord Literistic, Inc. Copyright © by H. R. F. Keating.

"Mysteries to Solve" by George Shannon from STORIES TO SOLVE: FOLKTALES FROM AROUND THE WORLD by George Shannon. Text © copyright by George W. B. Shannon. Reprinted by permission of Greenwillow Books (A Division of William Morrow and Co., Inc.).

"The Adventure of the Blue Carbuncle" by Arthur Conan Doyle from THE ADVENTURE OF THE BLUE CARBUNCLE as contained in Book Two of THE ADVENTURES OF SHERLOCK HOLMES by Catherine Edwards Sadler, copyright © 1981 by Catherine Edwards Sadler. Used by permission of AVON BOOKS, a division of The Hearst Corporation.

"River" and "Fisherman" by Dionne Brand. Thanks to the author Dionne Brand for the inclusion of these poems from EARTH MAGIC.

"Niagara Daredevils" by Linda Granfield from ALL ABOUT NIAGARA FALLS. Text copyright © 1988 by Linda Granfield. Reprinted by permission of Kids Can Press Ltd., Toronto, Canada.

"I Shall Wait and Wait" by Alootook Ipellie. Copyright © Alootook Ipellie. Used by permission of the author.

"The Fateful Night" and "Discovery of the Titanic" from EXPLORING THE TITANIC by Dr. Robert Ballard. Text copyright © Ballard and Family, 1988. Reprinted by permission of Penguin Books Canada Limited/Madision Press Books.

"Survivor: An Eyewitness Account of the Sinking of the Titanic" by Maggie Goh. Copyright © 1989 Nelson Canada, a division of International Thomson Ltd.

"The Shark" by E.J. Pratt from THE COLLECTED POEMS of E. J. Pratt reprinted by permission of University of Toronto Press. Copyright © 1958 by University of Toronto Press.

"Dear Bruce Springsteen" by Kevin Major excerpted from DEAR BRUCE SPRINGSTEEN by Kevin Major, Doubleday Canada, Toronto. Copyright © 1987 Kevin Major.

"Wonderkid" by F.N. Monjo from LETTER TO HORSEFACE by F.N. Monjo. Copyright © 1975 by Ferdinand Monjo and Louise L. Monjo. All rights reserved. Reprinted by permission of Viking Penguin, a division of Penguin Books USA, Inc.

"New Morning" by Bob Dylan. Copyright © 1970 by BIG SKY MUSIC. International copyright secured. Reprinted by permission.

"Turn Me Round" by K.D. Lang. Copyright © 1987, BUM-

STEAD PUBLISHING/ZAVION MUSIC. Administered by Copyright Management, Inc.

"Red River Valley II" Traditional. Reprinted by permission of the CANADIAN EOLK MUSIC BULLETIN

"She's Called Nova Scotia" by Rita MacNeil. Copyright © Big Pond Publishing. Reprinted by permission.

"Down Here Tonight" by Bruce Cockburn copyright © 1985 Golden Mountain Music Corp. Words and music by Bruce Cockburn. Taken from the album "World of Wonders."

"May I Have Your Autograph?" by Marjorie Sharmat from SIXTEEN: SHORT STORIES FOR YOUNG ADULTS edited by Donald R. Gallo. Copyright © by Marjorie Sharmat. Reprinted by permission of Delacorte Press, a division of Bantam, Doubleday, Dell Publishing Group, Inc.

"I Was a Beatlemaniac" by Ron Schaumberg from GROWING UP WITH THE BEATLES by Ron Schaumberg. Copyright © by Delilah Communications Ltd. Reprinted with permission of the Berkely Publishing Group.

"Melody For A Bull" by John V. Hicks. Copyright John V. Hicks. Used by permission of the author.

"A Writer's Education" by Jean Little from LITTLE BY LITTLE by Jean Little. Copyright © Jean Little, 1987. Reprinted by permission of Penguin Books Canada Limited.

"Mixed Up Messages" by Gary Larson from THE FAR SIDE cartoons are reprinted by permission of Chronicles Features, San Francisco, CA.

"Cultural Frustration" by Barry Elmer, reprinted from MYSTERIOUS SPECIAL SAUCE – POEMS BY CANADIAN STUDENTS © the Pandora Charitable Trust of the Canadian Council of Teachers of English, by permission of the Canadian Council of Teachers of English.

"The Dying Story" by Jannis Allan-Hare used by permission of the author.

"Give Us This Day" by Raymond Souster from THE COLLECTED POEMS OF RAYMOND SOUSTER by Raymond Souster used by permission of Oberon Press.

"Let Me Hear You Whisper" by Paul Zindel excerpted from LET ME HEAR YOU WHISPER by Paul Zindel. Text copyright © 1970 by Paul Zindel. Reprinted by permission of Harper & Row, Publishers, Inc. CAUTION: Professionals and amateurs are hereby warned that LET ME HEAR YOU WHISPER, being fully protected under the Copyright Laws of the United States of America, the British Commonwealth, including the Dominion of Canada, and all other countries of the Berne and Universal copyright Conventions, is subject to royalty. All rights, including professional, amateur, motion picture, recitation, lecturing, public reading, radio and televison broadcasting, and the rights of translation into foreign languages are strictly reserved. Particular emphasis is laid on the question of readings, permission for which must be secured in writing from the author's agent, Gilbert Parker, at Sterling Lord Agency. The amateur acting rights of LET ME HEAR YOU WHISPER are controlled exclusively by the Dramatists Play Service, 440 Park Avenue South, New York, New York 10016. No performance may be made without permission in writing.

"Zoot Capri" by Colleen Nielsen-Hyde. Copyright © 1989 by Nelson Canada, A division of International Thomson Ltd.

"On Camera" by Elizabeth MacLeod. Copyright © 1989 by Nelson Canada, A Division of International Thomson Ltd.

"The Forever Flavour File" by Harold Eastman. Copyright © 1989 by Nelson Canada, A Division of International Thomson Ltd.

"The New Kid" by Morley Callaghan from THE LOST AND FOUND STORIES by Morley Callaghan. Used by permission of the author.

"Heritage" by Lola Sneyd from THE CONCRETE GIRAFFE by Lola Sneyd. Copyright © 1984 by Lola Sneyd. Published by Simon and Pierre Publishing Co. Ltd. Used by permission.

"The Earth and the People" from SONGS AND STORIES OF THE NETSULIK ESKIMOS translated by Edward Field from text collected by Knud Rasmussen. Reprinted by permission of the estate.

"An Affair of Honour" by L. M. Montgomery published with permission from David Macdonald, Ruth Macdonald and Farrar, Straus and Giroux, Inc.

"Casey at the Bat" by Ernest Lawrence Thayer is reprinted with permission of the San Francisco Examiner. Copyright © 1988 The San Francisco Examiner.

"The Power of Light" by Issac Bashevis Singer from STORIES FOR CHILDREN by Issac Bashevis Singer. Copyright © 1980, 1984 by Issac Bashevis Singer. Reprinted by permission of Farrar, Straus and Giroux, Inc.

"Whatever Happe.. :d to Hope" by Kathy Wilmore from Action Magazine, Nov. 6/2 1987. Copyright © 1987 by Scholastic Inc. Reprinted by permission of Scholastic Inc.

"Salt-Water Sarah" by Joseph Schull from THE SALT WATER MEN by Joseph Schull. Copyright © Helen Gougeon Schull. Reprinted by permission.

"Like Father, Like Son" by Don Lemna. Copyright © Don Lemna. Used by permission of the author.

Permission to reprint copyright material is gratefully acknowledged. Information that will enable the publisher to rectify any error or omission will be welcomed.